Kerbis,

I hope you enjoy the book.
Thanks for being so encouraging.
God bless you.

[signature]
06

P.S. I'm proud of you.

POWER OF THE MUSTARD SEED

Jimi Clemons

Bloomington, IN Milton Keynes, UK

authorHOUSE™

AuthorHouse™
1663 Liberty Drive, Suite 200
Bloomington, IN 47403
www.authorhouse.com
Phone: 1-800-839-8640

AuthorHouse™ UK Ltd.
500 Avebury Boulevard
Central Milton Keynes, MK9 2BE
www.authorhouse.co.uk
Phone: 08001974150

First published by AuthorHouse 5/24/2006

ISBN: 1-4259-2358-5 (sc)

Printed in the United States of America
Bloomington, Indiana
This book is printed on acid-free paper.

Dedication
This book is dedicated to Michelle M. Fredricks
Although God was my source and my reason for writing this book,
He made you my greatest inspiration.
Jimi

ACKNOWLEDGEMENTS

First and foremost I would like to give all honor, glory, and credit to my Lord and Savior Jesus Christ. Thank you Lord for the sacrifice you made when you died on the cross so that I may live. Thank you for loving me and forgiving me for all of my sins. Thank you for setting me free from a drug habit that eventually would have taken my life. Thank you for giving me the gift of writing to create love and peace on paper to heal the world. Thank you for being better to me than I could ever be to myself. I simply thank you Lord for being my friend. To my mother: You are my role model, my queen, and my friend. We've been through the worst of the worst. We've cried, we've laughed, we've suffered, and to God be the glory, we've survived. Thanks for teaching me how to love people without seeing their skin color. You are the epitome of what a mother should be and more. I love you. To my sisters: Thank you for being your best when I was at my worst. I love you. To the rest of my family, I love you, and thank you. To Tunisha Barnett: The Christ- like life you lived in front of me when I was killing myself with drugs is the very thing that led me to the throne of salvation. Thank you for fighting the battle when I didn't have the strength to fight on my own. We won the war. I love you. To Pastor Kenneth Pugh: Thank you for teaching me what being a real man is all about spiritually, mentally, and emotionally. I never had a father in my life to teach me these things. Thanks for filling in the gap. To my boy Fats: Words can't describe the love you showed me when I was dying from the addiction. Thanks man. I'll never forget it. To my friend Yo Sobha: Thank you for trusting God's will even when you didn't understand it. That trust made me a better man. I love you. To Pastor J. Allen Lewis: Thank you (R.I.P). To A.J. Jones: You taught me what forgiveness is really about, and for that I thank you. To Joe Farrah: Thanks for always being there. To Candace Errato: (Miss Angel Eyes). Your anointing made this book beautiful, thanks. To Alice Remedios: The ultimate mom, wife, and friend, I love you. To Gerald Culbreth: Thanks for always having my back. To Dot and Glenda Culbreth: You loved me with no limits, thanks. To Flint and Jody Bradley: I love you, thanks. Thanks to the Croniser family. To Mr. and Mrs. Gerald Lampley: You'll always own a piece of my heart, always. To Joey and Presha Bradley: You guys are the best, thanks. To Marty and Gayle Allen: Thanks for making me look so good, I love you. To Mrs. Nancy Perry: You're the world's greatest teacher. You taught me, you encouraged me, and you loved me, thanks.

To Vic and Jo Brown: I love you. To Phil and Karen Keren: Thanks. To Tyrone and Tina Bailey: Thanks for taking care of me. To Tracy Carter: You helped me see, thanks. To Tim Joyce: I love you so much. Special thanks to my good friend, Jennifer Mundy: I miss you, and I love you. To Pastor Joseph Ragland: You really made the difference. Thanks to: Angello Cox, Rebecca Lopez, The Golden Girls, Kathrine Ellis, Sidney Linney, Bruce Ham, Todd Walton (R.I.P), Shari Smith, Sha Bryant, Jennifer "Willie" Williamson, Nicole Burdick, Aaron Croniser, Tracy Justice, Leanne Murray, Erica Bach, Robert Mason, Scott Cooper, Jamie Bradley, E.J. Bradley, Big Mike Whiting, Alice Shorts, Nick Errato, Fred and Mary Barnett, Brittany Cherry, Ariel C. Brown, Miss Lilly Jones, Micheal McKinney, and Erez Halfon. Last and certainly not least, to my best friend Amy Croniser. Thank you for your unconditional love, your friendship, and your support, we did it. I love you.

CHAPTER ONE

Minister Joe Ragland, who has been driving now for three and a half hours, is on his way to Bailey, South Carolina to pay a surprise visit to an old college friend. Bailey, South Carolina is about two hours from Charlotte, North Carolina, which is where Minister Ragland is from. Realizing that he's been driving an hour longer than usual, Minister Ragland looks at his map, looks up at a road sign, and realizes that he's lost. The road sign he sees says, "Welcome to Swamp Fox South Carolina."

MINISTER: Swamp Fox, South Carolina. Where in the world am I?

(Knowing he should have reached Bailey by now, he decides to stop in the small town to use the bathroom and grab a bite to eat. As he walks through the door of a little restaurant called Breakfast Time, he notices that all of the black people are sitting on one side of the restaurant, and all of the white people are sitting on the other. He stands there for a minute in absolute shock before walking up to the counter and taking a seat. Sitting at the counter a couple of seats to his right are four white people talking and laughing with a white waitress. After about five minutes of being ignored, Minister Ragland tries to get the attention of the waitress.)

MINISTER: Excuse me.

(The waitress ignores him)

MINISTER: Excuse me ma'am.

(She slowly turns and looks at him with an irritated look on her face.)

MINISTER: May I get some service please?

(She grudgingly makes her way over to him, pulls out her pencil and pad, crosses her arms, and stands there not saying a word.)

MINISTER: I was wondering if you could help me with some directions.

FAYE WATERS: Why don't you buy a map?

MINISTER: Well, actually I have a map and somehow I still got lost.

(He unfolds his map on the counter and tries to explain where he thinks he went wrong.)

MINISTER: See, right here is where I'm getting confused. I don't understand how highway 85...

(The waitress cuts him off in mid sentence.)

FAYE WATERS: Look I don't have time for this. I've got work to do. Now do you want to order something or not?

(Minister Ragland is blown away and left speechless by the waitress's behavior and attitude towards him.)

MINISTER: Okay, forget the directions. How about a menu? Can I see a menu?

(She grabs a menu and throws it on the counter in front of him.)

FAYE WATERS: Figure out what you want. I'll be back!

(As he sits there in awe looking around the restaurant, he realizes that something strange is going on. After about ten minutes have passed the waitress returns.)

FAYE WATERS: What do you want?

MINISTER: I'll have the Breakfast Time Special to go.

FAYE WATERS: Is that it?

MINISTER: Yes.

(She rudely snatches the menu out of his hands and walks away. As the Minister is sitting in his seat at the counter looking at his map, the waitress is standing at the cash register with his food waiting for him. After standing there for a couple of minutes her patience runs out and she yells to him from across the restaurant.)

FAYE WATERS: Do you want this food or not?

(The entire restaurant becomes silent and all eyes are on Minister Ragland. He gets up and makes his way to the register as everybody stares.)

FAYE WATERS: Three dollars and eighty cents!

(He pulls out his wallet and gives her a five. Instead of handing him his change, she throws it on the counter and walks away. After picking up some of his change that fell on the floor, he heads for the door still the center of attention. Once he reaches the door, he looks around the restaurant one more time and then he leaves. As Minister Ragland stands outside of the restaurant, he looks around and again notices that neither blacks nor whites are interacting. He turns to his right and sees a barber pole about 4 doors down from the restaurant and heads that way. When he gets to the barbershop, he peeks in the window and sees three old, heavyset, white men all wearing dingy denim overalls, sitting in their chairs talking. Curious of what kind of reaction he'll get, he decides to go in and ask for some directions. As soon as he enters the barbershop, the chit chat stops and all eyes are on him.)

MINISTER: Good afternoon, gentlemen.

(No one responds.)

MINISTER: I'm sorry to disturb you, but I was wondering if one of you could help me with some directions.

(One of the old farmers pulls his short, wet cigar out of his mouth, tucks his thumb behind his overall strap, and leans to his left to see what the Minister is holding in his hand.)

MAN IN CHAIR: That looks like a map in your hand. Can't you read boy?

(The men in the other chairs snicker and laugh at the Minister. Insulted by the comment, Minister Ragland stands there for a second, looks at each one of the men, and then walks out.)

MAN IN CHAIR: That's right boy, get on out of here! Directions, yeah! I'll give you some directions, directions to the hardware store to get me some rope!

(Once again, he finds himself outside looking around trying to figure out what is causing all of the tension. And it is at that very moment he finds his source for information. Across the street shooting hoops in a small park, is a seventeen-year-old black kid named Corey. With no hesitation, Minister Ragland walks on to the court and approaches the young man.)

MINISTER: Excuse me!

(The young man turns to see who is talking to him.)

MINISTER: I was wondering if you could help me with some directions.

(The young man hesitates at first and then responds.)

COREY WILLIAMS: Where are you headed?

MINISTER: I'm trying to find a town called Bailey.

COREY WILLIAMS: Bailey? You're a long way from Bailey. Where are you coming from?

MINISTER: Charlotte, North Carolina.

COREY WILLIAMS: Charlotte! If you left Charlotte, headed for Bailey, how did you end up here in Swamp Fox?

MINISTER: I took a wrong turn somewhere along the way.

COREY WILLIAMS: Let me see your map.

(Corey points at the map to show him where he went wrong.)

COREY WILLIAMS: See, look right here. Here's Charlotte, here's Bailey, and here's Swamp Fox.

MINSTER: I don't get it. I've probably driven 50 or 60 miles out of my way.

COREY WILLIAMS: At least. What you should have done is gotten off right here and taken I-85 South, but you somehow ended up on Highway 310.

(The Minister stands there shaking his head, surprised by his mistake.)

MINISTER: I just don't understand how I missed that exit. Oh well, tack on another two hours of extra driving I guess. What's your name?

COREY WILLIAMS: Corey Williams.

(They shake hands.)

MINISTER: Well it's nice to meet you, Corey. Minister Joe Ragland.

COREY WILLIAMS: Nice to meet you, Minister.

MINISTER: Corey, one more thing before I go. I've noticed that there is a lot of tension in this town. I stopped in at that restaurant over there and the waitress did everything but tell me she didn't want to help me. Then, I went to this little barbershop and was laughed right out the door. What's going on around here?

COREY WILLIAMS: Hatred. A lot of racial hatred, but it wasn't always like this. It's just been the last year and a half that things have gotten so bad. At one time it was peaceful in this town and everybody got along just fine. We even worshiped at the same church, both black and white, which is where it all started. The adult choir at church had been practicing a song for about two weeks. The song had four solo parts, one of which was being sung by a white girl named Jennifer Mundy. But because she had been sick, she missed a lot of practice. So, after about a week of being gone, she came back; That was on a Friday. The song they had been practicing had to be ready by Sunday morning service, and it pretty much was except for Jennifer's part. So the choir director, Ronald Hanks, who is black, suggested that she call her parents and ask them if she could stay a little while after practice to work on her part. Now because they knew and trusted Ronald, they said it was all right and let her stay. After they were finished and it was time to go, her parents had not arrived, so Ronald Hanks offered her a ride home, but she insisted on waiting for her parents. Before walking to his car, he asked her one last time if she wanted a ride, and again, she refused. So he gave her a hug, got in his car, and left her standing in front of the church. And that's where everything went wrong. As she waited in front of the church, somebody pulled up and offered her a ride home. More than likely it was somebody she knew and trusted. I know Jennifer, and I know there is no way she would get in the car with just anybody. So, considering the fact that her parents were now 45 minutes late, she accepted the ride. Now Ronald Hanks, who at this time is on his way home after stopping at the grocery store, decides to take a short cut which eventually put him at a stop sign at the corner of Potter and Wilson. After he takes a right on to Wilson Road he passes a car. That car, as it continued down Wilson Road headed in the opposite direction, would eventually find Jennifer walking. She was crying and her clothes were torn to shreds. It was obvious that she had been beaten up. So after picking her up and taking her to the hospital, they ran some tests and everybody's worst fears came true. The tests revealed that she had indeed been raped. With people standing around her bed, including the Mayor and the Chief of police, who are friends with her parents. Jennifer's father asked her who had raped her and that was the beginning of the end. Instead of telling the truth she lied and told them Ronald Hanks, the black choir director was the one that raped her.

MINISTER: Let me guess. Because they were left alone at the church, and his car was seen on the same road she was walking on, he was guilty before the trial even started.

COREY WILLIAMS: Exactly. I know Mr. Hanks. I've known his family all my life. His son and I are best friends, and I know there's no way in the world he would do something like that.

MINISTER: How long did the trial last?

COREY WILLIAMS: Two weeks. He never had a chance. They gave him mandatory fifteen years. You should have seen it. People were picketing outside the courthouse; there were reporters all over the place. People wanted to lock him under the jail; some of them wanted him dead. It got really bad around here. His poor wife couldn't even walk down the street without someone spitting on her or calling her all sorts of foul names.

MINISTER: What about their son?

COREY WILLIAMS: Larry? He couldn't take it. Things got so bad for him, his mom sent him to Connecticut to live with her sister. Oh yeah, it was re-election time, too. I forgot about that. The mayor wanted another term and he knew that Ronald getting off would kill any chance he had of getting that second term. So, I personally think that he fixed the whole thing, everything from the judge to the jury.

MINISTER: This Jennifer girl, where is she now?

COREY WILLIAMS: Last I heard, she and her family had moved to Cary. It's a small town about 50 miles from here.

MINISTER: That is some kind of story.

COREY WILLIAMS: That is also the reason why I study as hard as I do. I'm going to law school next year so I can prevent catastrophes like this from ever happening again.

MINISTER: Well, I tell you what. If you know that's God's will for your life don't ever let anybody convince you that you can't achieve it. Because what God has for you, is for you.

COREY WILLIAMS: That's what my mama tells me all the time.

MINISTER: She knows what she's talking about. You better listen to her.

COREY WILLIAMS: Oh, I do!

(Minister Ragland looks at his watch.)

MINISTER: Well, I need to get on the road. Corey, it has been a pleasure talking to you.

(They shake hands.)

COREY WILLIAMS: Same here. You drive careful.

MINISTER: I will. And don't forget what your mama said.

COREY WILLIAMS: Yes sir, I won't.

MINISTER: Take care.

COREY WILLIAMS: You too.

(Once Minister Ragland reaches the highway and is on his way to Bailey, he can't help but think about what Corey told him. Then, as if time suddenly stood still, he has a revelation. Everything comes into perspective and he realizes that him getting lost was no accident. God sent him to Swamp Fox for two reasons and two reasons only. To get an innocent man out of prison, and to bring the people of Swamp Fox back together to live in peace. After taking the first exit he sees, Minister Ragland

6

goes back to Swamp Fox, where he begins a journey that will change his life, and the tiny town of Swamp Fox forever.)

CHAPTER TWO

(After turning around and going back to Swamp Fox, Minister Ragland sees Corey walking down the street. So he blows his horn and yells.)

MINISTER: Hey, Corey!

(Corey turns to see who is calling him. As Minister Ragland pulls up to the curb, Corey walks up to the passenger side door and kneels down.)

COREY WILLIAMS: Let me guess, you don't know how to get back to the highway?

MINISTER: No, I do. I want to talk to you about something.

COREY WILLIAMS: What's up?

(Minister Ragland walks around to the other side of the car where Corey is standing.)

MINISTER: How would you like to get an early start on your career as a lawyer?

COREY WILLIAMS: What are you talking about?

MINISTER: Have you ever heard of a discerning spirit?

COREY WILLIAMS: I have, but I can't remember what it is.

MINISTER: A discerning spirit is a spiritual gift from God. Just like prophesying, speaking in tongues, and preaching, they're all spiritual gifts from God. If God gives you the gift of discernment, he's giving you the ability to tell the difference between right, wrong, good and evil, on a level you can't even imagine. It is so powerful, that someone you don't even know can walk up to you and if there's something wrong, instantly, in your spirit you feel it. The bible calls it your spirit man. It will let you know something is not right about that individual. The very second I walked into that restaurant, I knew that something was wrong. I just didn't know what. The bible says that the Holy Spirit will lead you to all truths. The Lord revealed the truth to me as I was driving down the highway. He revealed to me that I was never lost. He sent me here for a reason. He sent me here to get Ronald out of prison, and to somehow, someway, bring these people back together.

COREY WILLIAMS: You're joking, right?

MINISTER: No, I'm not.

COREY WILLIAMS: How exactly do you plan on doing all of this?

MINISTER: With a whole lot of faith, a whole lot of prayer, and a little snooping around, which is why I need your help.

COREY WILLIAMS: My help with what?

MINISTER: You know people I don't, like Ronald's wife Mrs. Hanks. I want to talk to her.

COREY WILLIAMS: I don't know, Minister Ragland. She's been through enough already.

MINSTER: Maybe she has. But I'm sure she would rather have her husband at home instead of locked up in some eight by ten cell for the next thirteen and a half years. I know this all sounds a little strange to you, and I myself cannot tell you how I'm going to do this. But with the Lord on my side, it will be done. That man deserves to be at home with his family, not locked up like some caged animal.

COREY WILLIAMS: Yeah, I guess you're right.

MINISTER: So are you gonna help me?

COREY WILLIAMS: Yeah, I'll help you.

MINISTER: Well, let's get going, Mr. Future Lawyer.

(After agreeing to help Minister Ragland, Corey gets in the car and they take off to see Mrs. Hanks. Corey rings the doorbell and Mrs. Hanks answers).

CYNTHIA HANKS: Oh my Lord! What a surprise! How are you doing, Corey?

(Before he enters the house, she hugs him.)

COREY WILLIAMS: I'm doing fine, how are you doing?

CYNTHIA HANKS: I'm good. How are your mama and daddy doing? I haven't talked to them in a couple of weeks.

COREY WILLIAMS: They're fine.

CYNTHIA HANKS: Who is this you have with you?

COREY WILLIAMS: This is Minister Joe Ragland. Minister, this is Cynthia Hanks.

(They shake hands.)

MINISTER: Nice to meet you, Mrs. Hanks.

CYNTHIA HANKS: Nice to meet you, brother Minister. Please, come in.

(Once inside she offers them a seat.)

CYNTHIA HANKS: Can I get you something to drink?

MINISTER: I'll take some water if it's not too much trouble.

CYNTHIA HANKS: Corey, I know what you want.

COREY WILLIAMS: Some of your good old-fashion homemade iced tea.

(Cynthia leaves the room to get the drinks. When Minister Ragland hears the clanging of glasses being pulled out of the cubbard, he walks over to the mantle and picks up their family photo.)

MINISTER: I assume this is her husband and son?

COREY WILLIAMS: Yeah, that's them.

(Cynthia enters the room to find Minister Ragland holding the photo.)

MINISTER: I'm sorry I was just looking. I hope you don't mind.

CYNTHIA HANKS: No, I don't mind.

MINISTER: You've got a nice looking family.

CYNTHIA HANKS: Thank you.

(They all sit down and Cynthia hands them their drinks.)

CYNTHIA HANKS: So what brings you two all the way out here?

(Minister Ragland and Corey look at each other.)

MINISTER: Well ma'am, I asked Corey to bring me out here so I could talk to you.

(She looks at Corey and then turns back to Minister Ragland.)

CYNTHIA HANKS: Talk to me about what?

MINISTER: About getting your husband out of prison.

CYNTHIA HANKS: I don't understand.

MINISTER: Mrs. Hanks, I know your husband is innocent and I'm gonna prove it. He's coming home.

CYNTHIA HANKS: What are you, some kind of lawyer or something?

MINISTER: No ma'am, just a man with ordered steps.

CYNTHIA HANKS: How are you going to prove he's innocent? You know something we don't?

MINISTER: No ma'am, but I do know a man named Jesus, and I do know that he sent me here to get your husband out of prison.

CYNTHIA HANKS: Well Joe, I'm a believer myself, and I know everything happens for a reason. Now, I'm not saying it can't be done; I'm just having a hard time with how it can be done. There are a lot of people in this town that will fight you tooth and nail on this. They don't want him out of prison.

MINISTER: But God does.

(She looks him in his eyes.)

CYNTHIA HANKS: You're serious, aren't you?

MINISTER: Yes, I am. And I'm going to need your help.

CYNTHIA HANKS: What can I do?

MINISTER: I would like to start with Jennifer. What do you know about her?

CYNTHIA HANKS: Well, her mother and I are, or were, best friends. My mother worked for her mother cleaning their house when I was a child. Over the years we developed a very special relationship. I was in the delivery room when Jennifer was born.

MINISTER: So you were close to her parents?

CYNTHIA HANKS: Very close. When Jennifer was six, her mother wanted to take some night classes at the community college. And because she was working during the day, and her husband was working at night, Jennifer would stay with us.

11

She stayed with us all the time. We loved and took care of Jennifer like she was our own daughter…

(In mid sentence Cynthia stops talking as she begins to cry.)

CYNTHIA HANKS: I don't understand any of this. How can people who say they love you do this kind of damage? I just don't understand.

MINISTER: Mrs. Hanks, whoever raped that girl was someone she knew and trusted enough to get in the car with. And I think she's hiding the truth because she's afraid. Chances are, whoever raped her, probably threatened to kill her or even her family to keep her quiet. That's how so many rapists commit that terrible crime and get away with it. They figure as long as that spirit of fear dwells in the heart of their victim, their freedom is guaranteed.

CYNTHIA HANKS: But why Ronald? Of all people why would she do this to him? There is nothing in this world he wouldn't have done for her.

(With her face covered in tears, she buries her face in her hands.)

MINISTER: Mrs. Hanks, the two of them being left alone at that church made him the perfect target. Then, someone seeing his car on the same road a mile or so from where she was found walking, pretty much sealed the deal for him. Mrs. Hanks, do you have any idea who could have raped Jennifer?

CYNTHIA HANKS: No.

(Corey leans over and whispers to the Minister.)

COREY WILLIAMS: Maybe we should go.

(Minster Ragland leans forward and gently grabs her hands.)

MINISTER: Mrs. Hanks, I never intended to come out here and upset you, but I have a lot of questions that need to be answered, and I had to start with you. I'm sorry.

(Cynthia looks at him with tears still streaming.)

CYNTHIA HANKS: It's okay. I just wish we could get our lives back.

MINISTER: You will. Remember Mrs. Hanks, we serve a God that promised us that he would make a way out of no way. Your breakthrough is coming, just hold on.

(Knowing it's best for them to leave, Corey stands up.)

MINISTER: We're gonna take off. I'll get your phone number from Corey and I'll call you if I have any more questions.

(Minister Ragland stands, pulling Cynthia up with him and then gives her a hug.)

CYNTHIA HANKS: Okay.

(Cynthia walks over to Corey and gives him a hug.)

COREY WILLIAMS: Call us if you need anything.

(He steps back and puts his hands on her shoulders.)

COREY WILLIAMS: Anything, anytime, okay?

(She shakes her head yes as she smiles at him.)

MINISTER: Thanks again for talking to me.

(Corey and Minister Ragland get in the car and leave.)

MINISTER: The lawyer that represented Ronald, what's his name?

COREY WILLIAMS: He doesn't practice law anymore. After the Hanks trial he never set foot in a courtroom again.

MINISTER: What was his name?

COREY WILLIAMS: Pete Wilson.

MINISTER: Was he a good lawyer?

COREY WILLIAMS: He was incredible. Nobody could work a courtroom like he could. On teacher workdays I would go down to the courthouse and sit in on some of his cases. He was the man.

MINISTER: Well, if he was that good why did he just up and quit?

COREY WILIAMS: Nobody knows.

MINISTER: Is he still in Swamp Fox?

COREY WILLIAMS: Yes. He owns a drug store in town. But I seriously doubt if he's going to talk to you about the trial.

MINISTER: He doesn't have to talk to me about the trial. I'll ask him a couple of out of the way questions, and if he's hiding something, his facial expression will do all the talking for him.

(With all confidence that they are onto something, Minister Ragland and Corey are off to see Pete Wilson.)

CHAPTER THREE

(As they enter the drug store, Pete Wilson is standing behind the counter stocking merchandise on a small shelf. Pete turns to see who is walking in.)

PETE WILSON: Attorney Corey Williams!

COREY WILLIAMS: I like the sound of that!

PETE WILSON: Well, you better get used to it because I see it in you! What can I do for you gentlemen today?

MINISTER: I need some film for my camera.

PETE WILSON: Okay. What kind of camera do you have? And what exposure do you need?

MINISTER: It's the Meridian 480 and I need 100 ASA.

PETE WILSON: Nice camera.

(Pete grabs the film and rings it up.)

PETE WILSON: That will be $4.79.

(He hands him a $5.00. As Pete is ringing up the film, Minister Ragland decides to go for it.)

MINISTER: Corey tells me you were a lawyer.

PETE WILSON: I practiced a little law here and there.

MINISTER: He said you were the best.

PETE WILSON: I don't know about that.

COREY WILLIAMS: Don't let him fool you. He was the best.

MINISTER: I bet you were good. Let me ask you something, out of all the cases you've tried, how many have you lost?

(Surprised by the question and completely caught off guard Pete is left speechless. He looks at Minister Ragland.)

PETE WILSON: One.

MINISTER: One case! Is that it? What happened?

PETE WILSON: Look, I'd love to chat but I've got a million things to do around here. Maybe some other time, all right?

(Pete puts Minister Ragland's film in a bag and hands it to him suggesting that he leave.)

PETE WILSON: You gentlemen have a good day.

(Minister Ragland slowly reaches out and grabs his bag as their eyes are locked on each other.)

MINISTER: You do the same.

(Minister Ragland turns and heads for the door.)

COREY WILLIAMS: Mr. Wilson, you take care.

PETE WILSON: You too, Corey.

(Once they're in the car Minister Ragland looks at Corey.)

MINISTER: Did you see that?

COREY WILLIAMS: I saw it.

MINISTER: The man looked like he had seen a ghost. He's hiding something.

(As Minister Ragland stares out of the window, an idea comes to mind and again he turns to Corey.)

MINSITER: You guys have a library around here?

COREY WILLIAMS: About three blocks that way, why?

MINISTER: I want to check on something.

(While at the library they pull up old newspaper clippings about Pete from the last ten years.)

MINISTER: You were right, this guy was incredible! The Hanks case was the only one he ever lost. Now why would somebody with that much talent in the courtroom just up and walk away like that? It doesn't make sense.

(Minister Ragland looks at his watch.)

MINISTER: We need to go, it's five o'clock and I need to get a room. I've got a ton of phone calls to make.

COREY WILLIAMS: Can you give me a ride home?

MINISTER: Corey, with all the help you've given me, I'd carry you home piggyback.

(They leave the library and arrive at Corey's house.)

COREY WILLIAMS: Come on in for a second.

(He looks at his watch again.)

MINISTER: I really need to go.

COREY WILLIAMS: Come on, I want you to meet my parents.

(He pauses.)

MINISTER: All right, but I can't stay too long.

(As they enter the front door, Corey yells.)

COREY WILLIAMS: Mama! Daddy!

JEAN WILLIAMS: We're in the kitchen!

(They walk into the kitchen where his mom is preparing dinner.)

COREY WILLIAMS: Mama, daddy. This is Minister Joe Ragland. Minister Ragland this is my mom Jean, and my dad, Earl.

MINISTER: Nice to meet you both.

(He shakes her hand.)

JEAN WILLIAMS: Nice to meet you.

(He then shakes his dad's hand.)

EARL WILLIAMS: Brother Ragland.

MINISTER: Nice to meet you.

COREY WILLIAMS: He just got into town today.

JEAN WILLIAMS: Oh, okay. Where are you from?

MINISTER: Charlotte.

EARL WILLIAMS: You here visiting someone?

MINISTER: Well, it's a long story.

JEAN WILLIAMS: You can tell us all about it while we eat. How about you stay for dinner?

MINISTER: I don't know, I'm kind of pressed for time.

COREY WILLIAMS: You mean to tell me, that you're gonna pass up on some of the best cooking in the state of South Carolina?

MINISTER: I'm afraid I'm gonna have to.

COREY WILLIAMS: Come on, just stay. You said you needed to get some food in your system.

EARL WILLIAMS: We've got plenty to eat.

MINISTER: You sure it's not a problem?

EARL WILLIAMS: Not at all. We'd enjoy the company. It's not often we have dinner guest.

(He leans over and whispers to Minister Ragland.)

EARL WILLIAMS: Not everybody's brave enough to eat her cooking.

JEAN WILLIAMS: I heard that! It sounds like somebody's brave enough to sleep on the couch tonight.

MINISTER: Uh oh! Now, I heard that.

(Amused by the fact that his dad got busted, Corey laughs hysterically. As they all sit down at the table to eat, they join hands and bless the food.)

EARL WILLIAMS: Heavenly Father, we thank you for this food we are about to receive. And we ask you to please bless and provide for those that are less fortunate. Father, please allow this food we are about to receive to be nourishment to our bodies, so that we, your people, may continue to spread your gospel, all the days of our lives.

In Jesus name we pray, Amen.

(They all say Amen.)

JEAN WILLIAMS: So, what brings you to town?

(After looking at Corey, Minister Ragland turns to receive a bowl of mashed potatoes that are being passed to him.)

MINISTER: Thank you

(He puts a scoop on his plate and begins to explain.)

MINISTER: Ronald Hanks is why I came to town.

JEAN WILLIAMS: Are you two friends?

MINISTER: Not yet, but we will be.

(She looks at her husband and then turns back to the Minister.)

JEAN WILLIAMS: I don't understand.

(Minister Ragland takes a deep breath.)

MINISTER: I'm here to get him out of prison.

(Both Earl and Jean stop eating and look at each other.)

EARL WILLIAMS: Get him out of prison? What do you mean?

MINISTER: The Lord has sent me here to get him out.

JEAN WILLIAMS: Joe, you do know why he's locked up don't you?

MINISTER: Yes, I do. Corey told me everything.

(Corey's parents stare at Minister Ragland not really sure of what to say.)

MINISTER: Look, I know it sounds crazy, and it may even sound impossible, but one way or another I will get him out. You two know as well as I do that Jennifer is not the only one to blame for this mess. She's not the only one with dirty hands in the sink.

(Corey smiles.)

EARL WILLIAMS: Joe, I understand what you're saying, and if this is God's will, you're right, he will get out. But you had better be extra careful about who you talk to around here about that trial. You start asking questions and you're gonna make a lot of people nervous around here, a lot of people.

MINISTER: Yeah, I noticed that this afternoon when I talked to Pete Wilson.

JEAN WILLIAMS: You talked to Pete Wilson? What did he say?

MINISTER: He didn't have to say anything because his face said it all. He's dirty, and I know it. That man knows something, something that can blow this whole thing wide open.

COREY WILLIAMS: Or get somebody blown wide open.

(They all turn and look at Corey as the realization of his comment causes a cold blanket of silence to settle on the entire room.)

CHAPTER FOUR

(Minister Ragland, now in his hotel room, pulls a piece of paper out of his pocket with Mrs. Hanks' phone number on it and calls her.)

MINISTER: Mrs. Hanks, this is Joe.

CYNTHIA HANKS: Hey Joe.

MINISTER: How are you?

CYNTHIA HANKS: I'm doing okay.

MINISTER: Good. Mrs. Hanks, I need to talk to your husband. When can we go see him?

CYNTHIA HANKS: Well, they have visiting hours between one and four on Saturdays. But I'm a little skeptical about how he's going to react to you asking him questions about the trial.

MINISTER: I understand what you're saying, but it's very important that I talk to him.

CYNTHIA HANKS: Okay. We'll go see him tomorrow. But he's not going to be happy about this. He's trying to forget about the whole thing and serve his time with the little peace of mind he has left.

MINISTER: Mrs. Hanks, he can't forget. I don't care how hard he tries. That prison uniform he wears everyday won't let him forget. Those steel doors that slam shut behind him won't let him forget. Waking up day after day without his wife and child won't let him forget.

(Minister Ragland has made a very powerful point that opens her eyes.)

CYNTHIA HANKS: Be here tomorrow at 12:00 noon. We'll go see him.

(Before picking up Mrs. Hanks the next day, Minister Ragland decides to have some breakfast. As he's driving through town, he looks to his right and sees the restaurant he stopped at when he arrived in Swamp Fox the day before and he whispers to himself.)

MINISTER: He will make your enemy your footstool.

(He decides at that moment to go back to the restaurant in spite of the nasty service he got the first time. He walks in, sits at the counter, and there to his right is Faye, the same rude waitress he had the day before. Faye walks over and stands in front of him with her arms crossed.)

MINISTER: How are you...

(He leans forward to read her nametag.)

MINISTER: Faye?

(Minister Ragland smiles.)

FAYE WATERS: What do you want?

MINISTER: For starters, I'll have a menu.

(She throws a menu on the counter and impatiently waits for him to order as she taps her fingers on the counter.)

MINISTER: You sure do have a lot of good food on this menu, Faye.

FAYE WATERS: Are you gonna order or not?

MINISTER: Yes. I'll have a glass of ice water and the Breakfast Time special. How's that?

FAYE WATERS: Is that it?

MINISTER: That is it.

(She yanks the menu out of his hand and walks away. After the Minister has finished eating, he walks up to the register to pay.)

MINISTER: What's the damage?

FAYE WATERS: Look, you ordered the same thing yesterday! The price hasn't changed. It's still three dollars and eighty cents.

(Minister Ragland gives her a ten, and again, instead of handing him his change she throws it on the counter. Minister Ragland picks up his change and walks out smiling. As Faye begins to clean his area, something catches her eye. She sees that one of his napkins has something written on it, and it says... "Love your enemies, bless those who curse you, do good to those who hate you, and pray for those that spitefully use and persecute you." After reading the napkin, she looks around to see if anybody is watching, puts it in her apron pocket, and continues to clean. While on their way to the prison, Minister Ragland notices that Cynthia is a little nervous.)

MINISTER: You all right?

CYNTHIA HANKS: Just a little nervous, that's all.

MINISTER: Don't be nervous. Everything is going to work out.

(After sitting in the waiting room for a little while Ronald Hanks enters the room.)

CYNTHIA HANKS: Hey baby, how are you?

(They hug.)

RONALD HANKS: I'm doing all right, how about you?

CYNTHIA HANKS: I'm okay.

(After the hug they sit down.)

CYNTHIA HANKS: Ronald, are you getting enough to eat? You've lost so much weight.

RONALD HANKS: Yes, I'm eating, honey.

CYNTHIA HANKS: But look at you. You're getting so thin.

RONALD HANKS: Honey, I promise I'm getting enough to eat. Who's this?

CYNTHIA HANKS: Honey, this is Minister Joe Ragland. Joe, this is my husband Ronald.

(They shake hands.)

MINISTER: It's a pleasure to meet you, Mr. Hanks

RONALD HANKS: Nice to meet you.

CYNTHIA HANKS: Ronald, Joe is here to help you.

RONALD HANKS: With what?

CYNTHIA HANKS: He's gonna help you get out of here.

RONALD HANKS: What?

MINISTER: Mr. Hanks, I know what happened and I know you're innocent. I'm gonna get you out of here.

(He looks at his wife.)

RONALD HANKS: What's going on here Cynthia?

CYNTHIA HANKS: Ronald, he's here to help you, baby.

RONALD HANKS: How are you gonna prove I'm innocent?

MINISTER: By finding out who really raped Jennifer, and a little prayer of course. Prayer changes things you know.

RONALD HANKS: Does it really? Well, I've been praying since they threw me in this rat hole and not a thing has changed for me.

MINISTER: Mr. Hanks, don't allow a lie and crooked justice destroy your faith. You have to hold on.

RONALD HANKS: I have to hold on? No, the only thing I have to do is survive in here. That's what I have to do. But I don't expect you to understand that. See, you don't know what it's like living day-to-day worrying about somebody sneaking up behind you and shoving a shank through your skull. I don't expect you to know what it's like to worry about being raped or getting dragged off to a room by one of these racist guards and getting your brains beat out. When I wake up in the morning, the first question I ask myself, is am I going to die today? I shouldn't even be here. I did not rape Jennifer!

MINISTER: I know that, and that's why I'm here. I need you to tell me everything that happened that night at the church. Give me every detail.

RONALD HANKS: For what? There's nothing you can do!

MINISTER: Mr. Hanks, please. Tell me what happened?

RONALD HANKS: Don't you get it? Without the truth there's nothing you can do. So just let it go.

MINISTER: Mr. Hanks, I don't know where your faith is, but mine is in Christ Jesus. So whether you help me or not, I will find out who raped that girl. But I want you to remember something. There is an entire town divided because of one lie, which in turn is divided because of color. The Bible says a house that is divided cannot stand. Swamp Fox is that house Mr. Hanks, and the foundation it's sitting on is about to cave in. Sooner or later that house is going to collapse, and when it does, people are going to die. Do you understand what I'm saying? People are going to die. You think about that.

(Minister Ragland grabs his coat and stands up.)

CYNTHIA HANKS: Mrs. Hanks, I'll see you in the car.

(As Minister Ragland turns to walk away, Mrs. Hanks looks at her husband. After about 5 seconds of silence Ronald speaks.)

RONALD HANKS: Where do you want me to start?

(Minister Ragland stops, turns around, looks at Ronald, Ronald looks at his wife, and she slowly shakes her head yes as reassurance to her husband that he's doing the right thing. After talking with Ronald and getting back on the road to Swamp Fox, Minister Ragland offers to buy her dinner.)

MINISTER: What do you say we grab a bite to eat? It's on me.

CYNTHIA HANKS: You don't have to do that.

MINISTER: I know I don't have to, but I want to. What do you say?

CYNTHIA HANKS: Sure, why not.

MINISTER: There's a little Mexican restaurant around the corner from my hotel?

CYNTHIA HANKS: Not Border-to-Border?

MINISTER: Yeah, that's it. What's wrong? Is the food not good?

CYNTHIA HANKS: No, it's not that. It's just that I'm not too crazy about being in town.

MINISTER: You can't spend the rest of your life shut up in your house.

CYNTHIA HANKS: I know. But it's hard to deal with the whispering and pointing I get when I'm in town. They treat me like an outcast, and please stop calling me Mrs. Hanks. Call me Cynthia.

MINISTER: You can't let them intimidate you, Cynthia. We'll go in, eat some good Mexican food, and we'll leave. Just ignore them.

(As they enter the restaurant, almost immediately the pointing and whispering begins. After being escorted to their table, they sit down and she leans forward to talk to Minister Ragland.)

CYNTHIA HANKS: See what I mean?

MINISTER: Just ignore them.

(Sitting in the back of the restaurant in a large corner booth, is the Mayor of Swamp Fox, the Chief of police, a city councilman, and Pete Wilson.)

MAYOR: Well, well, well, isn't this a surprise?

RAYMOND CLETTER: What?

MAYOR: Cynthia Hanks.

(They all turn to look at her.)

RAYMOND CLETTER: Looks like the dead has risen. Who is that she's with?

PETE WILSON: I was wondering the same thing. He came into my store yesterday with the Williams kid acting very strange.

(Raymond, feeling a little uncomfortable with what Pete has just said stops eating.)

RAYMOND CLETTER: What do you mean strange?

PETE WILSON: I don't know. He said he came in to buy some film for his camera, but I got a feeling he was looking for more than that. He started asking all kinds of questions about me being a lawyer and how many cases I had lost.

(Raymond nervously looks at Pete.)

HAYWOOD BURGESS: Pete, don't be so paranoid. That man coming to your store was probably nothing.

(Raymond, with a very concerned look on his face turns around to look at Minister Ragland one more time.)

MINISTER: Cynthia I want you to do me a favor. When I tell you to, I want you to slowly turn around and look towards the far right corner of the restaurant.)

(He tells her it's safe and she slowly turns to look.)

CYNTHIA HANKS: You talking about the big booth?

MINISTER: Yeah. That's an awfully interesting looking bunch sitting with your husband lawyer back there. By the way, Corey and I dropped in on Mr. Wilson after we left your house.

(Surprised by what he just said, Cynthia leans forward and whispers.)

CYNTHIA HANKS: Did you ask him about the trial?

MINISTER: No, I just went by to see where his head was. Who are the others?

(Again she turns to look and then quickly turns back to Minister Ragland.)

CYNTHIA HANKS: The one in the blue shirt, that's Sidney Linney. He's a City Councilman. The one to his right wearing the glasses is Mayor Haywood Burgess. And the one in the uniform is Raymond Cletter. He's the Chief of Police.

MINISTER: The Mayor, what's his story?

CYNTHIA HANKS: Your typical politician. He owns half the land in Swamp Fox and didn't pay one dime for it. He's cheated people out of land that's been in their families for generations.

(Minister Ragland shakes his head in disgust.)

MINISTER: That's all right he'll get his sooner or later. Cynthia do you have a picture of Jennifer?

CYNTHIA HANKS: Plenty of them. Why?

MINISTER: I'm going to drive to Cary tomorrow to find her and I need to know what she looks like.

(As Cynthia is putting her glass of water up to her mouth to drink she freezes, puts the glass back on the table, and sits straight up in her chair.)

CYNTHIA HANKS: You're gonna do what?

MINISTER: I was thinking about driving to Cary to find her.

CYNTHIA HANKS: You can't do that Joe.

MINISTER: Why not?

CYNTHIA HANKS: She doesn't even know you. You're going to scare her to death.

MINISTER: Well, that's a chance I'm willing to take. It's very important that I talk to her. She's the eye of the storm.

CYNTHIA HANKS: It's too dangerous Joe.

MINISTER: I'm not worried about it being dangerous. I'm worried about not being able to find her.

CYNTHIA HANKS: Finding her is the easy part. She's a senior and there's only one high school in Cary.

MINISTER: Well that's it. I'll catch up with her at school.

26

CYNTHIA HANKS: What are you going to say to her? "Hey, Jennifer, I know you lied. How about coming back to Swamp Fox and telling the truth." Joe, if you approach that girl and you say something to scare her, the first thing she's going to do is run home and tell her parents, and then there will be trouble. I know Sam Mundy, and when it comes to his little girl, nothing else in the world matters. You mess with her, and all hell is going to break loose.

MINISTER: No, hell is what Swamp Fox will be like if this situation isn't resolved soon. There are a lot of angry people in this town that are dying to release a little tension. Once that tension is released Cynthia, there is going to bloodshed. I'm talking full-scale race war. The kind of war that will make something as simple as going to your mailbox dangerous. Now as far as Sam Mundy and his little temper tantrum, I'm not worried about that. The only thing I'm concerned about is finding Jennifer.

(Realizing there's no changing his mind, she sighs.)

CYNTHIA HANKS: I assume there's no way to talk you out of this, is there?

MINISTER: Not a chance. So you may as well give me a picture and some directions. If not, then I'll break out my trusty old map and get there myself.

CYNTHIA HANKS: No, please. The last time you broke out your trusty old map you ended up South, trying to go North. You need to leave trusty where it is. I wouldn't want you to leave here and end up in Zimbabwe or somewhere. I'll give you directions.

(Amused by her sarcasm, Minister Ragland smiles as he shakes her hand and thanks her.)

CHAPTER FIVE

(The next morning before driving to Cary, Minister Ragland decides to have breakfast at his favorite new eating spot, Breakfast Time.)

MINISTER: Good morning, Faye! How are you this fine sunny morning?

FAYE WATERS: Why do you keep coming around here? There are three other restaurants in this town where you can get breakfast. Why do you insist on coming in here bugging me?

MINISTER: Because there is no way I can start my day without doing two things. One is praying, and two is seeing your beautiful face.

FAYE WATERS: Whatever. What do you want?

(Minister Ragland laughs.)

MINISTER: I'll have the usual.

FAYE WATERS: Look, I don't have time for your games! Now what do you want!

MINISTER: A tall glass of ice water and a menu. How's that for now?

(A short while later, after eating his food, Minister Ragland walks up to the register to pay.)

MINISTER: What's the damage?

(Irritated by him asking her what the damage is again, she shakes her head.)

FAYE WATERS: Once again, the cost, not the damage, is three dollars and eighty cents. The same as it was yesterday, and the day before when you ordered it.

(He gives her a ten.)

MINISTER: Keep the change.

(Faye looks down at the money and then looks up at Minister Ragland.)

FAYE WATERS: You do realize that you gave me a ten don't you?

MINISTER: Yeah, I know. Have a nice day, Faye.

(Faye, surprised that she even got a tip after the way she treated him, and such a large one, stands there and watches him as he walks out. After putting the money in her apron pocket, Faye walks over to the area where he was eating and begins to throw away his trash. Out of the corner of her eye, she sees another napkin in the trashcan with writing on it. She didn't notice the writing at first, but when she does, she grabs the napkin and reads it. It says: "Romans chapter 12, verses 17 and 18, "Repay no one evil for evil. Have regard for good things in the sight of all men. If it is possible as much as depends on you, live peaceably with all men." After reading the napkin, again she looks around to see if anybody is watching her, and again puts it in her apron pocket. Two hours later after getting lost a couple of times, Minister Ragland arrives at Jennifer's school. He sees a student sitting on a bench and approaches him.)

MINISTER: Excuse me.

(The young man looks up at him only to find the glare of the sun. So he puts his hand up to block the sun as he talks to Minister Ragland.)

YOUNG MAN: Yeah.

MINISTER: Do you know a Jennifer Mundy?

YOUNG MAN: Yes.

MINISTER: Do you know where I can find her?

(The young man looks around and then points.)

YOUNG MAN: There she is right there.

(Minister Ragland turns to look and there she is standing at a water fountain talking to a couple of her friends. He looks at the picture that Cynthia gave him to make sure it's her and it is.)

MINISTER: Thanks.

YOUNG MAN: No problem, dude.

(Minster Ragland slowly makes his way across the school courtyard. Jennifer is saying good-bye to her friends as they walk off in different directions going to class. To make sure he doesn't tell a lie, Minister Ragland throws his directions back to Swamp Fox in a trash can while making his way towards Jennifer.)

MINISTER: Excuse me!

(Jennifer turns to see who is talking to her.)

MINISTER: I'm sorry to bother you, but I was wondering if you could help me with some directions?

JENNIFER MUNDY: Sure. Where are you headed?

MINISTER: I'm trying to find a small town called Swamp Fox. I'm not from around here and I don't have any directions.

(Somewhat surprised by his answer she hesitantly answers.)

JENNIFER MUNDY: Swamp Fox? Just get back on the highway, take exit 219, follow it for about 15 miles, and then get off on the Creek Crossing Road exit and turn left. Once you make that left, just stay on Creek Crossing Road and it will take you straight to Swamp Fox.

MINISTER: Creek Crossing Road, I got it. I appreciate it.

JENNIFER MUNDY: Sure thing.

(Minister Ragland turns to walk away. Jennifer's curiosity, which at this point has gotten the best of her, is wondering why he's going to Swamp Fox so she asks.)

JENNIFER MUNDY: Sir!

(Minister Ragland turns to face her.)

MINISTER: Yes.

JENNIFER MUNDY: Do you have family in Swamp Fox? I know some people that live there.

MINISTER: No. Just a friend, but I don't think you'd know him.

JENNIFER MUNDY: What's his name?

MINISTER: Ronald Hanks.

(Jennifer is lost for words as she stares at him.)

MINISTER: Are you all right?

(Jennifer continues to stare at him not saying a word.)

JENNIFER MUNDY: What, yeah. Look, I need to go. I'm gonna be late for class.

(Jennifer nervously turns and walks away. As she is walking, she looks back at Minister Ragland one more time and begins to walk even faster still shocked by his answer. Minister Ragland goes back to his hotel and calls Cynthia.)

MINISTER: Cynthia, I found her.

CYNTHIA HANKS: What happened?

MINISTER: Just what I expected. I mentioned his name and she panicked. She ran off.

CYNTHIA HANKS: I bet day-to-day life is an absolute struggle for that poor girl. I don't see how she sleeps at night.

MINISTER: Cynthia, I assure you that a good night's sleep is something she hasn't seen in a long time.

CYNTHIA HANKS: The best thing we can do is keep praying for her. Speaking of prayer, how would you like to come to church with me Sunday?

MINISTER: I'd love to.

CYNTHIA HANKS: Good, I'll pick you up in front of your hotel around 10:30 Sunday morning.

MINISTER: I'll see you then. Bye.

(After they hang up the phone, Cynthia looks up at a picture of her husband on the mantle and whispers.)

CYNTHIA HANKS: And this too shall pass. This too, shall pass.

(Just before Sunday morning service starts, Cynthia introduces Minister Ragland to some of her friends that are standing out front. After a few minutes of chitchat they all begin to make their way into the church as the service gets under way. After some high-spirited gospel singing, the Pastor, Pastor Fredricks, is coming to the end of his sermon and the spirit is high. There are people standing, some are clapping, and others are giving praise by waiving their arms.)

PASTOR FREDRICKS: See that's the problem with some Christians. We get so holy and so sanctified, that we start to think we're better than those non-Christians! We are so quick to point out their faults and sins, knowing that behind closed doors we are the devil's MVP! Saints, let me tell you something that some of you may not be aware of. We are not better than non-Christians; we're just better off! The only way we will ever be better than non- Christians is if we live a sin free and perfect life!

Now, I hate to bust your bubble folks, but I'm telling you that will never happen! We will never be perfect, none of us. If we were perfect, we wouldn't need Jesus! The same Jesus that died on the cross for you and me!

CONGREGATION: Amen!

PASTOR FREDRICKS: The same Jesus that will give you sixty years to live, when the doctors say you've only got six months.

(By this time most of the congregation are on their feet.)

PASTOR FREDRICKS: The same Jesus that called out to a man named Lazarus that had been lying in a tomb dead for four days! Jesus said to him, "Lazarus! Come out!" And do you know why he called him by his name? Because if he had not, every dead body in that tomb would have gotten up and walked out! Hallelujah! Hallelujah!

(The entire church has absolutely erupted in praise. Some are crying and some are clapping. But in the middle of the aisle, praising the Lord with all he has is Minister Ragland dancing and shouting to the heavens above as the sound of praise roars through the building. After the service, Pastor Fredricks is standing at the door greeting people as they leave.)

CYNTHIA HANKS: Pastor Fredricks, this is Minister Joe Ragland. Minister Ragland, this is Pastor Fredricks.

PASTOR FREDRICKS: Brother Minister, I hope you enjoyed the service.

MINISTER: Oh I did. I was truly blessed.

PASTOR FREDRICKS: Well, praise the Lord.

MINISTER: Pastor, I was wondering if I could talk to you when you're done here.

PASTOR FREDRICKS: I tell you what, if you can give me about a half hour, we'll go on out to the house and have some supper.

MINISTER: Sounds good to me.

(After finishing Sunday dinner, Cynthia and the Pastor's wife begin to clear the table.)

MINISTER: Here, let me help.

PASTOR'S WIFE: No, don't worry about it. We'll take care of it.

MINISTER: Are you sure?

PASTOR'S WIFE: I'm sure. You're a guest in this house, you don't do dishes.

(The ladies leave the room and it's just the two of them sitting at the table.)

PASTOR FREDRICKS: So where are you from Joe?

MINISTER: Charlotte.

PASTOR FREDRICKS: My brother-in-law has a church in Charlotte!

MINISTER: What's the name of it?

PASTOR FREDRICKS: Hatcher Grove Missionary Baptist.

MINISTER: Kenneth Pugh! He's your brother-in-law?

PASTOR FREDRICKS: Sure is. He married my baby sister.

MINISTER: I've visited his church many times. He is a powerful man of God.

PASTOR FREDRICKS: Yes he is. You got kinfolk here in Swamp Fox?

MINISTER: No sir.

PASTOR FREDRICKS: You just here visiting the Hanks?

MINISTER: I am now.

PASTOR FREDRICKS: What do you mean?

MINISTER: God has decided that it's time for Ronald to come home. And he's appointed me lawyer, slash middleman, slash detective.

PASTOR FREDRICKS: What are you telling me son?

MINISTER: The Lord led me here to get him out.

PASTOR FREDRICKS: To get him out?

MINISTER: Yes sir.

PASTOR FREDRICKS: And you said God has called you to do this?

MINISTER: Yes sir, he has.

PASTOR FREDRICKS: Do you have any idea how dangerous that's going to be?

MINISTER: Yes sir. I've already been warned.

PASTOR FREDRICKS: God sent you?

MINISTER: Yes he did.

PASTOR FREDRICKS: Okay. I don't doubt your calling, Joe, don't get me wrong. I just want you to be sure that your steps are ordered. Because there are folks around here that are willing to do whatever it takes to settle the dust you're about to kick up. So you make sure you watch yourself.

MINISTER: I will.

PASTOR FREDRICKS: You know I feel sorry for whoever raped her. I really do, because when the wrath of God comes down on them, and he deals with them for taking the innocence and purity from that child, they are going to suffer beyond their wildest imagination. She was so precious, Joe. And her voice was absolutely phenomenal.

MINISTER: She was that good?

PASTOR FREDRICKS: Anointed. She is truly anointed. When she sang on Sundays, you couldn't find a dry eye in the entire church, not one.

MINISTER: I met with Ronald the other day. He's struggling, and he's a little angry with God right now.

PASTOR FREDRICKS: Accept what God allows. As much as we sometimes hate to do it, good or bad we have to accept what God allows. He is still in control, and in the end, some good is going to come out of all of this. Regardless of how it may look now.

MINISTER: How long have you known him?

PASTOR FREDRICKS: Long enough to know that he would never do something like that. I'd trust him with everything I've got, including my children.

MINISTER: What do you know about Pete Wilson, Pastor?

PASTOR FREDRICKS: He was a natural born leader, but eventually he lost his focus and became a follower.

MINISTER: Who is he following?

PASTOR FREDRICKS: He's become Haywood's little shadow.

MINISTER: That's the Mayor, right?

PASTOR FREDRICKS: Yes.

MINISTER: Do you think Ronald's trial was fixed?

PASTOR FREDRICKS: I don't want to pass judgement on anyone, but if I had to guess I would say it was. Something illegal went on during that trial.

MINISTER: They're going down. If it takes me from now until judgement day, they will go down. People are walking around here afraid to stand up for themselves, but I'm not. I don't care if it's the Mayor, the Governor, the Chief of Police, or whoever. If I find out that trial was fixed, they are going to jail. And I'm willing to do whatever it takes to put them there.

(Pastor Fredricks shakes his head as Minister Ragland talks.)

PASTOR FREDRICKS: Wrong attitude, Joe. Look at you; you're sitting here practically on fire just talking about it. And you've got revenge written all over your face, that's the wrong attitude. Let me tell you something, son. You need to take those personal feelings of yours, and check them at the door. Don't make this a Joe thing; let it remain a God thing. You understand what I'm saying?

MINISTER: Yes sir.

PASTOR FREDRICKS: Joe, what's a surgeon's responsibility?

MINISTER: I'm sorry?

PASTOR FREDRICKS: A surgeon. What are some of their responsibilities?

MINISTER: Ahhh, I don't know. They find out why people are hurting. They mend things that are broken back together. They take things out of people that can hurt them and put in things that can help them.

(By the time Minister Ragland finishes his sentence, he realizes why Pastor Fredricks asks him the question. And by the look on his face Pastor Fredricks sees that he's got it.)

PASTOR FREDRICKS: Do you understand what I'm saying, son?

MINISTER: Yes sir.

PASTOR FREDRICKS: Then consider yourself a licensed MD. Go out and mend things that are broken, like hearts. Go out and take things out of people that can hurt them, like hate and racism. Go out and put things in them, Joe that can help them, like love, and the word of God. Lean not on your own understanding, Joe, but in all your ways acknowledge Him and he shall direct your paths.

(After coming to such a powerful understanding, Minister Ragland reaches across the table and shakes Pastor Fredrick's hand as they both smile at each other.)

CHAPTER SIX

(Cynthia Hanks, excited about the initiative that Minister Ragland has taken to help her husband, drives to the prison to tell him about his encounter with Jennifer in hopes of encouraging him. As Cynthia waits for Ronald to show up, she looks around at the other families in the visiting room and sees a little boy hug his father who is one of the prisoners there. Then the little boy climbs up onto his father's lap and lays his head on his shoulder causing Cynthia to think back to when their son, Larry, would do the same thing with Ronald when he was a child. As Cynthia continues to observe the other families and reminisce, Ronald sneaks up behind her.)

RONALD HANKS: Cynthia!

(Cynthia jumps and puts her hand over her heart.)

CYNTHIA HANKS: What are doing sneaking up on me like that? You scared me!

(She stands up and they hug.)

RONALD HANKS: I miss you so much.

CYNTHIA HANKS: I miss you too, baby.

(With their fingers intertwined, they sit down at the table across from each other with smiles of love on their faces.)

RONALD HANKS: What were you daydreaming about when I walked in?

CYNTHIA HANKS: I was just looking at the other families and thinking about you, and Larry, and how close we used to be.

RONALD HANKS: We're still close baby, and we always will be.

CYNTHIA HANKS: I know. But there's nothing like being together. That's what I miss the most. Not being able to hold you two at the same time, I really miss it. But guess what, I may not have to miss it much longer.

RONALD HANKS: What are you talking about?

CYNTHIA HANKS: Baby, Joe talked to Jennifer.

(With his mouth wide open, Ronald leans forward.)

RONALD HANKS: He talked to her?

CYNTHIA HANKS: Can you believe that?

RONALD HANKS: Where did he see her?

CYNTHIA HANKS: He drove to Cary and talked to her at school. He asked her how to get to Swamp Fox and she told him. Then she asked him who he was going to see. And when he mentioned your name, she panicked and ran off.

RONALD HANKS: Sam Mundy is going to have a fit if she tells him.

CYNTHIA HANKS: I know. I tried to tell him that, but he was dead set on going.

RONALD HANKS: What else did he say to her?

CYNTHIA HANKS: He didn't say anything. He didn't have a chance to because she ran off.

RONALD HANKS: You mean that's it? He mentioned my name and she ran off? That's it?

CYNTHIA HANKS: Yeah. What do you mean is that it?

RONALD HANKS: How does that help me? He said my name she got scared and ran off. Big deal, so what!

CYNTHIA HANKS: Ronald…

(Before she can say anything else, he interrupts.)

RONALD HANKS: See, I was right; it's a waste of time. And until she decides to tell the truth that's all it's ever going to be. A big waste of his time!

CYNTHIA HANKS: What is your problem? He is trying to help you.

RONALD HANKS: Help me. The best way for him to help is to leave me alone!

(Ronald, now upset, gets up and walks away leaving Cynthia sitting there. Later that day while Corey is getting his books out of his locker for his next class, along comes a girl named Jacy. He's had a serious crush on her since the day he first saw her. Jacy's locker is next to his.)

COREY WILLIAMS: What's up, Miss Jacy?

JACY ELLIS: Nothing much, Mr. Corey. What's up with you?

COREY WILLIAMS: Well, I'm just standing here thinking about how blessed I am to have survived another fifty minutes with the wonderful Mr. Washington.

JACY ELLIS: I know what you mean. My time of misfortune is seventh period.

COREY WILLIAMS: Let me warn you, he's giving a surprise test today, "The Duality of Man".

JACY ELLIS: It's only been two weeks! He said we had a month to study for that test!

COREY WILLIAMS: Good old Mr. Washington. You've gotta love him.

JACY ELLIS: Yeah, like a pimple. I'll see you later.

COREY WILLIAMS: Give him a hug for me.

JACY ELLIS: Yeah, right.

(After closing her locker door, Jacy turns and walks away, only to turn back around seconds later to ask Corey a question.)

JACY ELLIS: Hey, Corey!

(He turns to face her.)

JACY ELLIS: What are your plans for this weekend?

COREY WILLIAMS: Don't have any, why what's up?

JACY ELLIS: I was wondering if you would like to go to the Air Show on Saturday.

(Corey is completely caught off guard.)

COREY WILLIAMS: What, with you?

JACY ELLIS: Of course with me. Why is there something wrong with me?

COREY WILLIAMS: Oh no, not at all, not a thing.

JACY ELLIS: So it's a date?

COREY WILLIAMS: It's a date.

JACY ELLIS: Cool.

(Jacy walks up to him and opens her notebook.)

JACY ELLIS: Write your phone number down and I'll call you so we can finalize everything.

(Corey, who is about to explode from excitement, writes his number down.)

JACY ELLIS: Open your hand.

(She writes her number down in his hand.)

JACY ELLIS: Call me.

(Jacy turns to walk away.)

COREY WILLIAMS: When?

(Jacy turns around to face Corey as she walks backwards.)

JACY ELLIS: Anytime.

(Corey, overwhelmed by the fact that Jacy asked him out, steps behind his locker door after she's gone and does a little dance. As Jacy was holding Corey's hand to write down her phone number, her racist brother and two of his friends just happened to be passing at the other end of the hall.)

TOMMY KILGROE: Why can't those niggers stick with their own kind?

SHELTON ELLIS: What does she think she's doing?

KEVIN CAMPBELL: Looks like she made a new friend.

SHELTON ELLIS: Not if I can help it.

TOMMY KILGROE: Shelton, you need to talk to her, man. That's not cool.

SHELTON ELLIS: Oh, I will. You can believe that.

(Later that evening Jacy is in her room doing her homework when Shelton, her brother, walks in without knocking.)

JACY ELLIS: Have you ever heard of knocking?

SHELTON ELLIS: What were you doing with that nigger this afternoon?

JACY ELLIS: Excuse me?

SHELTON ELLIS: At school this afternoon right before 4th period, I saw you talking and laughing with that nigger in the hall!

JACY ELLIS: First of all, that's none of your business! Second of all, stop calling him that! He has a name!

SHELTON ELLIS: I don't care what his name is! He's a nigger and I want you to stay away from him!

JACY ELLIS: Shelton, who do you think you are coming in here trying to tell me what to do? You are not my father and I don't have to answer to you.

SHELTON ELLIS: Let me tell you something, Jacy. If you keep hanging out with that nigger you're gonna end up just like Jennifer Mundy.

JACY ELLIS: Jennifer Mundy! Jennifer Mundy is a liar!

SHELTON ELLIS: What is your problem Jacy? You want people calling you a nigger lover? Is that what you want? Because that's what you're going to get!

JACY ELLIS: I don't care what they call me; Corey and I are just friends.

SHELTON ELLIS: Well, I suggest you find some new friends. I don't want to see you talking to him again and I mean it!

JACY ELLIS: Whatever. Get out of my room.

SHELTON ELLIS: I'm serious, Jacy. Stay away from him. If mom and dad found out about this it would kill them.

JACY ELLIS: Mom and dad would not have a problem with Corey and I being friends. Not everybody's a racist pig like you, Shelton. Now get out of my room!

SHELTON ELLIS: You're making a big mistake.

JACY ELLIS: Get out of my room!

(Angered by the fact that his sister won't listen to him, Shelton storms out of the room and slams the door. Later that same night, Jennifer is in her room crying when the doorbell rings. Her mom answers, it's her friend Jill.)

JILL ASNER: Hi, Mrs. Mundy.

ANNE MUNDY: Hi, Jill. Come on in. Jennifer's upstairs in her room.

JILL ASNER: Hi, Mr. Mundy.

SAM MUNDY: Good to see you, Jill.

ANNE MUNDY: How's school?

JILL ASNER: School's good, I made honor roll.

ANNE MUNDY: Well, congratulations!

(Ann yells to Jennifer.)

ANNE MUNDY: Jennifer! Jill's here!

JENNIFER MUNDY: Come on up!

(Jill walks into the room to find Jennifer sitting on her bed crying.)

JILL ASNER: What is going on? You call me up crying, you don't tell me what's wrong. What is it?

JENNIFER MUNDY: You have to promise me that you won't tell my parents.

JILL ASNER: I promise.

(Jennifer wipes her eyes and takes a deep breath.)

JENNIFER MUNDY: Last Friday at school, this man stopped me and asks me for directions to Swamp Fox. He told me he was going to visit a friend. That friend is Ronald Hanks.

JILL ASNER: What?

JENNIFER MUNDY: He said he was going to visit him. Now tell me, out of all the places to get directions, why would he come to a high school? And out of all the students at Cary High, what are the chances of him running into me? I'm scared Jill. I'm afraid he may be watching me or something.

JILL ASNER: Jennifer, you have to tell your parents.

JENNIFER MUNDY: No way. If I tell them they'll freak out and I'll never be able to leave the house without one of them watching over me. Forget it.

JILL ASNER: Jennifer, some strange man comes to our school, and out of sixteen hundred students, not only does he run into you, but he just happens to be friends with the same man that raped you. You have to tell them, Jen!

JENNIFER MUNDY: Jill, they'll be worried sick.

JILL ASNER: I'd rather see your parents worried sick than a headline that reads: "Young Girl Found Dead, Murdered by Stalker." Jennifer, this guy very well could be watching your every move. You don't know what his intentions are.

(Jennifer takes a deep breath as she leans her head back and looks at the ceiling.)

JENNIFER MUNDY: I know I'm going to regret this.

JILL ASNER: So you will tell them?

JENNIFER MUNDY: As much as I hate to, yes.

JILL ASNER: You're doing the right thing. I promise. Come on.

(The girls get up and go downstairs. They walk into the kitchen and sit down at the table.)

JENNIFER MUNDY: Mom, dad! Can you come in here for a second please!

(Her parents enter the kitchen and instantly they can see that she has been crying.)

ANNE MUNDY: Baby, what's the matter?

(Her parents sit down at the table. Her mother, sitting across from her, reaches out and grabs her hands.)

JILL ASNER: Tell them, Jen.

(Jennifer turns to look at Jill.)

JILL ASNER: Go ahead.

SAM MUNDY: Jennifer, what is it?

(Again she takes a deep breath.)

JENNIFER MUNDY: Last Friday at school, this man approached me and asks me for directions to Swamp Fox because he was going to see a friend of his. I asked him what his friends name was, and he said Ronald Hanks.

SAM MUNDY: He said he was a friend of Ronald's?

JENNIFER MUNDY: Yes.

JILL ASNER: Mr. Mundy, don't you think it's strange that one of Ronald's friends would go to a high school campus of all places to get directions? And just happen to run into Jennifer?

ANNE MUNDY: Sam that gives me the creeps. What are we going to do?

(Sam stands up and heads for the phone.)

JENNIFER MUNDY: Dad, who are you calling?

SAM MUNDY: You said he was headed to Swamp Fox, right?

JENNIFER MUNDY: Yes! Who are you calling!

SAM MUNDY: I'm calling Haywood. If this guy is in Swamp Fox, Haywood will find him.

JENNIFER MUNDY: Dad, please don't!

ANNE MUNDY: Jennifer, we've got to find out who this man is and what he's up to. This could be a very dangerous situation.

SAM MUNDY: I need you to give me a description of this guy so Haywood will know what to look for.

JENNIFER MUNDY: I knew you guys were just going to freak out! I should have kept my mouth shut!

(Jennifer, now even more upset, gets up from the table and runs up to her room crying.)

ANNE MUNDY: Jennifer!

(Her mom calls her name in hopes of stopping her. But Jennifer wants to be left alone so she continues on to her room slamming the door behind her. Jill, her best friend, goes after her, calling her name.)

JILL ASNER: Jennifer! Jennifer, wait a second!

CHAPTER SEVEN

(The next day at Corey's school, as he's walking down the hall with a couple of his friends, Jacy's brother approaches him with two of his friends.)

SHELTON ELLIS: What do you think you're doing with my sister, boy?

COREY WILLIAMS: What?

SHELTON ELLIS: You heard me, nigger.

(Corey's friend Darren, who is standing behind him steps forward to grab Shelton but Corey stops him. At the same time, Shelton's friend Tommy, thinking there's going to be a fight, also steps forward and Shelton stops him.)

COREY WILLIAMS: Chill! I got this!

(The scuffling stops and once again Corey and Shelton are face to face.)

COREY WILLIAMS: Look man, I don't know who you are or what your sister told you. But for your own safety and good health, I suggest you have another talk with her and get your facts straight.

SHELTON ELLIS: The only thing I'm gonna get straight is you, nigger.

COREY WILLIAMS: Let me tell you something, as long as you live don't you ever call me a nigger again. I will crush you, son. Now if you don't believe me, then try me.

SHELTON ELLIS: You threatening me, boy?

COREY WILLIAMS: You can call it what you want baby, call it what you want.

(By this time a crowd has gathered.)

SHELTON ELLIS: Guys step back for a second.

(People on both sides make room.)

SHELTON ELLIS: You want some of me, boy? Come and get it.

COREY WILLIAMS: Let's dance.

(Both Corey and Shelton are now slowly moving around in a circle with their fist up ready to fight. And then out of nowhere a teacher suddenly appears and stands between them.)

TEACHER: Is there a problem, gentlemen?

(With their fists now unclenched and by their sides, they lock eyes.)

SHELTON ELLIS: No problem at all. We were just goofing around.

TEACHER: Go to class.

(They're still locked eye to eye.)

TEACHER: Now gentlemen!

(As the crowd begins to disperse, Shelton slowly backs up still facing Corey.)

SHELTON ELLIS: I'll see you later.

COREY WILLIAMS: And you better come correct.

(Shelton and his friends turn and walk away. Corey watches Shelton as he walks down the hall. One of Corey's friend's steps up beside him.)

DARREN MARTIN: Man what did you do to Jacy to set that dude off like that?

COREY WILLIAMS: Jacy? That's Jacy's brother?

DARREN MARTIN: Yeah that's her brother and you better watch him, because he will be watching you.

(As Corey continues to watch Shelton walk down the hall, he thinks about the dilemma he's now facing and the dangers that may come with it. A couple of hours later at the Mayors office, the phone rings and his secretary answers. She buzzes his office to see if he wants to take the call.)

MAYOR: Yeah, Merna?

SECRETARY: You have a call on line one.

MAYOR: Who is it?

SECRETARY: It's Raymond Cletter.

MAYOR: Put him through.

(The Mayor picks up his phone.)

MAYOR: Raymond.

RAYMOND CLETTER: Haywood, I got your message, what's the big emergency?

MAYOR: Do you remember that old boy we saw with Cynthia Hanks at the restaurant last week?

RAYMOND CLETTER: Yeah what about him?

MAYOR: I got a call last night from Sam Mundy. He told me that Jennifer was approached by a gentleman at her school that said he was friends with Ronald Hanks.

RAYMOND CLETTER: What?

MAYOR: Yeah, and I believe it's the same fellow we saw with Cynthia.

RAYMOND CLETTER: Why do you say that?

MAYOR: The man that approached her said he was headed to Swamp Fox to see an old friend, and guess who that old friend is?

RAYMOND CLETTER: Ronald Hanks.

MAYOR: Exactly.

RAYMOND CLETTER: So you're telling me that this guy drove all the way to Cary just to tell Jennifer that he was friends with Ronald Hanks?

MAYOR: No. When he stopped her he asked her how to get to Swamp Fox, and then he mentioned being friends with Ronald Hanks. Now why would he drive to another town, to get direction to a place he just left? That makes no sense.

RAYMOND CLETTER: If it's him.

MAYOR: According to the description she gave Sam it's got to be.

RAYMOND CLETTER: I knew there was something strange about that old boy when I looked at him. So what do you want to do?

MAYOR: For starters, find out who he is. Then find out where he's staying if he's still here. I've got a real funny feeling about this guy.

RAYMOND CLETTER: I'll call Clyde and see if anybody who fits his description has checked into the hotel and I'll call you back.

MAYOR: Call me as soon as you find out something. The Mundys are like family to me, and I don't want any of them harmed, especially Jennifer. She's been through enough pain to last her a lifetime.

RAYMOND CLETTER: I'm on it.

(After hanging up the phone, the Mayor rears back in his chair with a look of concern on his face trying to figure out what the Minister up to as he rubs his hands together. Later that same day, Minister Ragland picks Corey up at his house to go play basketball. As they're on their way to the court, Minister Ragland notices that something is bothering Corey.)

MINISTER: You all right?

COREY WILLIAMS: Not really. Minister Ragland I need to talk to you about something. I've got a little problem.

MINISTER: What's up?

COREY WILLIAMS: It's about this girl.

MINISTER: I should have known.

COREY WILLIAMS: There's a girl named Jacy at my school. She moved to Swamp Fox about a year and a half-ago right before this whole Jennifer thing started. I don't know what it was about her the first time I saw her, but something grabbed me that day. And it's still got a hold on me; I mean she absolutely blew me away.

(Minister Ragland looks at him and chuckles.)

COREY WILLIAMS: Today she asked me out.

MINISTER: And that's a problem?

COREY WILLIAMS: A big problem.

MINISTER: Wait a minute. The same girl that you're so crazy about, asks you out and that's a problem?

COREY WILLIAMS: She's white.

(Minister Ragland looks at Corey.)

47

MINISTER: Okay. Now we're getting somewhere.

COREY WILLIAMS: There's more.

(Minister Ragland turns to look at Corey again not knowing what to expect this time.)

COREY WILLIAMS: Her brother hates black people.

MINISTER: And how do you know that?

COREY WILLIAMS: Because we almost went to blows today.

MINISTER: You got in a fight with her brother?

COREY WILLIAMS: Almost. He got in my face and told me to stay away from his sister. He must have seen us talking or something.

MINISTER: You know if you two get in a fight it's just going to make things worse.

COREY WILLIAMS: Yeah, I know. I should have walked away.

MINISTER: Maybe he's just overly protective. You can't label the guy a racist because he wants to protect his sister.

COREY WILLIAMS: Minister Ragland, getting in my face and calling me a nigger is a strong indication that he's not too crazy about the brothers.

MINISTER: So what does she have to say about all of this?

COREY WILLIAMS: She doesn't know about it, I don't think.

MINISTER: Are you gonna tell her?

COREY WILLIAMS: I don't know.

MINISTER: Don't you think she has a right to know?

(Corey pauses before he answers.)

COREY WILLIAMS: Yeah, she does.

MINISTER: And what about your date, are you going?

COREY WILLIAMS: I'm not sure, what do you think I should do?

MINISTER: It doesn't matter what I think. This is a decision you have to make.

COREY WILLIAMS: It boils down to two things. Go out on a date I've been waiting on for the last year and a half and probably have the time of my life. Or, go out on a date I've been waiting on for the last year and a half and possibly have to fight for the rest of the school year.

MINISTER: Let me tell you something, Corey, people of different races fall in love everyday. Now I'm not saying you guys are in love, but it happens. True love only comes around once in a lifetime. It may come in black, it may come in white, but it will come. Don't you ever let the ignorance of this world deny you that true love, Corey. God has a special someone out there for all of us. We don't know what color they are, or what they look like until we meet them, but they are out there. And when God brings two people together, there is a love and a bond that is created that no devil or demon in hell can destroy. The devil will work as hard as he can to form weapons against that love and that bond, but they'll never prosper. Why? Because love never fails, Corey, it never fails.

COREY WILLIAMS: Weapons? What do you mean weapons?

MINISTER: Reach back there, grab my bible, and turn to 1st Corinthians chapter 13 verse 4.

(Corey grabs the Minister's bible from the back seat.)

COREY WILLIAMS: Got it.

MINISTER: Read.

COREY WILLIAMS: "Love is kind and patient, never jealous, proud, or rude."

MINISTER: Jealousy, pride, rudeness, weapons. Read.

COREY WILLIAMS: "Love is not selfish."

MINISTER: Selfishness, weapon. Read.

COREY WILLIAMS: "Or quick- tempered."

MINISTER: Bad temper, weapon. Read.

COREY WILLIAMS: "It doesn't keep records of wrongs that others do."

MINISTER: Not forgiving people when they do you wrong, weapon. Read.

COREY WILLIAMS: "Love rejoices in truth, but not evil."

MINISTER: Evil, weapon. Read.

COREY WILLIAMS: "Love is always supportive, loyal, hopeful, and trusting."

MINISTER: And last but not least?

COREY WILLIAMS: "Love never fails."

MINISTER: You see, the devil will try and bring these things into your relationship, but if the love is there, they will never prosper. Turn to Matthew chapter 19 verse 19.

(He flips through the pages.)

COREY WILLIAMS: Got it.

MINISTER: Read.

COREY WILLIAMS: "Honor your mother and father, and love others as you love yourself."

MINISTER: Now, it didn't say unless you're white, or black, or Asian, or Hispanic or Indian, did it?

COREY WILLIAMS: No.

MINISTER: I didn't think so. Read that last part again.

COREY WILLIAMS: "Love others as you love yourself."

MINISTER: There you have it, straight from God. Love is what it's all about. Whether it's friendship, or marriage, it's about love, not the color of your skin. And what people fail to understand is, every time someone says that people of different races shouldn't love each other, they're telling God He's wrong.

COREY WILLIAMS: So you're telling me I should go out with her?

MINISTER: Like I said before, that's a decision you have to make on your own. All I'm saying is, don't allow the ignorance of this world to dictate what you can and cannot do when it comes to loving someone.

(Later that night, Jacy calls Corey at home.)

COREY WILLIAMS: Hello?

JACY ELLIS: May I speak to Corey, please?

COREY WILLIAMS: This is Corey.

JACY ELLIS: Hey, it's Jacy!

COREY WILLIAMS: Hey Miss Jacy. What's going on?

JACY ELLIS: Nothing much. I just wanted to call and make some concrete plans for Saturday. You're still going aren't you?

(Corey doesn't answer.)

JACY ELLIS: Hello?

COREY WILLIAMS: Yeah, I'm here.

JACY ELLIS: Are you still going?

(After a short pause he answers.)

COREY WILLIAMS: Yeah, I'm going.

JACY ELLIS: Good. You scared me for a minute. I thought you were gonna say no.

COREY WILLIAMS: Jacy, I wouldn't miss it for the world.

JACY ELLIS: Well, I'm glad. Now, do you want me to drive or do you want to drive?

COREY WILLIAMS: I'll drive.

JACY ELLIS: Cool. Pick me up at my house around 10:00 Saturday morning and we'll have some breakfast before we leave.

COREY WILLIAMS: Pick you up at your house?

JACY ELLIS: Yeah.

COREY WILLIAMS: I don't think that's a good idea.

JACY ELLIS: Why not?

COREY WILLIAMS: Well, I didn't want to say anything. But yesterday, your brother got in my face and gave me a hard time because he saw us talking. He told me to stay away from you.

JACY ELLIS: He did that?

COREY WILLIAMS: Yeah, but don't say anything to him. He was just blowing a bunch of hot air.

JACY ELLIS: Don't worry about it. I won't say anything.

COREY WILLIAMS: It's no big deal.

JACY ELLIS: Okay. How about I drive to your house, and you drive from there?

COREY WILLIAMS: That would probably be better.

JACY ELLIS: Great. So I'll see you Saturday morning at 10:00?

COREY WILLIAMS: You better believe it.

JACY ELLIS: I'll talk to you later.

COREY WILLIAMS: Okay.

JACY ELLIS: Bye.

COREY WILLIAMS: See ya.

(After hanging up the phone, Corey smiles as he stretches across his bed feeling very confident about his decision to go to the air show with Jacy.)

CHAPTER EIGHT

(The next morning as Minister Ragland is driving through town he shakes his head in disgust as he looks around and is saddened by the separation of the races. But the sadness is short lived when he turns, looks to his left, and sees something that brings a huge smile to his face; he sees the Breakfast Time sign. After parking his car, he walks in and has a seat at the counter. As Faye turns the corner and sees him sitting there, she walks over to Janis Jones, another waitress, and pulls her to the side.)

FAYE WATERS: Janis, I need you to do me a favor.

JANIS JONES: What?

FAYE WATERS: You see that black man sitting at the end of the counter?

(Janis turns to look at the Minister and he gives her a big huge smile as he waves.)

JANIS JONES: Yeah, I see him. How can you miss him? What is he so happy about?

FAYE WATERS: Don't ask. He's a fruitcake. Look, I want you to take his order and wait on him.

JANIS JONES: Why don't you wait on him?

FAYE WATERS: Because he gets on my nerves. Every time he comes in here he sits at the counter and bugs me. Now I really don't feel like dealing with him today. Will you please take his order?

(Janis sighs.)

JANIS JONES: Fine.

(Janis walks over to take his order.)

JANIS JONES: May I help you?

MINISTER: No. But Faye can.

JANIS JONES: She's busy.

MINISTER: Okay, I'll wait.

(With a smile on his face he sits there as she stares at him. Janis walks over to Faye and tells her that he wants her to wait on him. Now at her wits end, Faye angrily walks over to him.)

FAYE WATERS: Why didn't you let her wait on you?

MINISTER: Because I want you to wait on me.

FAYE WATERS: What's the difference?

MINISTER: She's not you.

(Faye sighs.)

FAYE WATERS: What do you want?

MINISTER: I'll start with a...

(Faye interrupts him.)

FAYE WATERS: Let me guess, a tall glass of ice water and a menu.

MINISTER: Now you see that, you see what I'm talking about? You and me Faye, right here, we're right here.

(He points his index and middle finger at his eyes suggesting to Faye that they now see eye to eye. After giving him his water she throws a menu on the counter and waits for him to order and then trouble walks in. Raymond Cletter, the chief of police walks in and sits down beside Minister Ragland.)

FAYE WATERS: Hey, Raymond!

RAYMOND CLETTER: How's it going, Faye?

(She looks at the Minister.)

FAYE WATERS: It could be better.

(Minister Ragland smiles at her.)

FAYE WATERS: What can I get you, Ray?

RAYMOND CLETTER: Coffee, no cream.

(As Faye leaves to get the coffee Raymond introduces himself to Minister Ragland.)

RAYMOND CLETTER: How are you?

MINISTER: I'm good. How are you?

RAYMOND CLETTER: Good. Are you new in town?

MINISTER: Not for long, I'm just passing through.

FAYE WATERS: Here you go, Raymond, coffee, no cream.

RAYMOND CLETTER: Thank you, Faye.

(As she turns to walk away she gives Minister Ragland a mean look and once again he flashes her a big smile.)

RAYMOND CLETTER: Where are you from?

MINISTER: Charlotte.

RAYMOND CLETTER: Charlotte? I've been to Charlotte a couple of times; I hated it. To much traffic and to many people.

MINISTER: I guess the city's not for everybody.

RAYMOND CLETTER: I guess not. Are you here visiting somebody?

MINISTER: Not really.

RAYMOND CLETTER: What brings you to Swamp Fox?

MINISTER: I'm sorry, is there a problem?

RAYMOND CLETTER: I don't know, you tell me.

(There is a short pause of silence as they sit face to face with their eyes locked on each other.)

MINISTER: It was nice talking to you.

(Minister Ragland gets up and leaves. After walking out, Raymond calls Faye over.)

RAYMOND CLETTER: Faye, what do you know about that old boy?

FAYE WATERS: Nothing at all. Other than he's come in here for the last few days to eat, that's about it. Why?

RAYMOND CLETTER: No particular reason; just doing my job.

(While Raymond is talking, he's watching Minister Ragland walk to his car. The next day, Jacy arrives at Corey's house ready to go to the air show. She rings the doorbell and Corey answers.)

COREY WILLIAMS: Hey Miss Jacy, come on in!

(Jacy walks in.)

JACY ELLIS: You ready?

COREY WILLIAMS: Yeah, let me grab my keys.

(When Corey leaves the room to get his keys, Jacy begins to look at all of the pictures on the wall and she sees a baby picture of Corey wearing a little black suit.)

JACY ELLIS: Corey, is this you?

(Corey peeks around the corner.)

COREY WILLIAMS: That's me.

JACY ELLIS: You were so cute.

(Corey yells from the other room.)

COREY WILLIAMS: What do you mean, were?

JACY ELLIS: You know what I mean! And look at your little suit.

(With keys in hand Corey stands beside Jacy and looks at his baby picture.)

COREY WILLIAMS: Can you believe my mom still has that thing?

JACY ELLIS: You've still got it?

COREY WILLIAMS: Yeah, we do. You ready to go?

(Jacy and Corey walk out headed for the car.)

JACY ELLIS: You know what? When your son takes his baby pictures, you can let him wear that suit.

COREY WILLIAMS: Yeah, and I'd never have to punish him another day of his life. That suit would be punishment enough.

(Jacy laughs as she gives him a little nudge in his arm.)

COREY WILLIAMS: Have you decided on a college yet?

JACY ELLIS: Yeah, I'm going to North Carolina State.

(Corey, shocked by her answer, and somewhat disappointed because he is a die-hard North Carolina Tarheel fan, starts to give her a hard time.)

COREY WILLIAMS: North Carolina State! You've got to be kidding me!

JACY ELLIS: What's wrong with North Carolina State?

COREY WILLIAMS: It's not North Carolina. That's what's wrong with North Carolina State. What are you majoring in?

JACY ELLIS: I want to be a veterinarian. What about you? Where are you going?

COREY WILLIAMS: I'm settling for nothing less than the best. I'm going to Tar Heel Country. The University of North Carolina.

JACY: What do you want to do?

COREY WILLIAMS: Not what do I want to do, what am I going to do. I'm gonna be a lawyer.

JACY ELLIS: No way, really?

COREY WILLIAMS: Absolutely. I want to prevent catastrophes like the one we have at home. It never should have happened.

JACY ELLIS: Tell me about it. I don't know how she lives with herself.

COREY WILLIAMS: Speaking of that whole thing, I want to ask you something. Are you not at all worried about your brother finding out we're together?

JACY ELLIS: No I'm not. Don't get me wrong; I love my brother to death. But there is no way I'm going to let him tell me who I can and cannot be friends with.

COREY WILLIAMS: What about your parents, what would they say?

JACY ELLIS: My parents are cool; they wouldn't care.

COREY WILLIAMS: What if we started dating?

(Jacy turns and looks at Corey with a smile and a funny look on her face.)

JACY ELLIS: Are you trying to tell me something, Corey?

COREY WILLIAMS: Come on, I'm serious. What would they say?

JACY ELLIS: I'm telling you they would be okay with it. As long as you were good to me and I was happy, that's all they care about.

COREY WILLIAMS: That's cool.

JACY ELLIS: What about your parents? What would they say?

COREY WILLIAMS: Well, I've talked to my parents about it before. And they said that if I meet someone, whether they're black, white, or whatever, as long as I'm happy that's all that matters. Color means nothing in my house. It never has and never will. On the other hand, considering the situation we have at home and the way some people in the world feel about interracial dating, they told me that with the good comes some bad. People will sometimes say some negative things, and some of those things can hurt. But, if I love that person, they love me, and we're both willing to accept the good with the bad, they said, "go for it."

JACY ELLIS: Thank the good Lord for open minds.

COREY WILLIAMS: Amen sister, you didn't know?

(They both turn, look at each other, and at the same time say.)

BOTH: You better ask somebody.

(They reach over and give each other a high five as they laugh hysterically. After being on the road for about forty-five minutes, Jacy hears a jet off in the distance.)

JACY ELLIS: Shhh, listen. Did you hear that?

COREY WILLIAMS: Sounds like a jet.

JACY ELLIS: Have you ever been to an air show?

COREY WILLIAMS: No, this is my very first one.

JACY ELLIS: You are going to love this.

(They pull into the parking area and park the car.

COREY WILLIAMS: Hold on for a second.

(Corey walks around to the other side of the car and opens Jacy's door.)

JACY ELLIS: Thank you that was sweet, Corey.

COREY WILLIAMS: And I appreciate you inviting me. I've been looking forward to this all week.

JACY ELLIS: I'm glad you decided to come.

COREY WILLIAMS: Really?

(She gives him a kiss on the cheek.)

JACY ELLIS: Really. Come on, let's go.

(Side by side they start to walk towards the crowd.)

JACY ELLIS: I'll race you.

(Jacy takes off running laughing hysterically as Corey follows, smiling as if he had not one care in the world.)

CHAPTER NINE

(Later on that same day, Minister Ragland decides to drop in on Pete Wilson. Because Pete is sometimes in the back of the store, he has three small bells hanging on the back of the door so he will know when someone walks in. As Minister Ragland enters the store the bells ring, startling Pete who is sitting behind the counter reading a newspaper. Feeling a little uncomfortable about Minister Ragland being there, Pete nervously stands up and lays his paper on the counter.)

MINISTER: Mr. Wilson, how are you?

PETE WILSON: What can I do for you?

MINISTER: Well, Mr. Wilson, or can I call you Pete?

PETE WILSON: Mr. Wilson is fine.

MINISTER: Okay, Mr. Wilson. You can start by telling me why you stopped practicing law and tell me the truth.

(As he's talking he grabs a magazine off of the rack and begins to flip through the pages.)

MINISTER: See I checked you out. And after doing so, I had to ask myself why in the world would an ambitious, go getter like Pete Wilson with all the talent he has in the courtroom, just give up something he loved so much.

(Minister Ragland puts the magazine back on the rack and walks up to the counter.)

MINISTER: You lost the Hanks case and you quit. That's strange to me Pete.

PETE WILSON: I just didn't have the desire anymore.

MINISTER: And why is that?

PETE WILSON: Look, I don't have time for this I've got a lot of work to do. Now either you buy something, or you leave.

(Pete begins to fold up his paper.)

MINISTER: A lot of work to do? You were sitting down reading the paper when I walked in.

PETE WILSON: What is your big fascination with me? You're running around here checking up on me, asking all kinds of questions. What does it matter to you why I gave up law?

MINISTER: It matters a lot to me. Because there is an innocent man with a family sitting in prison for something he didn't do and you could have stopped it.

PETE WILSON: You have no idea what you're talking about.

MINISTER: Oh yes I do. I peeped your game from day one. I know you're dirty, and I know you left Ronald hanging in that courtroom. That's obvious. I just don't know why.

PETE WILSON: There was nothing I could do. She testified under oath that he raped her and the jury found him guilty. It was out of my hands.

MINISTER: Don't give me that Pete, you knew she was lying.

PETE WILSON: Look, I want you out of my store now!

(While Pete is talking, Minister Ragland is talking as well.)

MINISTER: What happened? Why did you let an innocent man go to prison?

(At this point Pete is yelling as they continue to try and talk over each other at the same time.)

PETE WILSON: Get out! Get out! Get out of my store now!

(All of a sudden there is silence throughout the store as they stand face to face. After standing there for about ten seconds, Minister Ragland turns and heads for the door. Just as he opens the door to walk out he notices a sticker on the door that has the stores operating hours on it. Minister Ragland leans back, looks at the sticker, and then turns toward Pete.)

MINISTER: It says here you open at 6:00 a.m.; I'm impressed, very impressed. It must be pretty tough getting up that early in the morning and opening this place, considering the fact that you don't get much sleep at night. You have a nice day, Pete. Oh, I'm sorry, Mr. Wilson.

(Minister Ragland walks out with a smile on his face. Over at the Mayor's office, Raymond is giving a full report on what he found out about Minister Ragland.)

RAYMOND CLETTER: Guess who I ran into?

HAYWOOD BURGESS: Our new friend?

RAYMOND CLETTER: You got it.

HAYWOOD BURGESS: Where?

RAYMOND CLETTER: Breakfast Time. I saw him walking in so I waited a few minutes and I ran his plates.

HAYWOOD BURGESS: Who is he?

(Raymond pulls a piece of paper out of his shirt pocket.)

RAYMOND CLETTER: Joe Ragland, Minister Joe Ragland.

HAYWOOD BURGESS: Minister?

RAYMOND CLETTER: Minister. He's from Charlotte.

HAYWOOD BURGESS: Minister. Now what would a Minister from Charlotte want with Jennifer Mundy? Did you find out where he's staying?

RAYMOND CLETTER: The Clark Seven Hotel, and it looks like he's gonna be here for a while. Old Walt said he paid for two more weeks this morning.

HAYWOOD BURGESS: I wonder what this guy is up to.

RAYMOND CLETTER: I don't know, but I can find out.

HAYWOOD BURGESS: How?

RAYMOND CLETTER: With this.

(Raymond pulls something out of his pocket.)

HAYWOOD BURGESS: What is that?

RAYMOND CLETTER: It's a bugging device.

HAYWOOD BURGESS: No way, you can forget it! The only time you're allowed to use one of those things in law enforcement is with a court order, and even then you have to have probable cause. Anything other than that is illegal.

RAYMOND CLETTER: Illegal? I could put this thing in his room and he would never know it.

HAYWOOD BURGESS: Absolutely not! Raymond, if he found about that thing and somehow traced it back to you, you have no idea of the trouble you'd be facing. Trouble not even I could get you out of.

RAYMOND CLETTER: I'm willing to take that chance.

HAYWOOD BURGESS: Yeah, well I'm not. Use your head Ray. What if he's with the NAACP or one of those crazy nigger groups? You get caught with that thing and we'll have more of those monkeys around here than you can shake a stick at.

(Raymond laughs.)

RAYMOND CLETTER: Well, Minister or not, it's obvious that he's up to no good which in turn affects me. I'm responsible for the safety of every individual in Swamp Fox and with this guy walking around I just don't feel they're safe.

HAYWOOD BURGESS: I understand your point, Ray. But we can't break the law trying to enforce the law. It doesn't work that way.

(The Mayor's phone rings.)

HAYWOOD BURGESS: Haywood Burgess.

PETE WILSON: Haywood, this is Pete. I called Raymond's office and they said he was on his way to see you. Is he there?

HAYWOOD BURGESS: He's right here, hold on.

(The Mayor hands Raymond the phone.)

RAYMOND CLETTER: Who is it?

HAYWOOD BURGESS: Pete.

RAYMOND CLETTER: What can I do for you, Pete?

PETE WILSON: You remember that fellow I told you about, the one we saw with Cynthia Hanks?

RAYMOND CLETTER: Yeah.

PETE WILSON: Well he came by again, only this time he came looking for trouble! I had to throw him out of the store.

RAYMOND CLETTER: He didn't hit you or anything, did he?

PETE WILSON: No, he didn't. He just asked me a bunch of questions about the Hanks trial.

(Curious of the conversation, Mayor Burgess whispers to Raymond.)

HAYWOOD BURGESS: What happened?

(Raymond puts up his index finger suggesting that he hold on.)

RAYMOND CLETTER: Okay, I'll take care of it. If he comes back, call me on my cell phone.

(Raymond hangs up the phone.)

HAYWOOD BURGESS: What's wrong with him?

RAYMOND CLETTER: Now the good Minister is harassing Pete.

HAYWOOD BURGESS: Pete? Why is he harassing Pete?

RAYMOND CLETTER: The Hanks trial.

HAYWOOD BURGESS: What about it?

RAYMOND CLETTER: I don't know. But I do know that this guy has to be dealt with and dealt with now. I'm telling you Haywood.

(The Mayor sighs out of frustration.)

HAYWOOD BURGESS: Fine. Go over to the hotel and ask him if I could see him for a few minutes.

RAYMOND CLETTER: You got it.

(Raymond stands up and heads for the door.)

HAYWOOD BURGESS: Raymond!

(Raymond turns to face the Mayor.)

HAYWOOD BURGESS: Keep that bugging device in your pocket.

(Raymond again walks towards the door giving the Mayor no response.)

HAYWOOD BURGESS: Ray!

(Again he stops and faces the Mayor.)

HAYWOOD BURGESS: I'm dead serious. You had better not plant that thing in his room.

(With a sarcastic smirk on his face Raymond responds.)

RAYMOND CLETTER: Whatever you say, Mr. Mayor.

(Raymond walks out of the office leaving the Mayor with a deep look of concern on his face.)

CHAPTER TEN

(Later that afternoon Corey and Jacy are on their way home from the air show.)

JACY ELLIS: Are you in a hurry to get home?

COREY WILLIAMS: Not really. Why?

JACY ELLIS: Last week they put up new swings at Clemons Community Park. Let's go swing for a little while

COREY WILLIAMS: You like swings?

JACY ELLIS: I love swings. When I was a little girl my dad would take me to the park and push me for hours. He would tell me how beautiful of a bride I was going to be one day, and how he was going to give me this big huge beautiful wedding.

COREY WILLIAMS: Well, let's go swinging then.

(Corey and Jacy arrive at the park. He pops the trunk and grabs his basketball.)

COREY WILLIAMS: You like basketball?

JACY ELLIS: Actually soccer is my favorite sport. But yeah, I like basketball.

COREY WILLIAMS: A woman after my own heart. Follow me.

(Corey, leading the way, heads for the basketball court.)

COREY WILLIAMS: I bet you lunch at school on Monday that I can hit this free throw with my eyes closed?

JACY ELLIS: I bet you lunch for two weeks that I can hit it before you do?

(Surprised by the challenge, Corey turns and looks at her while standing on the free throw line.)

COREY WILLIAMS: Oh, you're a trash talker. Okay, pay attention, rookie.

(Corey squares up on the free throw line, closes his eyes, and takes the shot. He misses the entire goal.)

JACY ELLIS: Looks like mommy and daddy may have to increase little Corey's allowance.

(Corey gives her a sarcastic smile.)

COREY WILLIAMS: Very funny. Let's see what you got.

(Jacy squares up on the line, takes the shot, and makes it. After making the shot she blows on her right hand, and then her left.)

JACY ELLIS: Skills. That's all I've got, nothing but skills.

(After making the shot, Jacy walks off the court leaving Corey standing there staring at the goal in awe over the shot she just made. After messing around on the court for a little while longer, they decide to take a walk. As they're walking down a trail, Corey, being taller that Jacy rests his arm on top of her head. Jacy reaches up, grabs his arm, hooks their arms together, and leans her head on his shoulder as they continue to walk down the path. After walking about another twenty yards, they spot the swings.)

JACY ELLIS: You thinking what I'm thinking?

COREY WILLIAMS: Let's go.

(Corey and Jacy take off running towards the swings eager to have some fun. As Corey pushes her higher and higher he reaches up and tickles her when she swings back towards him causing her to laugh hysterically. After swinging for ten minutes or so, Corey sits in the swing beside her and they begin to talk. As he watches her bury her feet in the sand, he tells her a joke that once again causes her to laugh like crazy. The hours have flown by, the sun is starting to go down, and it's time for them to go. While walking to the car Jacy spots a gazebo and decides she wants to hang out there for a little while. As they sit side-by-side holding each other's hand Jacy look up at Corey.)

JACY ELLIS: Why are you looking at me like that?

COREY WILLIAMS: I just can't believe that I'm actually here with you. Every since I first saw you I've wanted this. I've wanted your time.

JACY ELLIS: Are you serious?

COREY WILLIAMS: Yeah. I've spent many nights trying to figure out how to approach you.

JACY ELLIS: I don't get it. You're a good-looking guy, you're sweet, you're popular, and it seems like everywhere I turn some girl at school is talking about how they would love to go out with you. You could have any girl you want. Why are you here with me?

COREY WILLIAMS: Because this is where I belong. I'm here with you because I feel like I belong with you.

JACY ELLIS: But you don't even know me.

COREY WILLIAMS: You're right, I don't know you. But I do know how I feel whenever you come around. I do know that I sit in class staring at the clock, waiting for the bell to ring so I can go to my locker in hopes that you'll be standing there. I do know that you alone have done more for my heart in the last eight hours, than any other girl has been able to do in seventeen years. I do know that.

(Jacy stands up.)

JACY ELLIS: Stand up.

(Corey stands up and Jacy wraps her arms around him.)

JACY ELLIS: You are so sweet.

(After standing there for a few seconds starring into each other's eyes, Jacy gently touches the side of his face.)

JACY ELLIS: Explain to me what's happening here right now.

COREY WILLIAMS: Ask your heart for the answer. Don't ask me.

(As they stand face to face holding each other tight, the sun starts to set in the background. Jacy stands up on her tiptoes, Corey leans forward, and under that gazebo they kiss for the very first time. Back in town, Minister Ragland returns to his hotel room to find Raymond kicked back on his bed.)

MINISTER: What are you doing in my room!

RAYMOND CLETTER: Waiting on you, preacher man. The Mayor wants to see you.

MINISTER: For what?

RAYMOND CLETTER: He wants to talk to you.

MINISTER: Then you tell him to come and see me! Now get out of my room!

RAYMOND CLETTER: I don't think you understand, boy.

MINISTER: No, I don't think you understand. You had better get out of my room before I call...

(Before Minister Ragland can finish his sentence Raymond jumps up off of the bed and gets in his face.)

RAYMOND CLETTER: Who are you gonna call, the law? Boy, around here I am the law. Now I suggest you lock up your little room here and come with me before I have to enforce my law.

(They leave the hotel and arrive at the Mayor's office. As they come through the door, Mayor Burgess stands up and sticks out his hand for the Minister to shake.)

HAYWOOD BURGESS: How are you? I'm Mayor Haywood Burgess.

(Minister Ragland doesn't bother to shake his hand.)

MINISTER: Why don't you tell me what this all about!

(Realizing that the Minister is upset, the Mayor tries to settle him down.)

HAYWOOD BURGESS: Minister Ragland, if you will just have a seat, I'll explain everything.

MINISTER: Oh, you know who I am?

RAYMOND CLETTER: I ran your license plate, preacher man.

HAYWOOD BURGESS: Minister Ragland, I just want to ask you a couple of questions, and then you can go. Please have a seat.

(Minister Ragland finally sits down. Raymond sits in the chair next to him.)

HAYWOOD BURGESS: I received two phone calls, from two different individuals, that said you were harassing them. One was from Sam Mundy, and one was from Pete Wilson.

MINISTER: Look, I didn't harass anybody. All I did was ask a couple of questions: That's not harassment.

HAYWOOD BURGESS: Well, I'm not so sure now. It all depends on how and what you asked them.

MINISTER: You asked me if I harassed anybody and I answered your question. I'm out of here.

(As Minister Ragland is talking, he gets up out of his seat. When he turns to walk towards the door, Raymond steps in front of him.)

RAYMOND CLETTER: Sit down, boy.

HAYWOOD BURGESS: Raymond, sit down!

(After standing face to face for a few seconds, Raymond sits down.)

HAYWOOD BURGESS: Minister, please, have a seat.

(Minister Ragland and Raymond remain locked eye to eye as he sits down.)

HAYWOOD BURGESS: Minister Ragland, if you don't mind me asking, why exactly are you here?

MINISTER: To clean up somebody's mess, that's why I'm here.

HAYWOOD BURGESS: Mess? What mess?

MINISTER: The mess somebody made of an innocent man's life. What kind of sideshow system are you people running around here? I guess I shouldn't be surprised though. Any town that would allow a guy like that to wear a badge, something's gotta be wrong.

RAYMOND CLETTER: You better watch your mouth, boy.

HAYWOOD BURGESS: Raymond, be quiet. Minister Ragland, I'm not sure if you're aware of this or not, but Ronald Hanks made his own mess when he decided to rape that young girl. Now I suggest you get all the facts before you start throwing around accusations like that. She stood in that courtroom and swore on the Holy Bible that he raped her. He got a fair trial, was found guilty, and now he's paying for what he did.

MINISTER: He's paying because of a crooked system. He's paying because his lawyer left him hanging when he needed him most. He never got proper representation and you know that.

(Now upset, the Mayor stands up.)

HAYWOOD BURGESS: Now you just wait one minute. I don't know what you're up to, or what exactly you think you can change, but I'm telling you right now, if I get one more phone call about you harassing somebody, anybody, I'm gonna have you picked up, arrested, and thrown in jail. Do you understand me?

MINISTER: Yeah, I understand. And I'm telling you, that if I find out that you, or anyone else ran interference in that trial, you're going down. Now, do you understand me?

HAYWOOD BURGESS: Are you threatening me?

MINISTER: No, just making you a promise.

(Feeling satisfied that he got his point across, Minister Ragland gets up and walks towards the door to leave. Just before he walks out, Raymond again gets in his face.)

RAYMOND CLETTER: Ya know, I'd like nothing more than to lock you up in jail and throw away the key. I suggest you walk a straight line around here, nigger. Or I will personally make you wish you had.

MINISTER: And I suggest that you prepare for war. Because that's exactly what you're going to get until I get him out of prison. Have a nice day.

(Minister Ragland walks out leaving Raymond raging mad with a scowl on his face.)

CHAPTER ELEVEN

(Later on that evening just after dark, Corey and Jacy return to Corey's house. Corey, once again opens her door, gently grabs her hand, and walks her to her car.)

COREY WILLIAMS: Thank you for the best date I've ever had.

JACY ELLIS: You mean that?

COREY WILLIAMS: Absolutely.

JACY ELLIS: You're something else, Corey Williams.

(Corey looks at his watch.)

COREY WILLIAMS: You know it's seven o'clock don't you?

JACY ELLIS: It's okay my parents are cool.

(As they take a few more steps walking arm and arm, they reach her car and turn to each other.)

JACY ELLIS: So, where do we go from here?

COREY WILLIAMS: Wherever our hearts take us, I guess.

(After one last long hug, Corey steps back still holding her hands.)

COREY WILLIAMS: Have I ever told you how beautiful you are?

JACY ELLIS: Yeah, about a hundred times today. But I don't think one more would hurt. Go ahead.

(They both laugh.)

COREY WILLIAMS: You better get going.

JACY ELLIS: I'll call you when I get home.

COREY WILLIAMS: You do that.

(Jacy gets in her car.)

COREY WILLIAMS: Be careful.

JACY ELLIS: I will.

(They give each other a quick kiss.)

COREY WILLIAMS: I'll talk to you soon.

JACY ELLIS: Okay.

(Jacy puts the car in reverse and backs out of the driveway.)

COREY WILLIAMS: See ya!

(As Jacy drives off, she blows the horn and waves. With a smile on his face, Corey waves back as he watches her car disappear into the early evening darkness. When Corey walks in the house, he takes his shoes off at the door and looks up to find his dad staring at him from the living room couch with a smile on his face.)

COREY WILLIAMS: What?

EARL WILLIAMS: Looks like a brother's in love.

COREY WILLIAMS: What?

EARL WILLIAMS: I said it looks like a brother's in love.

COREY WILLIAMS: Get out of here. What are you talking about in love?

EARL WILLIAMS: I'm talking about you, standing up there, smiling, showing all thirty- two of your pearly whites.

(Corey laughs.)

COREY WILLIAMS: You're buggin', pop.

EARL WILLIAMS: Oh, I'm buggin'. How about we get a professional opinion? Jean!

(His dad calls his mom into the living room.)

JEAN WILLIAMS: What are you yelling about, Earl?

EARL WILLIAMS: I want you to turn and look at your son.

(She turns to look at Corey. After about ten seconds she starts to walk towards him with a smirk on her face causing him to laugh.)

COREY WILLIAMS: Are you kidding me? Mom is your professional opinion?

EARL WILLIAMS: Your mom knows about love. She got big daddy, didn't she?

COREY WILLIAMS: Big daddy? Now that's funny, and very twisted I must say.

(His mom begins to smell him and it completely cracks him up.)

COREY WILLIAMS: What in the world are you doing mama?

JEAN WILLIAMS: Do you remember what I said about taking your shoes off at the door so you don't track mud across the carpet?

COREY WILLIAMS: Yes.

JEAN WILLIAMS: That rule no longer applies to you. Because at the rate you're flying your shoes will never touch the floor.

(His mother, finding her comment funny, flops down on the couch next to his dad and they laugh hysterically. Corey, thinking they're both crazy, shakes his head and walks towards the stairs to go to his room. Before going up the stairs, he turns to look at his parents one more time as they continue to roll all over the couch laughing at him. His parents then stand up, embrace each other, and begin to sway side to side pretending to dance as his mother sings.)

BOTH PARENTS: He believes he can fly. He believes he can touch the sky. He thinks about her every night and day, she took his heart and she drove away. Corey thinks he can fly.

(His dad falls on the floor and his mom on the couch as they continue to laugh their heads off. Corey, now convinced his parents have truly lost it, continues up stairs to his room as he shakes his head. Jacy, who has just gotten home, walks in and sits on the couch next to her mother. Her dad is sitting in his recliner and her brother is sitting on the floor.)

JACY ELLIS: What are you guys watching?

CLINT ELLIS: Where have you been?

JACY ELLIS: The air show. I told you guys I was going.

(Her dad looks at his watch.)

CLINT ELLIS: That air show does not last until 7:20 at night.

JACY ELLIS: We stopped at the park on the way home and hung out there for a little while.

CLINT ELLIS: Who is we?

JACY ELLIS: Corey and I.

CLINT ELLIS: Who is Corey?

JACY ELLIS: He's a friend of mine from school.

SHELTON ELLIS: He's a nigger friend of hers from school.

JACY ELLIS: Shut up, Shelton! And stop calling him that!

CLINT ELLIS: You mean to tell me that you have spent the entire day with some black kid?

JACY ELLIS: Corey, dad. His name is Corey.

CLINT ELLIS: Jacy, what were you thinking about? Or were you thinking at all?

JACY ELLIS: What?

CLINT ELLIS: Have you lost your mind? What if somebody we know saw you with him?

JACY ELLIS: So what. Dad, why are you talking like that, what's wrong with you?

CLINT ELLIS: What's wrong with me, what's wrong with you? How dare you take the chance of embarrassing this family like that!

JACY ELLIS: Dad...

(Before Jacy can even start her sentence her dad cuts her off.)

CLINT ELLIS: Shut your mouth, young lady!

(Shelton, her brother, is sitting across the room smiling as her dad yells at her.)

CLINT ELLIS: Are you sleeping with him?

(Shocked and hurt by the fact that her dad doesn't trust her, and would accuse her of such a thing, Jacy begins to cry.)

JACY ELLIS: Dad, how could you say something like that? Of course I'm not sleeping with him; I've never slept with anybody!

CLINT ELLIS: Don't lie to me!

JACY ELLIS: I'm not lying! Mom, what's going on?

KATHRINE ELLIS: You know exactly what's going on. You took the chance, of embarrassing this entire family by doing God knows what with some black boy.

JACY ELLIS: Some black boy? Since when did color become an issue in this house? I don't understand!

CLINT ELLIS: Well, you better understand this, young lady, tonight was the last night of you hanging out with that boy. You see him again and you'll be hanging out with his whole family because you will not live here.

(Her dad storms off up to his room.)

JACY ELLIS: Dad!

CLINT ELLIS: I don't have anything else to say to you, Jacy.

(Her dad goes up stairs, walks into his room, and slams the door.)

JACY ELLIS: Mom, what is going on around here?

KATHRINE ELLIS: You heard your father. You are not going to date some black boy and live in this house.

JACY ELLIS: But mom, we're just friends.

KATHRINE ELLIS: I suggest you find some new friends.

JACY ELLIS: Mom, you and dad are contradicting everything you've ever taught us.

KATHRINE ELLIS: Jacy, what do you know about this guy? Do you know anything about his family, his background? How do you know you won't end up like Jennifer Mundy?

JACY ELLIS: Corey would never do something like that.

KATHRINE ELLIS: Listen Jacy, you have two choices: You can obey our rules and stay in this house, or you can continue to see him and get out; it's just that simple.

(Her mom gets up and heads for the bedroom to check on her husband. She gets half way up the stairs, stops, and turns around to face Jacy.)

KATHRINE ELLIS: You're gonna be the death of your father pulling stunts like this Jacy.

JACY ELLIS: Mom, why would you…

(Before she can finish her sentence her mother interrupts her.)

KATHRINE ELLIS: Go to bed, Jacy!

(Jacy's mom who is also upset with her walks into the bedroom and slams the door. As her brother passes by her on his way up stairs to his room, he stops right in front of her.)

SHELTON ELLIS: No nigger is worth your family, Jacy. Stop being so selfish.

(At this point Jacy is in absolute shock over what has happened. She sits down on the couch and buries her face in her hands as she cries. Later that same evening after doing a little snooping around, Minister Ragland goes back to his hotel room. As he throws his key on the nightstand beside the bed, he notices his briefcase is open on one side. As he tries to figure out why it's open, he remembers that Raymond has been in his room and decides to call Pastor Fredricks.)

MINISTER: Pastor Fredricks, this is Joe Ragland.

PASTOR FREDRICKS: Hey, Joe.

MINISTER: I didn't catch you at a bad time, did I?

PASTOR FREDRICKS: No I'm just doing a little reading, what can I do for you?

MINISTER: I was wondering if you could tell me a little bit about Raymond Cletter.

PASTOR FREDRICKS: Raymond Cletter. Raymond Cletter is a stick of dynamite burning at both ends. There is one thing and one thing only on his mind and that's revenge.

MINISTER: Revenge for what happened to Jennifer?

PASTOR FREDRICKS: No, it goes much deeper than that. Two years ago, his wife, daughter, and mother were coming home from his daughter's dance recital when a drunk driver crossed the centerline and hit them head on. The van they were driving was mangled and they couldn't get out. Some of the people that witnessed the accident tried to help them, but after about five minutes the van burst into flames. After that, there was nothing they could do. They all died trapped in that van. They were burned alive. By the time the fire department got there it was far too late.

MINISTER: That explains it.

PASTOR FREDRICKS: Explains what?

MINISTER: That look in his eyes. He looked at me as if I had killed them myself.

PASTOR FREDRICKS: In his eyes you did. That drunk driver was a black man.

To Raymond Cletter we all killed his family. You said you had a little run in with him today. What happened?

MINISTER: I stepped out for an hour or so, and when I came back he was in my hotel room.

PASTOR FREDRICKS: In your room?

MINISTER: Yes sir. He came by to pick me up and give me a ride to the Mayor's office.

PASTOR FREDRICKS: For what?

MINISTER: A couple of the people I questioned said I was harassing them.

PASTOR FREDRICKS: And?

MINISTER: And he told me that if he got one more phone call about me harassing somebody, he was going to throw me in jail.

PASTOR FREDRICKS: Joe, make no mistake about it. When he told you he would throw you in jail he meant it. Don't give him a reason to come after you.

MINISTER: Pastor, they want me to back off. They think a few threats are going to scare me right back to Charlotte. I'm not going anywhere. I was sent here to get him out and that's what I'm going to do.

PASTOR FREDRICKS: I understand that, and I'm behind you all the way. But if you start messing around with Raymond Cletter, going to jail will be the least of your worries. There's nothing more dangerous than a man that feels he has nothing to lose.

MINISTER: Do you think he could have raped Jennifer?

PASTOR FREDRICKS: I don't know. Anything is possible, I guess.

MINISTER: Pastor, I'm not going to keep you any longer. I appreciate your help.

PASTOR FREDRICKS: Anytime, Joe. You make sure you keep your eyes open out there.

MINISTER: I will. You take care of yourself.

PASTOR FREDRICKS: You do the same. Good night, Joe.

MINISTER: Good night, Pastor.

(As soon as Minister Ragland hangs up the phone, he picks it up and makes another phone call to Cynthia Hanks. And while talking to her about his plans for the next day, he is unaware of the fact that Raymond, even after he was told not to, has planted a bugging device in his room and can hear every single word he's saying.)

MINISTER: Cynthia it's Joe. How are you?

CYNTHIA HANKS: Hey, Joe. I'm okay.

MINISTER: Good. Cynthia, I was wondering if you happened to know the names of some of the people that testified against your husband.

CYNTHIA HANKS: I remember two of them. There was this schoolteacher named Nancy Perry. But I don't think she lives in Swamp Fox anymore.

MINISTER: And the other one?

CYNTHIA HANKS: His name was Tim Joyce. I know he still lives here.

MINISTER: Okay. Tomorrow I'm going to try and find these people to ask them some questions. I got a feeling that some of the people that testified against your husband were decoys. They didn't really know anything at all.

CYNTHIA HANKS: You think so?

MINISTER: Yeah I do.

CYNTHIA HANKS: I guess we'll find out soon enough.

MINISTER: Yes we will. I'll give you a call tomorrow sometime.

CYNTHIA HANKS: All right be careful.

MINISTER: Take care.

CYNTHIA HANKS: You, too.

(After the conversation is over and they hang up, Raymond calls one of his old friends.)

RAYMOND CLETTER: Cecil, this is Raymond.

CECIL WATERS: Raymond Cletter! What's going on, buddy?

RAYMOND CLETTER: Well, I've got a little bit of trouble and I need your help.

CECIL WATERS: Name it.

RAYMOND CLETTER: Do you remember those special friends you introduced me to last year when we went hunting?

(Raymond is referring to two of Cecil's friends that are members of the Ku Klux

Klan.)

CECIL WATERS: Yeah.

RAYMOND CLETTER: I think it's time we got re-acquainted.

CECIL WATERS: Trouble on the home front?

RAYMOND CLETTER: You could say that. We've got some loud mouth nigger stirring up unnecessary trouble that I don't need. I've got to get rid of him.

CECIL WATERS: Why don't you take care of it yourself?

RAYMOND CLETTER: I'd like to, believe me I would. But Haywood's watching me like a hawk on this one. My hands are tied.

CECIL WATERS: Meet me out at my place around seven thirty, tomorrow night. I'll call the boys. We'll get together and see if we can't take care of that little problem for you.

RAYMOND CLETTER: That sounds good, sounds real good.

CECIL WATERS: I'll see you tomorrow night.

RAYMOND CLETTER: You got it, buddy.

(The phone call ends and Raymond is grinning from ear to ear about the meeting at Cecil's. The next day at Corey's school, he's standing at his locker and along comes Jacy. When she reaches her locker, which is beside his, she doesn't say anything to him because she's worried that her brother may come along and see them talking.)

COREY WILLIAMS: You didn't call me last night. I was worried about you.

(Jacy answers him never even looking in his direction.)

JACY ELLIS: Sorry.

(Right away Corey knows something is wrong.)

COREY WILLIAMS: Jacy, what's wrong?

(Instead of answering him, Jacy hands him a piece of paper and walks off. The paper reads, "Meet me at the old barn on Wilson Road at 4:30." Corey, now more confused than ever, turns around and looks at her as she walks down the hall. Four thirty that afternoon comes and Jacy is at the barn sitting on an old log waiting for Corey. With tears in her eyes she looks up and from around the corner of the barn comes Corey on his bike. As soon as she sees him she immediately wraps her arms around his neck.)

COREY WILLIAMS: Baby, what's the matter?

(Corey puts his hands on her hips and leans back so he can look at her face to face.)

COREY WILLIAMS: Jacy, what's wrong?

JACY ELLIS: My parents freaked on me last night.

COREY WILLIAMS: Why?

JACY ELLIS: Because we were together. And they said if I see you again, they're going to kick me out of the house.

COREY WILLIAMS: Baby, I'm so sorry.

(He holds her tight.)

COREY WILLIAMS: I thought you said they would be cool with us hanging out.

JACY ELLIS: I did say that, that's what I thought. I'm just as surprised as you are.

COREY WILLIAMS: Surprised? I'm not surprised; I've seen it a million times. Parents tell their children all their lives to look at the person and not their color. But when it hits home, it's a totally different story; color is all they see. And don't think your parents are the only ones. There are black parents out there that are just as bad if not worse. There's ignorance on both sides of the fence, Jacy.

(Jacy sits Corey down on the log, kneels down in front, and gently grabs his hands.)

JACY ELLIS: Corey, listen to me. In the last three or four years I've been dating, I've had some good dates, and I've had some bad dates. But not one date I've ever had could compare to the one I had with you. I mean that. I can't tell you the last time I had that much fun. Everything felt so right and I could totally be myself. I was comfortable the entire time we were together. I didn't have to worry about how you would react to the things I'd say or do. Corey, there's something very special happening between us. I don't know where it's going to lead us, but I do know that I don't want to lose it, which means I don't want to lose you.

COREY WILLIAMS: But what about your parents? They threatened to throw you out of the house, baby.

JACY ELLIS: If we're really careful, they'll never know.

COREY WILLIAMS: Do you have any idea of the risk you'd be taking?

JACY ELLIS: Yes, and I'm willing to take that risk. But what I want to know is, are you willing to take it with me?

(Corey gently touches her right cheek with the back of his fingers.)

COREY WILLIAMS: Jacy, there is nothing I want more in this world than to be with you. You're everything to me. If being with you means I have to come all the way out here to spend time with you, then so be it. From this day forward, Jacy, I promise you with every ounce of love I have in my heart for you, that I will never ever allow anything or anybody to tear us apart.

(With tears in her eyes she stands up pulling him up at the same time.)

JACY ELLIS: Why are you so sweet to me?

(Corey smiles.)

COREY WILLIAMS: I'm just cool like that.

(Jacy smiles.)

JACY ELLIS: I thought guys like you were just made up characters in movies. I didn't think you really existed, but here you are, as real as they come.

COREY WILLIAMS: And to think, I was only one locker away.

JACY ELLIS: Promise me right now that I'm never going to lose you, Corey.

COREY WILLIAMS: I promise, baby. I promise.

(With smiles on their faces, Jacy and Corey have decided to love in spite of the danger and consequences they face if they ever get caught. They have made up their minds that nothing is going to stop them from following their young love stricken hearts.)

CHAPTER TWELVE

(The next day, Minister Ragland arrives at the home of Tim Joyce. Tim Joyce is one of five people that testified against Ronald Hanks. He rings the doorbell and Tim answers.)

TIM JOYCE: Yes?

MINISTER: Yeah, I'm looking for a Mr. Tim Joyce.

TIM JOYCE: I'm Tim Joyce.

MINISTER: Mr. Joyce, my name is Minister Joe Ragland.

(They shake hands.)

MINISTER: Mr. Joyce, I was wondering if I could have just a few minutes of your time to talk to you?

TIM JOYCE: About what?

MINISTER: Well, I was hoping I could talk to you about the Hanks trial.

TIM JOYCE: What about it?

MINISTER: You testified against Mr. Hanks, correct?

TIM JOYCE: Yeah, so?

MINISTER: I'm kind of curious, Mr. Joyce. What exactly did you testify about? What did you see?

(Tim's facial expression changes.)

TIM JOYCE: You should be ashamed of yourself.

MINISTER: Excuse me?

TIM JOYCE: You reporters are all the same. You lie and run all over people just to get your stupid story.

MINISTER: Reporter? I'm not a reporter.

TIM JOYCE: Yeah, right. I want you off of my property now!

(Tim tries to shut the door. Minister Ragland, while trying to explain, puts his foot in the door to stop him.)

MINISTER: Mr. Joyce, please listen to me! Give me a chance to explain! It's very important that we talk!

(While all of this is going on, Raymond is sitting in his patrol car across the street behind some trees watching them. Knowing that the Minister was going to be there because of the bugging device hidden in his room, Raymond arrived early and waited. As the confrontation continues, Raymond decides enough is enough. Hearing the car pull up, Minister Ragland turns to see who it is and is absolutely shocked.)

TIM JOYCE: There we go. I bet you'll leave now.

(Standing there in a daze, Minister Ragland is speechless as Raymond approaches the porch.)

RAYMOND CLETTER: Is there a problem?

MINISTER: Where did you come from?

TIM JOYCE: Yes officer, there is a problem. I've asked this gentleman to leave my property several times and he refused. I tried to shut my door and he wouldn't let me.

(Raymond turns to Minister Ragland.)

RAYMOND CLETTER: Is that true, sir?

MINISTER: I was trying to explain to him that I'm not a reporter. Will you tell him I'm not a reporter?

RAYMOND CLETTER: Sir, I don't know anything about you or who you are.

(Minister Ragland is starting to get a little angry.)

MINISTER: You liar!

RAYMOND CLETTER: Sir, would you like to press charges?

TIM JOYCE: Yes I would.

RAYMOND CLETTER: Sir, please put your hands behind your back.

MINISTER: I didn't do anything! Why am I being arrested?

RAYMOND CLETTER: You're being arrested for trespassing. Please put your hands behind your back.

MINISTER: Trespassing? I didn't trespass!

84

(Now fed up, Raymond grabs Minister Ragland and slams him against the wall face first. While twisting, Raymond pulls Minister Ragland's arms behind his back and puts the cuffs on.)

RAYMOND CLETTER: Sir, I'm going to need you to come down to the station and file a report.

TIM JOYCE: I'll meet you there.

RAYMOND CLETTER: That's fine.

(After putting the cuffs on, Raymond spins Minister Ragland around and they head for his patrol car. As they're walking towards the car, Raymond whispers in his ear.)

RAYMOND CLETTER: You sure are one hardheaded nigger.

MINISTER: Where did you come from? How did you know I was here?

RAYMOND CLETTER: Right now, that should be the least of your worries.

(Raymond opens the back door of his patrol car and throws Minister Ragland in headfirst. After a few adjustments Minister Ragland is able to sit up.)

MINISTER: You can't do this!

(Raymond turns around to face him.)

RAYMOND CLETTER: Boy, because I wear this badge I can do anything I want to do.

(Raymond hits him in the stomach with his nightstick.)

RAYMOND CLETTER: My advice to you is to sit back, and shut up!

(Again Raymond hits him in the stomach. Now crouched over in pain, Minister Ragland tries to catch his breath as Raymond pulls out of the driveway and heads for the station. Meanwhile, back in town, Pete is having lunch with the Mayor. Mayor Burgess looks up as he's eating and sees Pete staring out of the window.)

HAYWOOD BURGESS: Pete, you look troubled.

PETE WILSON: Troubled? Yeah, I am troubled, Haywood, and you should be too.

HAYWOOD BURGESS: About what, the Minister? Give me a break.

PETE WILSON: Give you a break? Haywood, this guy means business, I'm telling you. He is dead set on finding out what happened during that trial.

HAYWOOD BURGESS: So what?

PETE WILSON: What do you mean so what? I think he knows something.

HAYWOOD BURGESS: Don't be ridiculous. He doesn't know anything, and he won't know anything if you keep your mouth shut.

(The Mayor leans forward with a very serious look on his face and whispers to Pete.)

HAYWOOD BURGESS: Keep your mouth shut, do you understand?

(Pete sighs out of frustration.)

PETE WILSON: Yeah. I understand.

(Pete picks up his fork to eat and then nervously drops it on his plate.)

PETE WILSON: He's on to us Haywood, I'm telling you!

(The noise of the fork hitting the plate has people looking at their table.)

HAYWOOD BURGESS: Shhh.

(The Mayor looks around at the people that are looking at them and smiles. He then leans forward and whispers again.)

HAYWOOD BURGESS: Didn't I just tell you to keep your mouth shut? You're causing a scene.

(Pete looks around to find a couple of people still looking at them.)

HAYWOOD BURGESS: Listen to me. There is no way I could have gotten a second term if Ronald had gotten off and you know that. Pete, when you decided to buy the drug store, who put up half the money? I did. When you built your house, who got all of your permits passed in one day? I did. When you decided to get a new car, who talked old Jake into knocking off $3,000.00? I did. Now, do you think I could have done any of those things if I had not been re-elected? No, I couldn't. You did the right thing, Pete. So, why don't you sit back and reap all the benefits that come with it?

(Pete sits there for a few second and then responds with a smile.)

PETE WILSON: You know you're right, besides we covered our tracks. There is no way he can find out what went on.

(Pete raises his glass for a toast.)

PETE WILSON: To freedom!

HAYWOOD BURGESS: To freedom!

86

(They touch glasses.)

PETE WILSON: Freedom to do what ever we want.

(After they toast they both take a sip of their wine and smile at each other. Meanwhile, Raymond and Minister Ragland have been driving for 10 to 15 minutes when the Minister looks up and sees a sign that reads, 'Leaving Swamp Fox.' Knowing he's in serious trouble, Minister Ragland leans forward.)

MINISTER: Where are we going?

RAYMOND CLETTER: Where are we going? We're going to a very special place.

MINISTER: What special place?

RAYMOND CLETTER: The same place I take all niggers when they get out of line.

MINISTER: Look, I know what's gonna happen when we get to this so-called "special place." But is it really going to change anything? Do you think beating me is going to change what's happened?

(As Minister Ragland is leaning forward, Raymond reaches back and elbows him in the mouth knocking him back in the seat and busting his lip. Raymond, now completely irritated, yells.)

RAYMOND CLETTER: I told you to sit back and shut your mouth!

(After another fifteen minuets of driving they reach their destination. They're about 3 miles off of the main road in a clearing behind an old shack. There are no houses or people for miles. Raymond gets out and opens the back door.)

RAYMOND CLETTER: Get out!

(Because of the shot Raymond gave Minister Ragland in the stomach with his nightstick, Minister Ragland is moving extremely slow. Raymond grabs him, throws him on the ground, and kicks him in his ribs.)

RAYMOND CLETTER: I told you to move, boy!

(Raymond reaches down, grabs Minister Ragland by his shirt collar, and stands him up so that they are face to face.)

RAYMOND CLETTER: The other day in the Mayor's office you were running of at the mouth like a big man. You don't feel so tough now, do you?

MINISTER: You can bring me out here everyday of the week, beat me silly, and it still won't stop me. I will find out who raped her, and you had better hope it doesn't lead back to you. Because like I said before, if it does, you will be through.

(Surprised by Minister Ragland's boldness, Raymond steps back, looks him up and down from head to toe, and smiles.)

RAYMOND CLETTER: I can't believe it. I just can't believe it. I finally met a nigger I admire. Here you are about to get the whipping of your life, and you still stand up to me. I admire that.

MINISTER: When are you going to let them go and go on with your life?

(Raymond's smile quickly disappears. He walks up to Minister Ragland and stands so close that their noses are almost touching.)

RAYMOND CLETTER: What did you say nigger?

MINISTER: Do you think beating every black man you see is going to bring your family back? They are gone, and there is absolutely nothing you can do to bring them back.

(While Minister Ragland is talking, Raymond, at the same time, is telling him to shut up. The more the Minister talks, the louder Raymond gets. After a few more seconds of going back and forth, Raymond reaches his boiling point and snaps. He throws Minister Ragland on the ground and begins to punch him in the face as hard and as fast as he possibly can as he yells over and over and over again).

RAYMOND CLETTER: Shut up! Shut up! Shut up!

(Later that same evening, Jacy is at home having dinner with her family. As they begin to eat, there is a combination of silence and tension also sitting at the table. After about five minutes Shelton breaks the silence).

SHELTON ELLIS: So Jacy, did you talk to your little friend today?

JACY ELLIS: Shut up, Shelton.

CLINT ELLIS: Did you?

JACY ELLIS: Mom?

KATHRINE ELLIS: Answer your father, Jacy.

(Jacy sighs.)

JACY ELLIS: Yes, I talked to him.

CLINT ELLIS: And?

JACY ELLIS: And I told him that you guys didn't want us to hang out.

CLINT ELLIS: What did he say?

JACY ELLIS: He understood. Can we please change the subject?

CLINT ELLIS: Jacy, we don't want you to think that we're trying to run your life.

JACY ELLIS: Dad, that's exactly what you guys are trying to do and it's not fair.

CLINT ELLIS: But it's for your own good, Jacy.

JACY ELLIS: For my own good? Dad, let me ask you something, not as your daughter. I want you to consider me to be a complete stranger, okay?

CLINT ELLIS: Go ahead stranger. Ask away.

JACY ELLIS: Why are you so against interracial dating?

SHELTON ELLIS: Because it's sickening.

KATHRINE ELLIS: Shelton, shut up!

CLINT ELLIS: It's just not right. That's the way I was raised; it's not right.

JACY ELLIS: What's not right about it? If two people love each other, and they're happy, that's all that matters. Not the color of their skin. Love doesn't work that way.

CLINT ELLIS: You can call it what you want. But me personally, I think that blacks should be with blacks, and whites should be with whites. You start mixing the two and that's where I draw the line.

JACY ELLIS: So, just forget about love and happiness; it's the color that counts. Is that what you're saying?

KATHRINE ELLIS: What about the children, Jacy?

JACY ELLIS: What children?

KATHRINE ELLIS: The children that come out of these mixed relationships. They spend their entire lives confused and not knowing what they really are. Not to mention the verbal abuse they have to endure as children. They get picked on because of the way they look, and that's not something you can ignore because they do look different. Look at their hair, and their skin. It's just not fair to them, Jacy.

JACY ELLIS: Mom, kids are going to be cruel regardless of what color you are; they're just honest like that. When I was in elementary and middle school I was picked on all the time and most of the time it was by white kids. Now, as far as your comment about them not knowing what they really are, I had a friend named Tiffany King in middle school who was half- black and half- white. Her parents taught her about both cultures and she was proud to be who she was. I understand what you're saying, of course there will always be racism because there will always be some ignorant parent out there poisoning their child's mind, but that doesn't make it right.

CLINT ELLIS: Jacy, aren't you at all worried about what people in this town will say about you?

JACY ELLIS: No dad, that's your issue. You're worried about what they might say, not me. I cannot, and will not, live my life to satisfy people in this town. When I look at Corey, I don't see what everyone else in this town sees. I see a sweet, kindhearted guy that would never hurt anybody.

CLINT ELLIS: Well, like I said before, that's your opinion and you're entitled to it. When I was growing up it was forbidden in our house then, and it's forbidden in this house now.

JACY ELLIS: Okay, now as your daughter, I want to ask you one more question and then I'm through.

CLINT ELLIS: Go ahead.

JACY ELLIS: You guys love me, right?

CLINT ELLIS: Of course we do.

JACY ELLIS: And you want me to be happy in life, right?

CLINT ELLIS: Absolutely.

JACY ELLIS: Okay, then answer this question for me. Would you prefer that I marry a white guy that treats me bad and makes me miserable? Or a black guy that treats me like a queen and makes me happy?

(Her dad chuckles at her question.)

CLINT ELLIS: That's a ridiculous question.

JACY ELLIS: Just answer it dad.

CLINT ELLIS: That's ridiculous.

JACY ELLIS: Dad, why won't you answer the question?

CLINT ELLIS: I'm not going to answer that ridiculous question.

JACY ELLIS: Why? Because you know it'll prove you wrong?

(Knowing he's been hit with a question that requires an answer he doesn't want to admit to, Jacy's father gets angry and slams his fist on the table.)

CLINT ELLIS: I'm not going to answer that ridiculous question! Now this conversation is over and I don't want to hear anymore about it! Do you understand me?

JACY ELLIS: Yes, sir.

(He gets up from the table and storms off to his room once again, slamming the door behind him. Jacy turns to look at her mother, but her mother can't look her in the eye. She also knows that the answer to the question would prove them, and the ultimatum that they gave her about hanging out with Corey to be wrong. Later on that same evening, just as it's getting dark, Raymond brings Minister Ragland into the station and sits him down at one of his deputy's desk.)

RAYMOND CLETTER: Deputy Cox, take care of his paper work. He's being charged with trespassing and resisting arrest.

DEPUTY COX: You got it.

(Raymond goes to his office and sits down behind his desk. He leans back in his chair and takes a deep breath as he stares at the ceiling. After a couple of minutes he decides to call the Mayor who is now at home.)

RAYMOND CLETTER: Haywood, guess who I have in custody?

HAYWOOD BURGESS: Who?

MINISTER: Preacher man.

(The Mayor, who is comfortably sitting back in his recliner, quickly sits up.)

HAYWOOD BURGESS: What?

RAYMOND CLETTER: That's right. I got a call from a gentleman this afternoon that said a man was at his front door harassing him about the Hanks trial. Knowing exactly who it was, I drove out there and who is standing on this guy's porch trying to force his way into the house? Preacher man.

HAYWOOD BURGESS: Please tell me you're joking.

RAYMOND CLETTER: I wish I were. And on top of that, I had to physically wrestle this guy to the ground to get the cuffs on him. He was out of control.

HAYWOOD BURGESS: Listen to me. I want you to put him in a cell and hold him until I get there. I'm on my way.

RAYMOND CLETTER: I'll do it, but I won't be here when you get here. I have a very important meeting and I have to be there on time. But I will let Deputy Cox know that you're coming.

HAYWOOD BURGESS: Whatever. You just make sure the Minister is secured in a cell. And Raymond, tell him not to let anybody at all see him before I get there.

RAYMOND CLETTER: I'll do it.

(They hang up the phone and Raymond leaves to meet Cecil. On his way out he yells from across the room as he smiles).

RAYMOND CLETTER: Preacher man, you behave now, you hear?

(Minutes later, the Mayor arrives at the station.)

HAYWOOD BURGESS: Where is he?

DEPUTY COX: Cell-4.

(The Mayor walks up to the cell to find Minister Ragland lying on a cot.)

HAYWOOD BURGESS: Minister Ragland.

(Minister Ragland rolls over and the Mayor's eyes immediately grow wide. He is in absolute shock over the condition of Minister Ragland's face. The Mayor whispers to himself.)

HAYWOOD BURGESS: My goodness.

(Minister Ragland sits up.)

HAYWOOD BURGESS: What happened to your face?

MINISTER: Which side? My right cheek, I got that from the heel of your boy's shoe. Or do you mean my forehead? I got that from your boy's nightstick.

HAYWOOD BURGESS: Why did you have to fight him? Why didn't you just let him put the cuffs on you? He told me everything.

MINISTER: Oh yeah? Well did he tell you that he drove me out to the middle of nowhere and knocked me around for an hour? Did he tell you that he pulled his gun out, put it to my temple, and threatened to kill me? Did he tell you that?

HAYWOOD BURGESS: That did not happen.

MINISTER: Why would I lie to you? Look at my face. I stood almost nose-to-nose with that man this afternoon and I saw nothing but rage in his eyes. He is angry, he is out of control, and he is going to kill somebody if you don't do something!

HAYWOOD BURGESS: Why don't you just cut your losses and get out of town? You're not going to find anything and Ronald's not getting out of prison. He is exactly where he's going to stay.

MINISTER: Mr. Mayor, the word of God promises that whatever is done in the dark, shall be revealed in the light. Whoever is responsible for all of the pain, hatred, and anger in this town, will be exposed. I'm not going anywhere, so you may as well get use to seeing this face because everywhere you turn, there I will be.

HAYWOOD BURGESS: Suit yourself. But don't come crying to me when you end up in jail, or laid up in the hospital shot because you decided to trespass on someone's property, sticking your nose where it doesn't belong.

(Mayor Burgess walks out angry and frustrated. Out at Cecil's place, Raymond has just arrived. Cecil answers the door.)

CECIL WATERS: You're late, Raymond.

RAYMOND CLETTER: I know. I ran into a little trouble, I'm sorry.

(Cecil motions Raymond to come in. He walks in, turns the corner and there sits Buck Sanders and Willie Taylor.)

CECIL WATERS: Fellows, you remember Raymond. He went hunting with us last year up in Cotton County. Raymond, you remember Buck and Willie?

(Raymond shakes Buck's hand, and then Willie's.)

BUCK SANDERS: You still a cop?

RAYMOND CLETTER: Yeah.

BUCK SANDERS: How do we know that you're not setting us up?

CECIL WATERS: Because I'll vouch for him. He's all right.

RAYMOND CLETTER: I'm not gonna set you up. I'm a cop, but I'm your kind of cop.

BUCK SANDERS: You better be.

WILLIE TAYLOR: What is it exactly you want from us?

RAYMOND CLETTER: I need you guys to get rid of someone for me.

WILLIE TAYLOR: Get rid of someone? Who?

RAYMOND CLETTER: His name is Minister Joe Ragland.

(Both Willie and Buck look at each other.)

WILLIE TAYLOR: Are you crazy? You want us to kill a Minister?

CECIL WATERS: He's a nigger.

RAYMOND CLETTER: A nigger that's harassing a young white girl.

93

(Buck and Willie turn, look at each other, and smile.)

BUCK SANDERS: He's a nigger? Where do you want us to bury him?

RAYMOND CLETTER: I just want him out of town, no killing. Do whatever you have to do to get rid of this guy, and do it fast. But do not kill him.

WILLIE TAYLOR: No problem. All we need is an address, and we need to know what he drives.

(Raymond writes the information down.)

RAYMOND CLETTER: Here you go. It's the only hotel in Swamp Fox, and that's what he drives.

(Raymond hands the paper to Willie.)

WILLIE TAYLOR: Black Nissan Maxima. What's this John, 3-3?

RAYMOND CLETTER: That's his license plate.

BUCK SANDERS: We'll take care of it.

RAYMOND CLETTER: How much do I owe you fellows?

WILLIE TAYLOR: You said he was a nigger harassing a white girl, right?

RAYMOND CLETTER: Yeah.

WILLIE TAYLOR: This one my friend is on the house.

(Willie and Raymond shake hands to seal the deal, as they all smile smiles of revenge.)

CHAPTER THIRTEEN

(The next morning, Raymond walks into Minister Ragland's cell where he is sleeping. Raymond kicks his cot and yells.)

RAYMOND CLETTER: Hey, hey!

(He kicks the cot harder.)

RAYMOND CLETTER: Sleeping beauty!

(Minister Ragland rolls over and looks up at Raymond.)

RAYMOND CLETTER: You're free to go.

(Minister Ragland gets up and heads for the front desk to collect his belongings that they took from him when they booked him. As he's walking out of the cell, Raymond stops him.)

RAYMOND CLETTER: If I have to come and get you again, I'm gonna put a whooping on you so bad that when I'm finished, you'll go and curse your mama to her face for bringing you into this world. Do you understand me, nigger?

(Minister Ragland walks away, never responding to his threat. As he walks across the room, Raymond begins to mock him.)

RAYMOND CLETTER: Hallelujah!

(As Raymond yells Hallelujah and waves his arms in the air, some of the other deputies begin to laugh. When Minister Ragland gets back to his hotel room, he walks through the door to find the room completely trashed and most of his belongings destroyed. After grabbing what is salvageable, Minister Ragland drives

95

to Pastor Fredricks' office. After knocking, and Pastor Fredricks telling him to come in, Minster Ragland opens the door. Pastor Fredricks cannot believe what he is seeing.)

PASTOR FREDRICKS: Oh my Lord, look at your face.

MINISTER: I know, Pastor.

(Pastor Fredricks can only shake his head.)

PASTOR FREDRICKS: What happened?

MINISTER: Raymond took me for a little ride.

PASTOR FREDRICKS: I told you to stay away from him.

MINISTER: I did. He found me. Yesterday I went to talk to this guy about the trial. He thought I was a reporter and tried to slam the door in my face. I wanted to explain to him why I was there and that I wasn't a reporter so I stuck my foot in the door. Then out of nowhere comes Raymond. I mean he came out of nowhere. He just showed up. So when he pulls up, it looks like I'm trying to force my way into this guy's house. That's why I was arrested. But for the life of me, I just can't figure out where he came from. And on top of all that, I need somewhere safe to stay. Somebody destroyed my hotel room and I have a feeling that whoever did it will probably be back.

PASTOR FREDRICKS: Now do you believe me when I tell you this thing is getting out of control?

MINISTER: I know it looks that way, but it's not out of control. They're just trying to scare me off.

PASTOR FREDRICKS: You come in here with your face looking like that and you don't think things are getting out of control? Don't fool yourself, Joe.

(Pastor Fredricks reaches into a cabinet behind his desk.)

PASTOR FREDRICKS: Here.

(He throws the Minister a washcloth and a towel.)

PASTOR FREDRICKS: Go get yourself cleaned up. I'll make some phone calls and see if we can't find you somewhere to lay your head tonight, what's left of it, anyway.

(Minister Ragland takes the towel, the washcloth, and heads for the door.)

MINISTER: Thanks. Oh, where are the showers?

PASTOR FREDRICKS: Go right, take you're first left, and it's the second door on your right.

(As Minister Ragland is almost out of the door, Pastor Fredrick calls him.)

PASTOR FREDRICKS: Hey, Joe!

(He turns to face him.)

MINISTER: Yes sir?

PASTOR FREDRICKS: If this guy was standing right in front of you calling the police, why didn't you just leave?

MINISTER: He didn't call the police.

PASTOR FREDRICKS: Then how did Raymond know you were there?

MINISTER: That's what I'm saying, I don't know. I spent most of the night trying to figure that out and it just doesn't add up. I don't get it.

(After a few seconds of silence, Pastor Fredricks leans back in his chair.)

PASTOR FREDRICKS: Go on and take your shower. I'll make some calls.

MINISTER: Thanks Pastor. I appreciate it.

(Minister Ragland leaves and Pastor Fredricks immediately gets on the phone to find him a place to stay. Back at Raymond's office, Raymond is sitting at his desk when the phone rings; it's the Mayor.)

HAYWOOD BURGESS: Have you lost your mind?

RAYMOND CLETTER: Well, good morning to you, too.

HAYWOOD BURGESS: I'm not in the mood for games, Ray. Now, start explaining.

RAYMOND CLETTER: Explaining what?

HAYWOOD BURGESS: Why it looks like somebody ran a cheese grater across the Minister's face.

RAYMOND CLETTER: There's nothing to explain. He resisted arrest, attacked me, and I did what I had to do to get the situation under control.

HAYWOOD BURGESS: Well, that's not what he said.

RAYMOND CLETTER: So now you believe the criminals, not the cops?

HAYWOOD BURGESS: I never said I believed him.

RAYMOND CLETTER: Haywood, he was breaking the law, okay? Now last I heard when somebody's breaking the law it's our job to arrest him or her. If they get out of control, then it's our job to get them under control and that's what I did. That's the truth!

HAYWOOD BURGESS: It better be. Because if I find out otherwise you will be suspended, you will be arrested, and you will be charged with police brutality. Is that clear?

RAYMOND CLETTER: As a bell, Mr. Mayor.

HAYWOOD BURGESS: I want a full report on my desk by five o'clock today!

(The Mayor, who is extremely upset, hangs up on Raymond. Back at Pastor Fredrick's office, Minister Ragland is all cleaned up.)

PASTOR FREDRICKS: Joe, I found you somewhere to stay. I called a friend of mine named Bobby Medlin and explained everything. He said you're welcome to stay as long as you want.

MINISTER: I think I met him and his wife at your church.

HAYWOOD BURGESS: They live out in the country. He has a driveway that wraps around the back of his house so you can hide your car in the back yard next to the house.

MINISTER: Pastor, I really appreciate this. Thank you.

PASTOR FREDRICKS: Just promise me that you'll be more careful.

MINISTER: I will.

(At school, Corey is standing at his locker when Jacy walks by and slips him a note. Passing each other notes is the only way they can communicate considering they're not allowed to talk to each other. The note said, "Meet me at the old sawmill at four thirty this afternoon." At five o'clock that afternoon, Corey is at the old sawmill nervously pacing back and forth because Jacy is now a half an hour late. When she finally arrives, he walks up to her, wraps his arms around her, and hugs her as if it were his last.)

COREY WILLIAMS: I've been waiting all day for this.

JACY ELLIS: I know. I wanted to hug you so bad today when I saw you at your locker.

COREY WILLIAMS: It's not fair, Jacy. I remember last year at my family reunion when all of the old people were sitting around talking about how things were back in the day when they were growing up. They talked about the racism and segregation back in the sixties. I remember saying to myself, I'm so glad I don't have to deal with that. Now look at us. Here we are in the year 2006, and we're smack dab in the middle of it.

JACY ELLIS: Let me guess. You're having second thoughts about us?

COREY WILLIAMS: Second thoughts? No, I'm not having second thoughts. I'm just surprised that in this day and age people still hate each other because of skin color. I'll never understand it; it's just skin.

JACY ELLIS: That's the world we live in, baby. But you know what?

(As Corey is looking down, Jacy gently grabs his chin and lifts his head so that she can look into his eyes.)

JACY ELLIS: As long as we're together, that's all I care about. All the rest of that garbage, it doesn't even matter to me.

COREY WILLIAMS: I guess now it's my turn to ask. Why are you so sweet to me?

JACY ELLIS: Because you don't deserve anything less, nobody does.

COREY WILLIAMS: You know what I'm gonna do for you?

JACY ELLIS: What?

COREY WILLIAMS: I'm going to get a blanket, some food, and a radio. Then I'm going to take you out to Grant Lake, and give you the best picnic you've ever had.

JACY ELLIS: You mean the first picnic I've ever had. Nobody's ever taken me on a picnic before, but I'm confused. I understand the food, and I understand the blanket. But what's the radio for?

COREY WILLIAMS: The radio is for history. Tomorrow we're going to turn that radio on, and have our very first dance together.

(Completely swept off of her feet by Corey's romantic idea, Jacy looks down at the ground as she shakes her head. She then looks up at him.)

JACY ELLIS: You're incredible, Corey Williams. How is it you always know the right things to say and when to say them?

COREY WILLIAMS: Because of my dad. When I was fourteen and we had "the talk," he told me that any man can take care of a woman, but only a real man can take care of a woman's heart. In order for a man to do that, he should always be willing to put her need first, always. I figured you needed something nice considering everything you've been going through at home with your family. What can be nicer than a picnic on a beautiful day?

(Jacy hugs him.)

JACY ELLIS: You're so sweet.

COREY WILLIAMS: I try.

JACY ELLIS: May I make a suggestion?

COREY WILLIAMS: Sure.

JACY ELLIS: Biscuits. We've got to have biscuits.

(A little surprised by Jacy's request, Corey sits there for second in silence as he stares at her.)

COREY WILLIAMS: Biscuits? You're serious?

JACY ELLIS: Yes, I'm serious.

COREY WILLIAMS: Why biscuits?

JACY ELLIS: Because I love biscuits.

COREY WILLIAMS: Well, I love Silver Back Gorillas, but I don't want to take one on the picnic.

(Jacy looks at him funny because of his sarcastic remark.)

COREY WILLIAMS: Okay, okay. I'll figure out something. You know what? That's your new nickname, biscuit. No, I'll call you Biz, my Biz.

JACY ELLIS: Don't you dare call me that.

(Corey slides closer to Jacy, makes a funny face, and talks in a funny voice.)

COREY WILLIAMS: Why not? Don't you want to be my little Biz?

(Jacy begins to crack up.)

JACY ELLIS: You're crazy.

COREY WILLIAMS: That's right. I'm crazy about my Biz.

(Still laughing, Jacy wraps her arms around him as he too begins to laugh. Back in town, Walt Bedford, the owner of the hotel where Minister Ragland was staying, has called Raymond to come and look at the Minister's room. Raymond opens the door, sees the damage, and whispers to himself.)

RAYMOND CLETTER: My boys.

(Raymond thinks that Buck and Willie destroyed the room. Walt, who is standing behind him, hears him whisper to himself.)

WALT BEDFORD: What was that, Ray?

(Raymond comes out of his little daze.)

RAYMOND CLETTER: What? Oh, nothing. Does this phone still work?

(Raymond walks over, picks the phone up off the floor, and listens for a dial tone.)

RAYMOND CLETTER: Yeah, it works.

WALT BEDFORD: Look, I need to go back downstairs. Stop in and talk to me before you leave.

RAYMOND CLETTER: You got it.

(Walt leaves and Raymond calls the Mayor.)

RAYMOND CLETTER: Haywood, we've got a problem.

HAYWOOD BURGESS: Whatever it is, please tell me that it doesn't involve a certain Minister visiting from out-of-town.

RAYMOND CLETTER: Sorry to disappoint you.

(The Mayor puts his hand over his face and sighs.)

HAYWOOD BURGESS: What happened?

RAYMOND CLETTER: Looks like he got a little angry about being in jail and decided to take it out on his room. He destroyed everything from the mattress to the mirrors. You name it, he destroyed it.

HAYWOOD BURGESS: I don't understand this guy. He claims to be a man of God but he goes around harassing people and tearing up hotel rooms.

RAYMOND CLETTER: What do you want me to do?

HAYWOOD BURGESS: What do you mean what do I want you to do? He destroyed private property. That's against the law and now he has to pay. He's going to jail, I warned him.

RAYMOND CLETTER: I think that's easier said than done. It looks like he packed all of his stuff and hit the road.

HAYWOOD BURGESS: Raymond, that man is not going anywhere. He is truly

101

convinced that he can get Hanks out of prison. He's still here. I guarantee it and I want you to find him. If I we're you, I would start with Cynthia Hanks. I'm sure she knows where he is.

RAYMOND CLETTER: I'm on it.

HAYWOOD BURGESS: Raymond, when you find him, do not arrest him. I want you to call me, I'll meet you, and then you can arrest him. But not without me, do you understand?

RAYMOND CLETTER: Yes, sir.

HAYWOOD BURGESS: Go get him.

(Raymond hangs up the phone and heads for Cynthia's. Once he arrives, he loudly knocks on the door with his flashlight and Cynthia answers.)

CYNTHIA HANKS: What do you want?

RAYMOND CLETTER: Now what kind of greeting is that? Aren't you going to invite me in?

CYNTHIA HANKS: What do you want?

RAYMOND CLETTER: I need to know where your friend the Minister is.

CYNTHIA HANKS: Why?

RAYMOND CLETTER: That's none of your business, but if you must know, he destroyed his hotel room this morning. It looked like a tornado hit it.

(Cynthia chuckles.)

CYNTHIA HANKS: And you think he did it?

RAYMOND CLETTER: I wouldn't put it past him. You niggers are always messing up something. Look at your pervert husband.

CYNTHIA HANKS: My husband is innocent. He was set up the same way you're trying to set Joe up. Raymond, you look a little nervous. The Minister's not making you nervous, is he?

(Cynthia smiles.)

RAYMOND CLETTER: Listen to you; you're just as stupid as he is. If you think for one second that the Minister is somehow going get that freak you call a husband out of prison, you had better think again. He's staying right where he belongs, in a cage. If it were up to me, I'd put all of you niggers in a cage and send you back to Africa.

CYNTHIA HANKS: You're such a coward, Raymond. A coward hiding behind a badge. Take that badge away from you, and you're nothing.

RAYMOND CLETTER: Maybe so. But while I'm wearing it, I'm everything, including your worst nightmare. You had better be glad I'm a gentleman because if I weren't, I would drag you down these steps, tie you to that tree right there, and beat you like I owned you.

(Cynthia steps out of the door and right into his face.)

CYNTHIA HANKS: Take your best shot, you simple-minded redneck.

(Raymond laughs and takes a couple of steps back.)

RAYMOND CLETTER: That's funny. Simple minded redneck. I've got to remember that one. Listen, tell the good Minister that he had better turn himself in before I get to him. Because if doesn't, he won't have to worry about worshiping God from down here anymore. I'm going to send him to meet him personally.

CYNTHIA HANKS: I want you out of here now!

(Raymond puts his hat on, his dark sunglasses, and smiles.)

RAYMOND CLETTER: You have a nice day, Mrs. Hanks.

(As Raymond is walking down the steps, he looks down and sees her flowerbed, which runs along side of her walkway. He then turns, looks at her, smiles, and purposely walks through her flowerbed destroying all of her flowers. After Raymond leaves, her phone rings. It is Minister Ragland.)

CYNTHIA HANKS: Hello?

MINISTER: Cynthia it's Joe.

CYNTHIA HANKS: Joe, please tell me what is going on! Raymond Cletter was just here looking for you!

MINISTER: Looking for me? Why is he looking for me?

CYNTHIA HANKS: Something about you destroying your hotel room! He also said you had better turn yourself in before he finds you!

MINISTER: Well, once again it looks like they're going to charge me for something I didn't do.

CYNTHIA HANKS: Sounds like it.

MINISTER: Listen to me. I want you to go to Corey's house and stay there. It's too dangerous for you to be at home alone. I'll meet you there around seven o'clock tonight.

CYNTHIA HANKS: All right. I just need to grab a few things and then I'll leave.

MINISTER: Okay, I'll see you tonight.

(They hang up the phone and she begins to pack for Corey's. Back at the police station, Raymond has just walked into his office. He gets on the phone and calls Willie at work.)

WILLIE TAYLOR: "Carter's Auto, this is Willie."

RAYMOND CLETTER: Willie, its Raymond.

WILLIE TAYLOR: How's it going, Raymond?

RAYMOND CLETTER: From the looks of things, it's going pretty good. That job you guys did on his hotel room last night was excellent. Everybody thinks that he did it; it was perfect.

WILLIE TAYLOR: What are you talking about, Raymond?

RAYMOND CLETTER: The Minister's hotel room. The job you guys did last night was awesome.

WILLIE TAYLOR: Job? There was no job.

MINISTER: What do you mean there was no job? You guys didn't hit his room last night?

WILLIE TAYLOR: Raymond, we went straight home after we left Cecil's last night. Looks like you're not the only one that wants him out of town. Raymond, I'm gonna have to call you later. We're swamped over here.

(Willie hangs up the phone leaving Raymond puzzled. Night falls, it's seven o'clock, and Minister Ragland has just arrived at Corey's house. Corey's mom answers the door.)

JEAN WILLIAMS: Joe, what happened to your face!

MINISTER: Just Swamp Fox's finest sending me a message.

JEAN WILLIAMS: Come on in.

(Minister Ragland walks into the living room where everybody is sitting. When they see his face, they too are shocked.)

CYNTHIA HANKS: That's it! This has got to stop! Look at you! Why can't you just leave it alone and let it go!

MINISTER: You know I can't do that! I'm starting to make progress.

(Cynthia gets up, walks over to Minister Ragland, grabs his arm, and pulls him over to a mirror hanging on the wall.)

CYNTHIA HANKS: You call that progress, Joe? You call Raymond standing at my front door threatening to beat me, progress? You call me hiding out like some fugitive, progress? I don't think so Joe, that's not progress!

(Cynthia begins to cry. To comfort her, Minister Ragland puts his arm around her, walks her back to her seat, and kneels down in front of her on one knee as he gently holds her hands.)

MINISTER: Cynthia, I'm sorry that you ended up in this mess, I really am. You know the last thing I want is for you to get hurt; you know that. But there is no way I can stop now. The Lord has ordered my steps, and I have to follow them. Cynthia, if I turn around and walk away now there is going to be bloodshed around here like you can't even imagine.

(He puts his index finger under her chin and lifts her face so that they are eye to eye.)

MINISTER: Greater is he that is in me, than he that is in the world. We are more than conquerors, and if God is for us, then who can be against us? I know that things may look a little rough right now, Cynthia, and you feel like giving up. But if you'll just hold on a little while longer, God will bring this to pass. He told us in His word that after we've done all that we can do, just to stand, be still, and He will bring us out.

(Now comforted by his encouraging word, Cynthia gives him a hug. After the hug, he stands up.)

MINISTER: Earl, Jean. Do you mind if she stays here for a few days? It's probably safer for her here than at home.

EARL WILLIAMS: She can stay as long as she wants. She's like family.

CYNTHIA HANKS: Good.

JEAN WILLIAMS: What about you, Joe?

MINISTER: I'm gonna stay out at the Medlin's. Pastor Fredricks set everything up this afternoon.

JEAN WILLIAMS: They're good people. They'll take good care of you.

MINISTER: I'm gonna need somebody to rent me a car. I can't keep driving mine; I'm sure they're looking for it.

EARL WILLIAMS: I'll take care of it first thing in the morning.

MINISTER: I appreciate it, Earl.

(Minister Ragland shakes his hand.)

MINISTER: Well, I need to get going. Earl, if you can pick me up around eight tomorrow morning to get the car that would be great.

EARL WILLIAMS: Eight, it is.

MINISTER: I'll give you guys a call tomorrow.

(As Minister Ragland walks towards the door to leave, he remembers Corey.)

MINISTER: Oh, I almost forgot! Where's Corey?

JEAN WILLIAMS: Upstairs. He's probably on the phone with his little girl friend.

MINISTER: I'm gonna run up and say hello.

(Minister Ragland goes up to his room and knocks.)

COREY WILLIAMS: Come in!

(Minister Ragland walks in and Corey is pleasantly surprised.)

COREY WILLIAMS: Minister Ragland! What are you doing here? And what happened to your face?

MINISTER: I had a little accident so to speak. So, how did your date go?

COREY WILLIAMS: Oh man, you wouldn't believe it!

(The phone rings.)

COREY WILLIAMS: Hold on just a minute.

(Corey reaches across his bed and grabs his cordless)

COREY WILLIAMS: Hello. Jacy?

(Corey points at the phone to let the Minister know it's her. Minister Ragland stands up and slowly walks toward the door as he mimes to Corey that he'll call him later. Corey responds by giving him thumbs up.)

COREY WILLIAMS: Jacy, where are you?

JACY ELLIS: I'm at home.

COREY WILLIAMS: Baby, I thought we agreed that you wouldn't call me from your house.

JACY ELLIS: I know. I was just calling to remind you about tomorrow and to see if you needed a ride.

COREY WILLIAMS: Remind me about tomorrow? Baby girl, I wouldn't miss tomorrow for anything in the world. Tomorrow's going to be the best Tuesday you've ever had.

JACY ELLIS: Well, do you need a ride?

COREY WILLIAMS: No, I'm going to ride my bike. I like the trails out at Grant Lake. But I appreciate the offer.

JACY ELLIS: Okay. Well, I guess I'll see you tomorrow at 5:00 at the tire swing?

COREY WILLIAMS: I can't wait.

JACY ELLIS: Good night.

(Just before Jacy hangs up the phone, Corey calls her name.)

COREY WILLIAMS: Hey, Jacy.

JACY ELLIS: Yeah.

(Corey begins to sing. He gives her a hard time about her new nickname he gave her.)

COREY WILLIAMS: Nobody beats the Biz. Nobody beats the Biz.

JACY ELLIS: I'm gonna kick your butt tomorrow for giving me that silly nickname!

(Corey laughs.)

COREY WILLIAMS: Oh, I'm scared. I'll see you tomorrow, baby.

JACY ELLIS: Hey, Corey.

COREY WILLIAMS: Yes.

(Before Jacy answers she pauses for a few seconds.)

JACY ELLIS: Have you realized yet that I'm falling in love with you?

(Shocked by her statement, Corey is left speechless.)

JACY ELLIS: Corey, are you there?

COREY WILLIAMS: Yeah, I'm here.

JACY ELLIS: Did you hear what I said?

COREY WILLIAMS: I did.

JACY ELLIS: Did you know that?

COREY WILLIAMS: No, I did not.

JACY ELLIS: Well, now you do. I'll see you tomorrow.

COREY WILLIAMS: Okay.

JACY ELLIS: Good night.

COREY WILLIAMS: Good night, Jacy.

(After hanging up the phone, Corey lays back on his bed with a smile on his face. But if he only knew how big of a mistake he and Jacy have just made, his smile would surely disappear. As they talked about meeting at the tire swing and Jacy falling in love with him, Shelton, Jacy's racist brother, was listening in on the phone in his room and heard everything, which leaves him furious. But instead of telling their parents or confronting Jacy, he decides to take things into his own hands and calls one of his friends.)

SHELTON ELLIS: Kevin, what are you doing around four o'clock tomorrow afternoon?

KEVIN CAMPBELL: Nothing, what's up?

SHELTON ELLIS: I want you to pick me up at my house at four thirty tomorrow afternoon. And make sure you pull in the driveway and blow the horn.

KEVIN CAMPBELL: What's going on, Shelton?

SHELTON ELLIS: We're going coon hunting.

KEVIN CAMPBELL: Man, what are you talking about?

SHELTON ELLIS: Don't worry about it. I'll explain everything tomorrow.

(They hang up the phone and Shelton whispers to himself.)

SHELTON ELLIS: Nigger, it's time for you to go.

(Minister Ragland leaves Corey's house and is unaware of the fact that Willie and Buck are driving around looking for his Maxima. After driving around for two hours and not finding him, Buck decides to call Raymond.)

RAYMOND CLETTER: Hello?

BUCK SANDERS: Raymond, its Buck.

RAYMOND CLETTER: Did you find him?

BUCK SANDERS: No. We've been out here for two hours and he's nowhere to be found.

RAYMOND CLETTER: Well, just call it a night and we'll try it again tomorrow.

(As soon as Raymond finishes his sentence, Buck looks to his left and sees a black car sitting at a stop sign on a side street as they pass by. It's Minister Ragland.)

BUCK SANDERS: Did you see that?

WILLIE TAYLOR: Yes, I did.

BUCK SANDERS: Raymond, we've got him. He just took a right on Lake Forest. I'll call you back!

(They hang up the phone and turn around to go after Minister Ragland. Minister Ragland, having no idea they are following him, looks in his rear view mirror, sees headlights, and pays it no attention. After driving for another quarter of a mile, he looks in his mirror and notices that the headlights behind him are approaching extremely fast. As they gain on him he speeds up and before he knows it he's in an all out chase. Buck and Willie are driving a truck, which all of a sudden becomes Minister Ragland's advantage. They come up on a stretch of road that has three very sharp curves. Minister Ragland, in his car, is able to whip through the corners with no problem. As Willie and Buck chase him, they make it through the first curve, and through the second curve but the last curve gets the best of them. They lose control of the truck and end up in a ditch.)

CHAPTER FOURTEEN

(The next day, Minister Ragland decides to visit Ronald Hanks to let him know what's going on. Ronald enters the room and has a seat across from the Minister.)

MINISTER: How are you doing, Ronald?

RONALD HANKS: I've been better. How are you?

MINISTER: I'm all right. I just wish I could speed things up and get you out of here. But God's timing is not our timing.

RONALD HANKS: Have you talked to my wife? I called her five times last night and got no answer.

MINISTER: Well, that's why I'm here.

(Instantly a look of concern covers Ronald's face.)

RONALD HANKS: Please don't tell me that something has happened to her.

MINISTER: No, she's fine, but she's not staying at home. Raymond Cletter drove out there looking for me and he scared her a little. So right now she's staying with the Williams'. I figured she'd be safer there.

RONALD HANKS: Why was he looking for you?

MINISTER: They're trying to pin some phony charge on me so they can throw me in jail to keep me quiet. So, as of right now I'm on the run.

RONALD HANKS: Listen, Joe. In the last year and a half, I've lost my freedom, I've lost my rights, my peace of mind, and I've even lost my son. Cynthia is all I have left. Through all of this, she's suffered as much as I have, if not more. It never stopped her from loving and believing in me. Please promise me that you won't let anything happen to her, please.

MINISTER: Ronald, she's covered in the blood of Jesus and that I can promise you is the kind of protection that no man or one million men on this earth could ever provide. God's not going to allow one hair on her head to be harmed, that I will promise you.

RONALD HANKS: That's good enough for me. Hey look, I'm sorry about giving you a hard time before. I know you're out there putting your life on the line to help me and I just wanted to say, "thank you." I believe in what you're trying to do.

MINISTER: Don't believe in what I'm doing; just believe that it will be done.

RONALD HANKS: I do.

(Minister Ragland looks at his watch.)

MINISTER: I've got to get going. I'll stop by first chance I get. I don't know when it's going to be, but I will be back, the good Lord willing.

RONALD HANKS: Tell Cynthia I love her.

MINISTER: How about you call her at the Williams' and tell her yourself. I'm pretty sure she'd rather hear it from you.

RONALD HANKS: Yeah, I'll do that.

MINISTER: You take care of yourself, Ronald.

(As Minister Ragland walks out, the guard working the front desk gets on the phone and calls Raymond.)

GUARD: Raymond, he just left.

(Minister Ragland is on his way back to Swamp Fox with no idea that Raymond has been called. Two or three miles outside of Swamp Fox, Minister Ragland stops at a red light. While sitting at the light, he looks to his left and sees Raymond sitting at a stop sign waiting to take a right. Minister Ragland immediately leans to his right so that Raymond cannot see him. Once Raymond gets a break in traffic, he takes a right while talking on his radio.)

RAYMOND CLETTER: Yes. A black Nissan Maxima, License plate, John 3-3.

(Raymond has told his men to look out for a car that is not on the road. He has no idea that the Minister is driving a white rental car. Later that afternoon, Jacy and Shelton are at home sitting in the living room watching television when they hear a horn blow.)

111

JACY ELLIS: Who is that?

SHELTON ELLIS: Tommy and Kevin.

JACY ELLIS: Where are you guys going?

SHELTON ELLIS: Mikey Burne just got a new guitar and we're going over to his house and jam for a little while. You want to go with us?

JACY ELLIS: I've heard Mikey play. I don't think so.

SHELTON ELLIS: What are you gonna do?

JACY ELLIS: Probably kick back, listen to some music, and relax.

(As Jacy is talking about her plans for the afternoon, Shelton is standing behind her with a look of disgust on his face knowing she's going to meet Corey. After packing a few things into his backpack, Shelton heads for the door.)

SHELTON ELLIS: Try not to have too much fun.

JACY ELLIS: See ya.

(Shelton walks out of the front door. But what Jacy doesn't know is that he circled back around to the garage where her car is parked. Shelton opens the hood and loosens her distributor cap so her car won't start. He quietly closes the hood, leaves through the side door, and hops in the car to go to Grant Lake. Jacy, after hearing his friend's car drive away, gets up and looks out of the window to make sure they're gone. Once the coast is clear, she grabs her keys and heads for the garage smiling all the way. When she turns the key and it doesn't start, she whispers to herself.)

JACY ELLIS: No, not today. Please not today.

(Jacy sits there for a second, tries it again, and gets nothing. Knowing she's going be late meeting Corey, Jacy begins to panic. She gets out of the car and opens the hood to see if anything obvious is wrong. After checking the battery cables she tries it again and still it doesn't start. She goes back in the house and calls her dad at work.)

CLINT ELLIS: "South Farmville Insurance. This is Clint, how may I help you?"

JACY ELLIS: Dad, my car won't start!

CLINT ELLIS: What do you mean it won't start?

JACY ELLIS: It won't start!

CLINT ELLIS: Tell your brother to look at it.

JACY ELLIS: He's gone.

CLINT ELLIS: Well Jacy, what do you want me to do?

JACY ELLIS: Can't you come home and fix it? You're only five or six minutes away.

CLINT ELLIS: Jacy, I'm up to my neck in paper work honey. I can't leave now.

JACY ELLIS: Dad, I've got something very important to do today!

CLINT ELLIS: Go next door and ask Perry to take a look at it.

JACY ELLIS: Dad, Perry is like a major computer geek. He doesn't know anything about cars.

CLINT ELLIS: I don't know what else to tell you, Jacy. I have got to go, I'll see you when I get home.

(Now panicked and upset, Jacy hangs up the phone and runs next door. While she is dealing with her situation, Corey is peddling his way out to Grant Lake completely unaware of the danger that awaits him. After parking the car behind a little patch of woods, Shelton and his friends take off towards the tire swing where Corey and Jacy have agreed to meet. Once they reach the tire swing, they all pick a tree to hide behind as they anxiously wait for Corey to arrive. Back at Jacy's, Perry, her next-door neighbor, is under the hood.)

PERRY HAROLD: Try it now.

(Jacy turns the key and still gets nothing. She gets out and stands beside Perry.)

JACY ELLIS: Do you think you can fix it?

(Perry fiddles around with a couple of things.)

PERRY HAROLD: Try it again.

(Once again the car doesn't start. Jacy gets frustrated and bangs her hands on the steering wheel.)

JACY ELLIS: You piece of junk!

(Perry steps up to the driver side door.)

PERRY HAROLD: Take it easy. Banging on your steering wheel won't get it started any faster.

(Jacy sighs.)

JACY ELLIS: I'm sorry.

PERRY HAROLD: Just take it easy; we'll get it started.

(Jacy leans forward and rest her head on the steering wheel as she shakes her head. Back at Grant Lake, Corey has just arrived. He leans his bike against a tree and looks at his watch.)

COREY WILLIAMS: Four and a half miles on a bike and I still beat her here. Not bad, Corey Williams. Not bad at all.

(Feeling a little tight after riding for four miles, Corey begins to stretch. He grabs his backpack and begins to walk around looking for the perfect picnic spot. He walks about four or five steps, stops, turns to his right and out of nowhere jumps Shelton with a solid shot to Corey's nose. As Corey falls to the ground, blood begins to pour from his nose. Tommy and Kevin come out and they all begin to kick Corey without mercy. After receiving numerous kicks to the ribs and face, Corey tries to get up and run, but he has blood in his eyes and very little balance.)

SHELTON ELLIS: Where do you think you're going, nigger?

(Shelton trips Corey as he tries to run. As soon as Corey hits the ground, Shelton takes off his belt.)

SHELTON ELLIS: You guys hold him for me.

(Tommy and Kevin each grab one of Corey's arms as Shelton stands in front of him.)

SHELTON ELLIS: Nigger, didn't I tell you to stay away from my sister?

(With the little strength he has left, Corey yanks his arm away from Tommy and hits Shelton in the stomach. Tommy punches Corey in the jaw and he falls flat on his face. Shelton, after catching his breath, stands up.)

SHELTON ELLIS: Hold him up!

(Tommy and Kevin lift Corey up. Shelton, still holding his belt, gets down to eye level with Corey.)

SHELTON ELLIS: Nigger, you just signed your death certificate!

(Shelton kicks him in the stomach and again Corey falls forward, flat on his face.)

 SHELTON ELLIS: Hold him down!

(Tommy stands on Corey's ankles, and Kevin stands on his wrist as he helplessly screams in pain.)

SHELTON ELLIS: Shut up!

(Now completely out of control, Shelton rips Corey's shirt off and begins to violently beat him across his back and head with his leather belt. Back at Jacy's, Perry is still messing around under the hood when he happens to touch the distributor cap.)

PERRY HAROLD: Here we go! Here's your problem!

(Jacy gets out of the car to see what he's talking about.)

JACY ELLIS: What is that?

PERRY HAROLD: That is why your car won't start.

(Perry puts the cap back on.)

PERRY HAROLD: Try it now.

(Jacy turns the key and it starts.)

JACY ELLIS: Yes! Yes! Yes!

(She gets out and hugs Perry.)

JACY ELLIS: Thank you so much, Perry!

(He closes the hood.)

PERRY HAROLD: No problem.

JACY ELLIS: I have got to go! How much do I owe you?

PERRY HAROLD: No charge.

(She gives him a little peck on the cheek.)

JACY ELLIS: You're a sweetheart.

(Jacy gets in the car and backs down the driveway. As she pulls out she blows the horn and yells.)

JACY ELLIS: You're a genius, Perry!

(Feeling quite proud of himself, Perry smiles.)

PERRY HAROLD: I'm a genius.

(Back at Grant Lake, Corey is on his knees slumped over with his face covered in blood from the beating he's received.)

SHELTON ELLIS: Hey, boy!

(Corey doesn't respond.)

SHELTON ELLIS: Lift him up.

(Both Tommy and Kevin grab an arm and lift him up.)

SHELTON ELLIS: Hey, boy! Do you want to date white girls? Don't you know you have to be white to date white girls, nigger? I'll tell you what I'm gonna do. Knowing how much you want to date white girls, I'm going to help you out.

(Shelton grabs a can of white spray paint and begins to shake it.)

SHELTON ELLIS: You are now officially a member of the "I can date white girls club".

(Shelton begins to spray paint Corey's face white as they all laugh. As Jacy is speeding her way out to Grant Lake she looks at her watch and screams.)

JACY ELLIS: Why did you have to break down today, you piece of junk! God, please let him be there. Don't let him leave!

(Tommy, Kevin, and Shelton are standing over Corey's bloodied and beaten body as he lay motionless.)

KEVIN CAMPBELL: Well, looks like our work here is done. Let's go.

SHELTON ELLIS: We can't leave yet.

(Kevin looks at Shelton.)

KEVIN CAMPBELL: Why not?

SHELTON ELLIS: Because I'm not finished.

KEVIN CAMPBELL: What do you mean you're not finished? Look at him; he can't even sit up.

SHELTON ELLIS: I'm not finished. I told him to stay away from my sister but he was hard headed and wouldn't listen. I want to see just how hard his head really is. Hand me the bat.

(Again Kevin looks at Shelton.)

KEVIN CAMPBELL: What do you need the bat for, man? He's had enough.

TOMMY KILGROE: Kevin's right Shelton; he's had enough.

(Shelton gets mad and yells.)

SHELTON ELLIS: He's had enough when I say he's had enough!

(Startled by Shelton's yelling both Kevin and Tommy jump.)

KEVIN CAMPBELL: Shelton, I didn't come out here to kill anybody. You said we were going to rough him up and scare him a little. Killing was not apart of the plan.

SHELTON ELLIS: What's your problem, Kevin? What if it was your sister? Would you let some spook ruin her life?

(While Shelton is talking, Corey is slowly starting to sit up.)

SHELTON ELLIS: Would you let some nigger get her pregnant just to turn around and leave her to raise some half-breed baby by herself living on welfare?

(After talking about, Corey and Jacy, Shelton has worked himself into a frenzy. Now at his boiling point, Shelton lunges forward and snatches the bat out of Kevin's hand. He draws back, tightens his grip, and looks Corey in his blood soaked eyes. As Corey raises his weakened arms, he lightly whispers, begging for his life.)

COREY WILLIAMS: Please don't hit me.

SHELTON ELLIS: Shut up! I hate niggers! I hate niggers! I hate niggers!

(Shelton, with all the strength he has, repeatedly hits Corey in his back and head. Both Tommy and Kevin grab Shelton to stop the beating.)

KEVIN CAMPBELL: Stop man, you're gonna kill him! Shelton, stop it!

(After several blows they get him under control and take the bat. As they stand there holding Shelton, they're looking down at Corey waiting for some kind of response. A few seconds pass and Corey still has not moved. Tommy kneels down next to Corey.)

KEVIN CAMPBELL: What are you doing man?

TOMMY KILGROE: I want to see if he has a pulse.

KEVIN CAMPBELL: Don't touch him! They can trace your prints off of his body. Let's just go.

(As Shelton is standing there, he's looking down, staring at Corey, feeling absolutely no remorse for what he's done.)

KEVIN CAMPBELL: Shelton, let's go! We've got to get out of here!

(Before stepping over Corey to leave, Shelton coughs up phlegm and spits on him.)

SHELTON ELLIS: Next time I'm gonna kill you.

(Jacy is now less than a mile from Grant Lake.)

JACY ELLIS: Please let him be there, please let him be there.

(Tommy, Shelton, and Kevin are now driving down the highway going home and nobody is talking. Kevin, troubled by the fact that Corey could die, breaks the silence.)

KEVIN CAMPBELL: We have got to go back.

(Tommy, as he drives looks over at Kevin.)

TOMMY KILGROE: Do what?

KEVIN CAMPBELL: We have got to go back. If we leave him out there, he's going to die.

SHELTON ELLIS: We can and we will leave him out there. We're not going back.

KEVIN CAMPBELL: Shelton, if we leave him out there, he's going to die, man!

SHELTON ELLIS: If he does, then he got what he deserved! We are not going back!

TOMMY KILGROE: Kevin's right, maybe we should go back. What if he dies?

SHELTON ELLIS: Who cares?

KEVIN CAMPBELL: I care, Shelton! I care! This thing got way out of hand today and the end result could possibly be a dead seventeen-year kid! I can't live with that!

TOMMY KILGROE: We should go back, Shelton. I don't want to get nailed for murder.

SHELTON ELLIS: How can we get nailed for murder if nobody saw us? The only way we can get caught is if one of us starts running our mouth. But that's not going to happen, right?

TOMMY KILGROE: I'm not saying anything.

SHELTON ELLIS: Right, Kevin?

(Kevin doesn't answer, so Shelton, who's sitting in the back seat, leans forward and puts the bloody end of the bat next to Kevin's face.)

SHELTON ELLIS: Let me tell you something, Kevin, I am not going to spend the rest of my life behind bars because you all of a sudden have a conscience. My suggestion to you is to suck it up, deal with it, and keep your mouth shut. If I find out you talked to anybody, you'll be next.

(Jacy, who has just arrived at Grant Lake parks her car and takes off running towards the tire swing. Once she gets there she sees Corey's bike leaning against the tree.

Feeling relieved, she takes a deep breath. As she walks towards his bike she's looking around.)

JACY ELLIS: Corey! Corey! Corey, if you're trying to scare me it's not going to work! I see your bike, you're busted!

(As Jacy is talking, she's walking backwards when all of a sudden she trips over something. When she sits up to see what caused her to fall, what she finds causes her to gasp for air as if she were drowning. There before her, covered in blood, and barely alive is Corey. With tears wailing up in her eyes, Jacy leans forward to help him, but she's confused, panicked, and doesn't know if it's even safe to touch him. As she's on her knees rocking back and forth she begins to scream.)

JACY ELLIS: Somebody help me!

(Desperately wanting to help him, Jacy again reaches out towards Corey and then pulls her hands back in fear that she could hurt him worse.)

JACY ELLIS: Somebody, please help me! Please, somebody please! Help me!

(Jacy's tear-soaked mouth produces a cry that travels throughout the entire lake only to return to her in vain echoes. Tommy, Kevin, and Shelton have just pulled up in Shelton's driveway. Shelton gets out and talks to them from Kevin's side of the car.)

SHELTON ELLIS: Listen, I want you guys to go home, stay home, and keep your mouths shut. Don't call anybody, and don't go anywhere. Stay home, I'll call you later. Tommy, get rid of the bat.

TOMMY KILGROE: Okay.

SHELTON ELLIS: All right, go.

(Tommy pulls off and heads for Kevin's house. Now that Shelton is out of the car, Kevin tries to talk some sence into Tommy.)

KEVIN CAMPBELL: I'm going to the police.

TOMMY KILGROE: What?

KEVIN CAMPBELL: You heard me. I'm going to the cops. I can't handle this.

TOMMY KILGROE: You heard what Shelton said. There's no way we can get caught if we don't say anything.

KEVIN CAMPBELL: Forget about Shelton, Tommy! Don't you realize that we may have taken part in a murder today? A murder, Tommy!

TOMMY KILGROE: Okay, forget about Shelton, what about us? I don't want to go to jail, Kevin.

119

KEVIN CAMPBELL: This is not about us, Tommy. It's about that human being we left out at Grant Lake barely hanging on to life. If we end up in prison for the rest of our lives then that's exactly what we deserve!

TOMMY KILGROE: Shouldn't we at least call Shelton and let him know what's going on? He has just as much to lose as we do.

KEVIN CAMPBELL: You just don't get it, do you? You think Shelton is your friend but I'm telling you, he's not! If he knew I was going to the cops he'd kill me in a second, and you're no exception.

(They get to Kevin's house and park along side of the curb.)

KEVIN CAMPBELL: What are you gonna do, Tommy?

TOMMY KILGROE: Kevin, we really need to talk about this.

(With his mind made up, Kevin gets out of the car.)

TOMMY KILGROE: All right, Kevin, all right!

(Kevin stops and turns to face Tommy.)

TOMMY KILGROE: Let's go.

(Kevin gets in the car and they take off to the police station. At the local hospital, Corey has just arrived. Jacy has followed them bumper-to-bumper in her car. She pulls up behind the ambulance and leaves her car sitting there not caring at all about what happens to it. As they wheel Corey down the hall, Jacy is walking alongside his gurney with her face streaked with black mascara filled tears. After having an oxygen mask placed on him, Corey coughs and covers the entire mask with blood. He's so broken up inside from being kicked in the stomach and ribs that he is starting to choke on his own blood. While Jacy is holding Corey's hand, he tries to talk to her, but his words only come out in a gurgling murmur. To understand what he's trying to say, Jacy leans over putting her ear closer to his mouth not knowing that what she is about to hear, will be etched in her mind for the rest of her life. After making out what he said, she stands up and immediately bursts into tears. Finally, they reach the emergency room and wheel him in.)

NURSE: I'm sorry, you're not allowed in the ER.

JACY ELLIS: Please don't do this! I need to stay with him!

NURSE: I'm sorry, but you're going to have to stay out here.

(The nurse walks away and leaves Jacy standing out in the hall. She walks over to a chair, sits down, and begins to pray as she rocks back and forth. Tommy and Kevin are standing at the front door of the police station.)

TOMMY KILGROE: Are you sure you want to do this?

KEVIN CAMPBELL: Yes. Come on.

(As they enter the station they see a Deputy, Deputy Durant, sitting at his desk talking on the phone. After walking up to his desk and just standing there waiting for him to finish his call, Deputy Durant tells whoever he's talking to to hold so he can find out what the boys want.)

DEPUTY DURANT: Can I help you?

KEVIN CAMPBELL: Can we talk to you in private?

DEPUTY DURANT: What's on your mind?

KEVIN CAMPBELL: We'd really rather talk to you in private.

(Deputy Durant tells the person he's talking to that he'll call them back and hangs up the phone.)

DEPUTY DURANT: Follow me.

(Tommy and Kevin walk into an empty room and they all sit down.)

DEPUTY DURANT: Okay gentlemen, we're in private.

(Tommy and Kevin look at each other. Kevin then takes a deep breath and begins to explain everything that happened. Meanwhile at Corey's house, his dad is cutting the grass while his mom and Cynthia Hanks are in the kitchen talking and laughing when the phone rings.)

JEAN WILLIAMS: Hello?

NURSE SMITH: May I speak to Mr. or Mrs. Williams please?

JEAN WILLIAMS: This is Mrs. Williams.

NURSE SMITH: Mrs. Williams, my name is Shari Smith. I'm a nurse at Warsack County General Hospital.

JEAN WILLIAMS: Yes.

NURSE SMITH: Mrs. Williams, your son Corey has been in an accident.

(As her eyes grow wide she covers her mouth.)

JEAN WILLIAMS: Is he all right?

NURSE SMITH: Mrs. Williams, I can't discuss that over the phone. We need you and your husband to come down here right away.

JEAN WILLIAMS: Can you at least tell me if he's alive!

(After hearing some of the conversation, Cynthia Hanks walks over to Mrs. Williams and begins to rub her back to comfort her.)

NURSE SMITH: Yes, he is alive.

JEAN WILLIAMS: How bad is he hurt?

NURSE SMITH: Mrs. Williams, again, I can't discuss that over the phone.

JEAN WILLIAMS: We're on our way!

(She hangs up the phone and faces Cynthia.)

CYNTHIA HANKS: What wrong?

JEAN WILLIAMS: Corey's been in an accident!

CYNTHIA HANKS: Is he okay?

JEAN WILLIAMS: She couldn't talk about it over the phone!

(With tears in her eyes, Mrs. Williams darts out of the front door. She runs up to her husband, tells him what's going on, and he leaves the mower sitting in the middle of the yard. As they all run towards the car, Minister Ragland pulls up in the drive way behind them.)

MINISTER: Where is everybody going?

EARL WILLIAMS: To the hospital! Corey's been in an accident!

MINISTER: Cynthia, ride with me!

(Cynthia gives Jean a kiss on the cheek and gets in the car with Minister Ragland. Back at the station, Deputy Durant leans back in his chair amazed by the story he's just heard.)

DEPUTY DURANT: So let me get this straight. You two and this Shelton person sat in the woods, waited for this guy to show up, jumped on him, beat him with a bat, and left him out at Grant Lake?

KEVIN CAMPBELL: Yes sir.

(As Deputy Durant talks to the boys, another Deputy knocks on the door. Deputy Durant motions him to come in.)

DEPUTY ALLEN: I just got a call from Don down at the hospital. He said some girl found a kid beaten half to death out at Grant Lake. I was wondering if you wanted me to go down there and find out what's going on.

(Tommy, Kevin, and Deputy Durant all look at each other.)

DEPUTY DURANT: This kid, is he still alive?

DEPUTY ALLEN: From what Don told me he's barely hanging on.

DEPUTY DURANT: What about the girl? Is she still there?

DEPUTY ALLEN: Yes sir. Don said she was pretty upset.

DEPUTY DURANT: Get Don on the phone and tell him to keep her there. Under no circumstances is she allowed to leave.

DEPUTY ALLEN: Yes sir.

(The officer shuts the door and Deputy Durant leans forward.)

DEPUTY DURANT: You boys better thank the good Lord above that he's still alive, and you may want to ask him to keep him that way.)

(Deputy Durant gets on his radio.)

DEPUTY DURANT: Unit 7, come in.

UNIT 7: This is unit 7, go ahead.

DEPUTY DURANT: Mack, I want you to go to 604 Reedy Creek Road and pick up a Shelton Ellis for questioning. And make sure somebody's covering the back of the house in case he tries to run.

UNIT 7: We're on our way.

(Deputy Durant stands up.)

DEPUTY DURANT: All right boys. I'm going to go on down to the hospital to check on this kid and see what's going on. Deputy Cox is going to take a written statement and let you call your parents.

(After Deputy Durant walks out, Kevin leans forward and rests his head in his hands. Tommy stares at the floor wishing that they could somehow rewind the hands of time. As Mr. Williams is driving, he's holding his wife's left hand. In her right hand she's holding a bible, which is pressed close to her heart as she begins to pray.)

JEAN WILLIAMS: Precious father, I know all things work together for the good of them that love the Lord. We don't always understand why you allow certain things to happen Lord, but we do understand your perfect will. So Lord Jesus, if it's your perfect will to take Corey today, let your will be done.

EARL WILLIAMS: Yes, Lord.

JEAN WILLIAMS: But God I ask of you in the name of Jesus, to please give us one more chance to see him alive so we can tell him we love him.

(As she prays, with tears streaming down her face, her husband's emotions get the best of him and he too begins to cry. In the Minister's car, he notices that Cynthia is nervously bouncing her leg. So he reaches over and places his hand on top of hers, which she's resting on her left knee.)

CYNTHIA HANKS: Sorry.

MINISTER: It's okay. Just relax.

CYNTHIA HANKS: I've always considered Corey one of my own. Up until the day Larry left, they were inseparable. Wherever you saw one, you saw the other. I remember when Corey was seven years old; he walked up to me with that beautiful smile and asked me, "Can I call you my second mama?"

(Cynthia's tears slowly begin to slide down her face.)

CYNTHIA HANKS: That was one of the sweetest things I'd ever heard.

MINISTER: He's gonna be okay. Whether God decides to take him today or leave him here with us, he will be okay.

(As she turns to stare out of the window, she begins to pray within hoping that Corey's young life will continue on. Down at the hospital, two police officers are questioning Jacy. She can't erase the image of Corey's bloodied face from her mind as she stares at the floor. Corey's parents, Minister Ragland, and Cynthia Hanks have just arrived. They run up to the receptionist desk to find out where Corey is.)

EARL WILLIAMS: We're here to see my son. His name is Corey Williams!

(The receptionist checks her computer.)

RECEPTIONIST: He's in the Emergency Room right now.

JEAN WILLIAMS: Where is that?

RECEPTIONIST: I'm sorry you're not allowed on that hall. You'll have to go to the waiting room and a doctor will see you there.

(Now even more anxious to see her son, after looking to her right and seeing a sign on the wall that says, 'To Emergency Room' with an arrow pointing in that direction, she immediately takes off running, headed for the Emergency Room with the others right behind her. As the receptionist is chasing them down the hall, she's yelling.)

RECEPTIONIST: Stop! You are not allowed on this hall!

(When they come to the end of the hall, they take a right and at the other end of that hall is the emergency room. Jacy and two Police officers are sitting down just a few feet away from the emergency room doors when they look up and see Minister Ragland, Mr. and Mrs. Williams, Cynthia Hanks, and the receptionist running full blast down the hall making all sorts of noise. The two officers stand up.)

RECEPTIONIST: Officer, stop them! Stop them!

(The two officers immediately walk over and stand in front of the emergency room doors. When they finally reach the ER, they find themselves face to face with the two Deputies. One of the deputies is Deputy Durant.)

DEPUTY DURANT: You're not going in there!

JEAN WILLIAMS: We want to see our son!

(Mrs. Williams steps forward to enter the ER and the officer grabs her, which starts a scuffle. Mr. Williams, not liking the fact that the officer has grabbed his wife, tries to push the officer's hand away, which in turn causes the other officer to get involved. Knowing that things are getting out of hand, Minister Ragland tries to separate all of them and calm things down but it doesn't work. Now, in front of the emergency room are Corey's parents and the police yelling and screaming at each other. Then out of the emergency room comes a doctor who puts an immediate halt on all of the commotion.)

DOCTOR: What in heaven's name is going on out here?

EARL WILLIAMS: Our son is in there and we want to see him!

JEAN WILLIAMS: Right now!

(Mrs. Williams, determined to see her son, steps forward with all intentions of getting into the emergency room which sets off the second wave of scuffling and yelling. As the confrontation escalates, the doctor tries to calm them down.)

DOCTOR: Please stop it! Stop it! You are in a hospital! Mrs. Williams, please calm down! Mrs. Williams!

(After trying to quiet things down and having no success, the doctor does the one thing that he knows will silence them all.)

DOCTOR: Mrs. Williams! Mrs. Williams! Mrs. Williams, he's gone!

(As if time froze, they all turn and look at the doctor.)

DOCTOR: He's gone, Mrs. Williams. We did everything we could to save him, but he was too far-gone when he got here. His body was too weak to fight and he didn't make it. He's gone. I'm sorry.

(As they all stand there in silence, Jacy, who is standing off and away from the

125

commotion, can tell by everybody's facial expression that Corey has died. As tears slowly fill her eyes, she backs up against the wall sliding down into a crouching position. She buries her face in her hands as if she were trying to hide from the overwhelming pain that has just settled on her heart. Cynthia Hanks leans on the wall as she cries, stares at the floor, and whispers to herself.)

CYNTHIA HANKS: Why God? He's just a baby. Seventeen years old, Lord he's still a baby. Why?

(Mrs. Williams, with her mouth quivering and tears slowly streaking down her face, turns to face the two officers.)

JEAN WILLIAMS: I want to see my son. Now either I'm going in, or you're going to take me to jail for trying.

(The officers look at the doctor.)

DOCTOR: It's okay. Let her in.

(The officers move aside and let them in. As they enter the room they look to their left and there on a gurney lying motionless, with a severely swollen face, is their dead child. Minister Ragland looks in the other direction across the room as he tries to fight back the tears. After a few seconds he turns around to look at Corey, and it is at that time the emotional battle ends. Minister Ragland walks over to his bedside, grabs the side of the gurney, and cries as he whispers his name.)

MINISTER: Corey, please open your eyes.

(Mr. Williams, who's trying to be strong for his wife can't take it anymore. He tries to hold back the tears but he just can't do it. He walks over to Corey's bedside and cries as he holds his son's limp, lifeless hand. Mrs. Williams, straight-faced and serious, starts to walk around and pick up Corey's things that the doctors have either cut off or taken off.)

JEAN WILLIAMS: Look at you, Corey. You've got this hospital looking like your room. Speaking of your room Mr. Man, you didn't make up your bed this morning. What did I tell you about that?

(Minister Ragland and Mr. Williams look up at each other. Mrs. Williams grabs Corey's shoes off the floor and tries to put them on his feet.)

JEAN WILLIAMS: Come on Corey, get up, let's go. You have homework to do and I still have to make dinner.

(Mrs. Williams begins to weep as she tries to prepare her son for a trip she knows he'll never take.)

JEAN WILLIAMS: I'm not playing with you, Corey. I want you to get up now so we can go home.

(With his chin quivering, Mr. Williams quietly whispers.)

EARL WILLIAMS: God, please help her.

JEAN WILLIAMS: Baby, I won't make you do your homework if you come home, I promise.

(Cynthia Hanks walks into the emergency room and almost immediately turns around and walks out. Her heart sinks when she sees Jean trying to put Corey's shoes on. Minister Ragland looks at Mr. Williams and slowly shakes his head no, suggesting that he stop his wife. Mr. Williams walks over and stands behind her. He puts his hands on her shoulders as she continues to talk to Corey.)

EARL WILLIAMS: Jean, stop.

(She pushes his hands away and begins to tie up the laces of one of the shoes she's put on his foot.)

EARL WILLIAMS: Jean, you can't take him home.

(Again she pushes his hands away.)

JEAN WILLIAMS: He's my baby, and I'm taking him home. He doesn't want to stay here. Do you baby?

(Minister Ragland walks over to where they're standing.)

MINISTER: Jean, please.

EARL WILLIAMS: Jean, you can't take him.

(Again, she pushes his hands away. Knowing that he has to stop her he spins her around, grabs both of her arms, and looks her in her tear filled eyes.)

EARL WILLIAMS: You can't take him he's gone! You cannot take him home! He's dead, Jean! You hear me? He's dead! Our baby is dead. He's dead.

(Mr. and Mrs. Williams are now standing face to face in tears. Minister Ragland steps forward and wraps his arm around them both. Bringing the three of them together for one big hug. As they hold each other, Mr. Williams looks over his wife's shoulder to find reality staring him in the face. The reality that he will soon have to make the cold ground his baby's bed. A couple of hours have passed and Jacy's mom is pacing the floor waiting for her to get home. The police notified her parents and let them know that she was at the hospital and she was okay. As Jacy's mom continues to pace the floor, she sees headlights pull into the driveway and it's Jacy. When she walks through the door the first thing her mom notices is all of the blood that is on her clothes.)

KATHRINE ELLIS: What happened to you? Are you all right?

JACY ELLIS: I'm fine, it's not my blood. It's Corey's.

(Jacy looks directly at her dad.)

JACY ELLIS: He's dead.

(Her dad takes a deep breath.)

CLINT ELLIS: We know, honey.

JACY ELLIS: How do you know?

CLINT ELLIS: The police called us this afternoon.

JACY ELLIS: They called just to tell you that Corey was dead?

CLINT ELLIS: No honey. Sit down. There's something we need to tell you.

JACY ELLIS: Can't it wait, dad? I just want to take a shower and go to bed. The sooner this day is over, the better.

CLINT ELLIS: No, it can't wait. Now sit down.

(Jacy sits down on the couch. Her dad grabs the ottoman, sits in front of her, and begins to gently rub her hands as he talks to her.)

CLINT ELLIS: Jacy, the police called to tell us that your brother is in jail.

JACY ELLIS: In jail! Why is he in jail?

(Clint pauses.)

CLINT ELLIS: Your brother and two of his friends are responsible for Corey's death.

JACY ELLIS: What?

CLINT ELLIS: I'm sorry, honey.

JACY ELLIS: That can't be! They've got the wrong person!

CLINT ELLIS: I thought the same thing, but it's true. They confessed to it this afternoon, all three of them.

JACY ELLIS: This is not happening! This is not happening!

(Jacy takes off upstairs to her room. As her mother turns to go after her, her dad grabs her arm.)

CLINT ELLIS: Let me talk to her.

(Her dad goes up to her room and knocks on the door.)

CLINT ELLIS: Jacy.

(He can hear her crying as he talks to her.)

CLINT ELLIS: Baby, why don't we talk about it?

(Clint walks in.)

JACY ELLIS: I don't want to talk about it, dad.

CLINT ELLIS: It might make you feel better, honey.

(Clint walks over to the bed and attempts to put his arm around Jacy to comfort her. But that attempt is short lived as she pushes him away and jumps up off of the bed.)

JACY ELLIS: Get your hands off of me! How dare you come in here and try to comfort me? You deserve just as much blame as they do! You know what might make me feel better? If you tell me why you didn't do your job as a father by telling Shelton he was wrong!

CLINT ELLIS: What are you talking about, Jacy?

JACY ELLIS: You know what I'm talking about! You tell me that the three of them are responsible for Corey's death. Well, what about you, dad? The whole time Shelton was walking around here talking about how much he hated black people you never said a word. And when he would make those stupid jokes about black people you would laugh right along with him. You condoned the very same hatred that eventually caused him to murder another human being!

CLINT ELLIS: But…

(Jacy cuts him off.)

JACY ELLIS: No, let me talk! I've seriously dated two guys in my life who both treated me like trash, but you acted as if they were the greatest thing walking! Then along comes Corey who respected me, cared about me, treated me like a queen, and you hate him. Dad, he wanted to be with me for me, not for what was under my clothes! You never gave him a chance! Not even a simple hello!

CLINT ELLIS: I never said I hated him.

JACY ELLIS: You didn't have to. Your actions said it for you! When you allow your son to sit in your presence and talk about setting black people on fire, you are saying it! When you allow your son to sit in your presence and say that he hates niggers and

129

not correct him, you are saying it! You were wrong, Dad, and you know it!

(Clint stands up and yells as he begins to cry.)

CLINT ELLIS: What do you want me to do? What do you want me to do? I can't bring him back. If I could I would, but I can't! If I could give my life for his right now I would, but I can't do that, Jacy! And as far as me giving him a chance, my pride just wouldn't let me! Jacy, I was too afraid of what people might say and what they'd think of me! But do you really want to know why I never gave him a chance? It was because I didn't know how. All of my life, I was taught to tolerate black people but never to love and accept them for who they are; that's all I've ever known. And because my parents never taught me, I didn't know how to teach him. Sometimes you just can't do something unless somebody takes the time to show you how to do it. I just didn't know how! And now that poor kid's parents have to face every parent's nightmare. They have to bury their child, their only child! And as much as I want to, there is absolutely nothing I can do about it!

(With rage in her eyes and her face covered in tears, Jacy takes off running towards her dad. When she reaches him she grabs him by his shirt collar, pushes him up against the wall, and begins to yell.)

JACY ELLIS: You could have done something about it! Why didn't you tell him he was wrong? Why?

(Every time Jacy asks him why, she shakes him. As Jacy continues to yell at him, and the reality of his mistakes set in, Clint can only shake his head and cry as he answers her.)

CLINT ELLIS: I don't know! I'm sorry!

JACY ELLIS: Why, Dad?

CLINT ELLIS: I'm sorry!

JACY ELLIS: Why didn't you tell him, Dad?

(With his back pressed against the wall and Jacy in his face, Clint begins to slowly slide down the wall. As he goes down, Jacy goes down with him.)

CLINT ELLIS: Baby, I'm sorry!

(When they finally get down to the floor, her dad puts his fists over his eyes, curls up in a ball, and cries. Jacy, now emotionally drained, gives him one last shake as she yells.)

JACY ELLIS: You could have told him, Dad!

(After finally letting go of his shirt collar, Jacy remembers what Corey told her about love and hate living in the same heart. She then realizes that she has to forgive her father, regardless of the damage he's done. After a few seconds of watching him cry and regretting what she's done, Jacy slowly reaches out, wraps her arms around her heartbroken father, and embraces him. As Clint feels the arms of forgiveness wrap around him, he embraces his daughter, knowing that in his life, a change has to come. Back at the hospital, Cynthia, the Williams', and Minister Ragland are walking down the hall on their way to their cars. Mr. Williams is walking with his arm around his wife, and Minister Ragland is doing the same with Cynthia Hanks. When they round the corner and are near the front exit, they hear someone whistle. At once, they all look to see who it is and immediately they all stop walking. Standing to their left, in the waiting area, swinging a pair of handcuffs back and forth on his index finger is Raymond, along with the Mayor, and two other police officers.)

MINISTER: Cynthia, I want you to go and call Pastor Fredricks. Tell him to meet me at the police station.

CYNTHIA HANKS: But Joe...

(Minister Ragland cuts her off.)

MINISTER: Go on and call him, Cynthia, I'll be all right. Earl, Jean, you two go home and try to get some rest.

EARL WILLIAMS: Is there anything we can do, Joe?

MINISTER: Yeah. Go home and get some rest.

(Raymond walks up to Minister Ragland and right away he turns around and puts his hands behind his back so Raymond can put the cuffs on.)

RAYMOND CLETTER: You didn't think you could hide from old Raymond forever, did you? Tell me something. Where are you hiding out?

(Somewhat amused by the fact that Raymond couldn't find him, Minister Ragland chuckles.)

RAYMOND CLETTER: Oh, you think this is funny. You think this is some kind of game, don't you?

(Raymond gets right up to Minister Ragland's ear and whispers.)

RAYMOND CLETTER: Do you really think that I'm going to let you run loose in my town and make a fool out of me, nigger? Do you? If you do, you're sadly mistaken. The Mayor is the only thing that's keeping me, from sending you to the morgue. But sooner or later, he won't be around to save you. You had better get out while you can because your days are numbered.

(After whispering in his ear, Raymond steps back.)

131

RAYMOND CLETTER: Officer Durant, take this parasite to jail and lock him up.

(Officer Durant grabs Minister Ragland by his arm and escorts him out of the front entrance and into his patrol car. Back at home, Jacy has just gotten out of the shower. She slips on her pajamas, sits down in front of the mirror, and brushes her hair. After sitting there for a few minutes in daze, she decides it's time to end the day and go to bed. As she gets in bed and leans over to turn off the light, she sees something near the door out of the corner of her eye. What she sees is Corey's backpack that he carried out to Grant Lake. She picked it up and threw it in the back seat of her car as the paramedics were taking Corey away. As all of the day's events play back in her mind, Jacy gets out of bed. She grabs the bag and gets back into bed. As she begins to go through it, the first thing she sees is a radio. With a gleam in her eye, she smiles and remembers what Corey said about the radio and their first dance. She places the radio on her nightstand and continues to go through the bag with a smile on her face. The next thing she finds is a blanket. She moves the bag aside, spreads the blanket over her lap, and continues on with her search. After pulling out a couple of sodas and some chips, she comes across a light blue container. What she finds in that light blue container causes her to smile from ear to ear. There is a note that reads, "I know they don't look all that great, and they may not taste all that great, but I wanted to show you that there's nothing more important in the world to me than making you happy. I asked my mother how to make biscuits and she told me. At first she offered to make them herself, but I didn't want her to take care of you; I wanted to take care of you, myself. Surprise baby, here are the biscuits you asked for. I hope you like them. Love, Corey." With tears resting in her eyes, Jacy looks down, and there in that light blue container are several very odd shaped biscuits. As her tears begin to fall, she smiles. Once again Corey has proven to her that all he wanted to do was take care of her heart. With her body completely worn out, Jacy decides to call it a night. She puts the container in the bag and puts the bag on the floor. Jacy then pulls Corey's blanket over her, turns the light off, and peacefully cries herself to sleep.)

CHAPTER FIFTEEN

(The next morning at Corey's house, Corey's mom and Cynthia are sitting on the couch looking at his baby pictures. As they smile and gaze at the pictures, Corey's dad Earl is standing in the doorway looking over his wife's shoulder at the pictures. Earl leans over and gives his wife a kiss on the cheek.)

EARL WILLIAMS: I'm gonna go get the paper.

(His wife looks up at him, smiles, and goes right back to the photos. As Earl is walking down the driveway, a patrol car pulls up; it's Officer Durant. Feeling somewhat confused and a little hesitant about Durant because of the whole hospital incident, Earl stops walking and waits for Durant to get out of his car. As Officer Durant walks up the driveway, he picks up Mr. Williams's newspaper, which is just to the side of the driveway in the grass. With the newspaper in his hand and a blank look on his face, Officer Durant once again comes face to face with Mr. Williams.)

EARL WILLIAMS: I guess now you're gonna tell me I can't read my own newspaper.

(Officer Durant hands him his paper.)

DEPUTY DURANT: Mr. Williams, I was only doing my job yesterday at the hospital. It was nothing personal.

EARL WILLIAMS: Is there a reason for this unexpected visit?

DEPUTY DURANT: Unfortunately, there is. After all that happened yesterday I felt like I owed it to you to come out here and give you all the facts before you read the paper.

EARL WILLIAMS: Well, it looks like your timing is perfect. What is it?

DEPUTY DURANT: Mr. Williams, what happened to your son was no accident. Your son was murdered.

(Mr. Williams is so shocked all he can do is stare at Deputy Durant.)

EARL WILLIAMS: Murdered? What do you mean he was murdered?

DEPUTY DURANT: We have three young men in custody that have given us a full confession.

EARL WILLIAMS: How young?

DEPUTY DURANT: All eighteen.

EARL WILLIAMS: Why did they kill my son?

(Deputy Durant takes a deep breath.)

DEPUTY DURANT: Well, from what we were told, the brother of the girl your son was dating got upset when he found out they were seeing each other, he just couldn't handle it. He overheard the two of them making plans to go out to Grant Lake and have a picnic. So he and two of his friends went out there, waited for Corey to arrive, and they attacked him.

(A tear slowly rolls down Mr. Williams's face.)

DEPUTY DURANT: They beat him for almost an hour and left him for dead.

EARL WILLIAMS: So you're telling me that my son, my only child, was beaten to death because of who he was dating and the difference in their skin color?

(With a lump in his throat, Officer Durant fights back the tears as he answers.)

DEPUTY DURANT: I'm afraid so.

(With his face covered in tears, Mr. Williams tries to figure out how one human being, can kill another human being, over something as simple as skin color. Officer Durant puts his hand on Mr. Williams' shoulder to comfort him.)

DEPUTY DURANT: I'm sorry.

(As he's standing in front of Mr. Williams facing the house, Officer Durant looks up and sees Mrs. Williams staring at them out of the window. When Mr. Williams looks up, he notices that Officer Durant is looking at something behind him. Mr. Williams turns around to see what he's looking at only to find his wife staring back at him. Their eyes instantly lock and the reality of having to tell her sets in.)

DEPUTY DURANT: I'm gonna go ahead and take off so you can talk to her.

(Durant pulls out one of his cards.)

DEPUTY DURANT: Here's my card. Call me if you have any questions at all.

(Mr. Williams takes the card.)

DEPUTY DURANT: You take care of yourself.

(Officer Durant turns and heads for his car.)

EARL WILLIAMS: Hey, Durant.

(Officer Durant turns to face him.)

EARL WILLIAMS: Thank you.

DEPUTY DURANT: You're welcome. No hard feelings about yesterday?

EARL WILLIAMS: None at all.

(Durant gets in his car, waves, and drives off. Knowing that he has to tell his wife the bad news, he takes a deep breath, turns around, and walks towards the door. Once he is in the house he shuts the door and leans against it.)

JEAN WILLIAMS: What did he want?

EARL WILLIAMS: Why don't you sit down, honey?

JEAN WILLIAMS: I don't want to sit down, Earl. Now what did he want?

(Mr. Williams takes a deep breath.)

EARL WILLIAMS: He said what happened to Corey was no accident. Corey was murdered.

(As she continues to stare out of the window, Mrs. Williams's eyes fill up with tears.)

JEAN WILLIAMS: Do they know who did it?

EARL WILLIAMS: Yes. It was the brother of the girl Corey was seeing and two of his friends.

(She turns and looks at her husband as a tear dangles from her chin.)

JEAN WILLIAMS: And why exactly did they take my baby's life?

(Mr. Williams, who at the time is looking down at the floor, looks up at his wife.

Mrs. Williams, remembering that Jacy is white, realizes why Corey was murdered without her husband ever saying a word. After turning back to the window for a few seconds, Mrs. Williams heads for her bedroom. Mr. Williams, who is now standing at the bottom of the stairs, sticks his arm out to stop her. As they stand in silence facing in opposite directions, Mrs. Williams looks at her husband bearing no facial expression whatsoever. Mr. Williams then turns and looks up at his wife only to find her face covered in pain. His heart longs to make her feel better, but he realizes that there really isn't much he can say or do to help. So he decides that it's best to let her have some time alone. Feeling absolutely helpless, Mr. Williams slowly lowers his arm and lets his wife go by. When she's about half way up the stairs, he turns and watches her as she slowly climbs the stairs, dragging her hand along the railing as if she had been climbing for days. The next morning, Minister Ragland is sleeping on a cot in the cell. Raymond walks into the cell and stands over him for a few seconds as he sleeps. He then takes out his nightstick and loudly rakes it across the cell bars.)

RAYMOND CLETTER: Wake up, sleeping beauty! You made bail!

(Minister Ragland, still half asleep, rolls over and looks up at Raymond.)

MINISTER: Nice alarm clock.

RAYMOND CLETTER: Get out of my cell, boy.

(Minister Ragland gets up and they both walk to the front desk so he can sign some papers. After signing the papers, Minister Ragland gets his things and heads for the front door.)

RAYMOND CLETTER: I'll see you next time!

(Raymond smiles as he watches Minister Ragland walk away. Sitting in front of the station in his car waiting for Minister Ragland is Pastor Fredricks. Once Minister Ragland gets in the car, he takes a deep breath.)

MINISTER: Thank you so much for getting me out of there.

(Minister Ragland pulls out his checkbook.)

MINISTER: How much do I owe you for bail?

PASTOR FREDRICKS: You don't owe me anything.

MINISTER: Oh yes I do! Now, you've done enough already! I'm going to pay you back. Now, what do I owe you?

PASTOR FREDRICKS: Joe, your bail was seventy- thousand dollars.

MINISTER: Seventy- thousand dollars! That can't be right!

PASTOR FREDRICKS: Joe, in this town, in this system, you shouldn't be surprised.

MINISTER: And I assume there's absolutely nothing we can do about it, right?

PASTOR FREDRICKS: Not a thing.

MINISTER: I'm really sorry. That was probably your life savings.

(Pastor Fredricks looks at Minister Ragland.)

PASTOR FREDRICKS: I don't have seventy thousand dollars, Joe.

MINISTER: Where did you get the money?

PASTOR FREDRICKS: Nowhere. We put our house up as collateral.

(Minister Ragland is shocked.)

MINISTER: What?

PASTOR FREDRICKS: There was no other way, Joe.

MINISTER: I can't believe you did that. How did you get your wife to go along?

PASTOR FREDRICKS: It was her idea.

MINISTER: Pastor, I promise you right now...

(He cuts him off in mid sentence.)

PASTOR FREDRICKS: Don't even say it, Joe. I'm not worried about you leaving town. If it were the wrong thing to do, the Lord would have made another. This is just His way of testing our faith; that's all He's doing. What you need to do is get back out there and finish what you started.

MINISTER: Yes sir.

PASTOR FREDRICKS: If you go to trial, you do know that their going to throw you in jail don't you?

MINISTER: Yes sir.

PASTOR FREDRICKS: Okay. Then get out there and do what God sent you here to do.

MINISTER: Yes sir.

CHAPTER SIXTEEN

(The next day at school, Jacy is walking to her locker. People are pointing at her and whispering as she passes by. When she finally reaches her locker, which seems like an eternity, she looks over at Corey's locker and sees that it's decorated with small signs that say, "Heaven just got a new angel," "I love you," and "We're going to miss you." After reading the signs, she opens her locker to get her books, unaware of the trouble that awaits her. Across the hall and down a few lockers, three black girls are talking when one of them spots Jacy. She points her out to the rest of her friends and immediately they walk straight to Jacy's locker. The girl that noticed Jacy first grabs her by her shoulder and spins her around. Jacy, who is completely caught off guard, drops her books.)

BRITANY CHANCE: You got a lot of guts, girl!

JACY ELLIS: Excuse me?

BRITANY CHANCE: You heard me! You got a lot of guts showing your face around here after what you did to Corey!

JACY ELLIS: I didn't do anything to him!

(Ashley Moore, one of the three black girls that walked up to Jacy, pushes Jacy on the forehead causing her to hit the back of her head on the locker.)

AHSLEY MOORE: Don't try and lie your way out of it now! You got him killed, and now we're gonna kick off in your tail for it.

(Just as Ashley steps forward to grab Jacy, out of nowhere comes a six-foot-one black girl named Shannon. She steps between the two of them and gets in Ashley's face.)

SHANNON KELLY: I don't think so!

ASHLEY MOORE: Shannon, what are you doing?

SHANNON KELLY: I am not gonna let you jump on her. It's not happening.

(One of the other girls named Tammy steps up into Shannon's face.)

TAMMY CARL: And who do you think you are?

SHANNON KELLY: I think I'm about 6'1 and you're about 5'8.

TAMMY CARL: And?

(Shannon raises both of her fists and puts them in Tammy's face.)

SHANNON KELLY: And I'm all about feeding you this two-piece dinner if you don't get up out of my face.

(Tammy steps back, realizing that messing with Shannon is not the smartest thing to do.)

BRITANY CHANCE: You're wrong, Shannon! How are you gonna stand up here and protect that white trash after what she did to Corey?

SHANNON KELLY: Now see, there you go. All in the crayon box and don't know the colors. She didn't have anything to do with what happened to Corey. That's why you need to mind your own business.

BRITANY CHANCE: Check you out. Now that you got your little basketball scholarship you think you're all that. Taking that white girl's side. You're a sellout!

SHANNON KELLY: And you're about to get knocked out, if you and these two hood rats don't get up out of my face.

(As they stand there in silence eyeing each other down, Shannon raises both of her arms suggesting that they make a move.)

SHANNON KELLY: What's up?

(They decide to let it go for the time being. They know Shannon and they know she is nothing to mess around with.)

TAMMY CARL: That's all right. We'll catch you next time. You better watch your back, Jacy.

(Shannon watches them as they all turn and walk away.)

SHANNON KELLY: They're just a bunch of mouth; always trying to start something. Are you all right?

JACY ELLIS: Yeah. Why did you do that?

SHANNON KELLY: I know who you are, Corey mentioned you a few times. Actually, he mentioned you all the time, Jacy this, Jacy that. That boy loved himself some Jacy. There must be something really special about you. I know a whole lot of girls that couldn't even get a date with Corey. And here you come along and get his heart. He was really something special. And he was fine too, won't he girl? Just fine, for no reason at all!

(Jacy laughs.)

JACY ELLIS: I take it you guys were friends?

SHANNON KELLY: Oh yeah, we were tight, have been for a long time. I still can't believe he's gone. I just can't believe it. You know, one of the things I'm gonna miss most about him is playing basketball. Once a year, they block off the street downtown and have a 3 on 3-basketball tournament. I remember the very first year of the tournament I wanted to play in the coed division, but I couldn't find a partner because all of the guys wanted to play with their boys. Ten minutes before Corey's team was scheduled to play, he told them to find somebody to replace him because he wanted to play in the coed division with me. We've won the division every year since.

(As Shannon is talking to Jacy, she begins to stare off into space as she reflects on all of the good times she had with Corey.)

SHANNON KELLY: Oh, well, I guess its time to hand the trophy over to somebody else because I will never, ever play in that tournament again.

(As a tear falls from Shannon's eyes, Jacy can plainly see the empty void that Corey has left in her life. The bell rings and it's time to go to class.)

SHANNON KELLY: Third period bell.

(Shannon looks up at the clock on the wall and wipes her eyes.)

SHANNON KELLY: Time for gym. Listen, if anybody starts bugging on you, just let me know. I got your back.

JACY ELLIS: All right.

SHANNON KELLY: I'll see you around.

JACY ELLIS: Okay.

(Shannon turns and heads for the gym.)

JACY ELLIS: Hey, Shannon!

(Shannon turns to face Jacy.)

SHANNON KELLY: Yeah.

(Jacy pauses for a couple of seconds before she responds.)

JACY ELLIS: Thanks.

(Shannon smiles back at Jacy.)

SHANNON KELLY: It's all good.

(After Shannon walks away Jacy bends over and picks up her books. After picking them up she glances over at Corey's locker and decides that it's time to confront her brother. Jacy puts her books back in her locker and takes off to the courthouse where her brother is being held until his trial. Shortly after she arrives, they escort her to the visiting area where she nervously waits for Shelton. Finally, after sitting there for five minutes or so in anticipation, the heavy steel door slowly squeaks open. Jacy, with her stomach in knots, looks up to her left and in walks Shelton. He is wearing an orange one-piece jail suit with brown open-toed sandals. Shelton and Jacy are separated by a thick piece of glass. To communicate they have to use phones that are on the walls in each of their little booths. When Jacy looks at Shelton's face, she is instantly reminded of the day she found Corey at Grant Lake. As they sit in silence, in her mind she's starting to second-guess her decision to go see him, and then Shelton speaks.)

SHELTON ELLIS: Please talk to me.

(Jacy continues to stare at him a few seconds longer and then finally breaks her silence.)

JACY ELLIS: Do you have any idea how much damage you've done?

(Not expecting that question, Shelton sits there for a second or two before he answers.)

SHELTON ELLIS: Yes.

JACY ELLIS: Are you sure? I don't think you do.

SHELTON ELLIS: Jacy, I know what I've done.

JACY ELLIS: No, Shelton. In your mind you imagine how much damage you've done. Me, I've seen up close and personal the damage you've done. So how about I give you a little run down on what you missed out on. Do you know who found him out at Grant Lake? I did.

(Jacy has to stop talking as she begins to cry.)

141

JACY ELLIS: Shelton, the back of his head look like somebody put a softball under his scalp, it was so swollen. His nose was broken so bad, that it was turned almost completely sideways.

(Through her tears Jacy continues to explain the horror she experienced that day.)

JACY ELLIS: When they were wheeling him down the hall at the hospital, he kept murmuring something, but I couldn't understand what he was saying. So I leaned closer to hear him, and what he was telling me is that he couldn't see.

(Again Jacy has to stop talking as she cries.)

JACY ELLIS: Shelton, he didn't even know his eyes were wide open.

(As Jacy reminds Shelton of the damage he's done, he begins to cry. The guilt and shame is overwhelming.)

JACY ELLIS: I saw his parent's faces when the doctor told them that he was dead. I see mom and dad walking around in a daze all day. I've seen dad cry off and on for two days straight, and you know dad never cries. He didn't even cry at his own mother's funeral. I see revenge in faces everywhere I go. I've seen it all, Shelton.

SHELTON ELLIS: I was only trying to protect you.

JACY ELLIS: Shelton, there was nothing to protect me from. He was never going to hurt me. He loved me too much to hurt me. You were trying to protect me from his color, not from him.

SHELTON ELLIS: I couldn't handle it Jacy. You and him together, I just couldn't handle it. But I think more than anything, I wanted to protect myself from the things people might say and how it would make me feel.

JACY ELLIS: How it would make you feel? What about everybody else, Shelton? What about his parents? What about all of the people that loved him? How do you think they feel now that he's gone? You had no right to touch him. Do you know who they're starting to blame? Me, Shelton, they're blaming me. People are threatening me, telling me I'm next, and cornering me at school wanting to beat me up. Shelton, I'm afraid to leave the house and it's all because you were worried about how it might make you feel! We're all targets now, Shelton; me, mom and dad! You had no right to touch him!

(Shelton, who is still crying wipes his eyes with the sleeve of his uniform.)

SHELTON ELLIS: I know everybody hates me, even mom and dad. And I know that things are ten times worse than they were before because of what I've done. Last night in my cell I tried to figure out why I hated them so much. I wanted to know what was fueling that fire and producing all of the hate.

(Shelton slowly raises his hands to chest level and shrugs his shoulders.)

SHELTON ELLIS: Nothing. I came up with absolutely nothing. The reason I took another human being's life is because I never took time to control my own. I never took the time to think for myself. I just followed everybody's lead. I hated because everybody else hated. No black person has ever done anything to hurt me, never. Now look at me. Because I followed everybody else, I'm going to be in this uniform and behind these bars for the rest of my life.

(As Shelton begins to cry, Jacy, feeling every ounce of his pain, also begins to cry.)

SHELTON ELLIS: Will you please forgive me? You're all I have now, Jacy.

JACY ELLIS: Yes, I do forgive you. And whether you're right or wrong, you're still my brother, and I love you. I could never hate you, Shelton. Maybe smack you around a little bit, but never hate you.

(Jacy makes a joke to lighten the mood a little which causes both of them to laugh.)

JACY ELLIS: Shelton, for the rest of my life I will remember what you've done. There's no way I can forget it, ever. If I sat here and told you that I wasn't angry, I'd be lying to you because I am. But in spite of what you've done, I do forgive you. Because love and hate can't live in the same heart. Corey told me that.

(With a lump in his throat, Shelton responds.)

SHELTON ELLIS: That's good advice, Jacy. You hold on to it.

(The guard walks up and taps Shelton on his shoulder. Shelton turns and looks up at him.)

GUARD: Times up.

(Shelton turns back to Jacy and takes a deep breath.)

SHELTON ELLIS: I have to go.

JACY ELLIS: Okay.

SHELTON ELLIS: Tell mom and dad I said hello and that I love them.

JACY ELLIS: I will. They told me they were coming to see you tomorrow.

SHELTON ELLIS: Good. When can you come back?

JACY ELLIS: I don't know. It was pretty hard coming out here today knowing that I was going to see you locked up in this place. I don't know when I'm coming back.

SHELTON ELLIS: I understand. Just promise me you'll come back.

JACY ELLIS: I promise.

(The guard taps him again.)

GUARD: Let's go!

SHELTON ELLIS: I'll see you next time, okay?

(Jacy starts to cry again.)

SHELTON ELLIS: Don't do that. Please don't do that.

(Jacy's tears trigger Shelton's tears.)

JACY ELLIS: You hang in there and take care of yourself.

SHELTON ELLIS: I will.

(Jacy kisses her index finger and presses it against the glass.)

JACY ELLIS: I love you.

(Shelton does the same.)

SHELTON ELLIS: I love you, too.

(While Shelton is being walked to the door in cuffs, he and Jacy lock eyes. They continue to hold eye contact even as he is leaving the room. After walking out of the visiting room, Shelton and the guard take a left, which takes them past a large window. And even though it's only for a brief moment, Jacy and Shelton catch one last glimpse of each other and mime I love you as their tears continue to fall. Four days have now gone by and the day that nobody is looking forward to has arrived. It's the day of Corey's funeral. Pastor Fredricks is in the pulpit speaking as the service is under way.)

PASTOR FREDRICKS: Whether we want to accept it or not, this is a time to rejoice!

(Throughout the church, people are responding to what he is saying with words like, 'Hallelujah,' 'Yes, Lord' and 'Amen.')

PASTOR FREDRICKS: Corey's soul has crossed over into glory. The Bible says to be absent from the body is to be present with the Lord. Corey's soul is resting in a place each and every one of us still has to make it to. I loved Corey...

(As Pastor Fredricks begins to cry he has to take a couple of seconds to gather his composure.)

PASTOR FREDRICKS: Of course we would rather have him here with us, but my soul rejoices when I think about that boy being with the Lord. I feel blessed to the utmost knowing that I'm going to see him again one day. But the next time I see him, there won't be any black or white.

(Voices ring out all over the church in praise responding to the powerful truth he's speaking.)

PASTOR FREDRICKS: There won't be any death! There won't be any racism! There won't be any ignorance! There won't be any upper class! There won't be any lower class! No more sickness! No more sadness! And no more hatred! But there will be praise!

(Most of the people at this point are standing. Some have their hands raised towards heaven. Some are crying with their hands clasped together under their chin. Some are sitting down, slowly rocking back and forth as tears of joy fall from their eyes. They stop mourning the death, and begin to celebrate the new life.)

PASTOR FREDRICKS: Now as I close, I ask all of you, to let the reason we are here today be a lesson learned. Let today be a reminder of just how precious life can be, and how so very important it is to get your lives right with God before you leave this earth. Any one of us could be lying here next week in a casket, and that's the truth. In the book of James, the fourth chapter and the fourteenth verse. The bible says, "For what is your life but a vapor that appears for a little time, and then vanishes away." None of us are promised tomorrow, so let's make sure we do the right thing today! Now if anybody wants to come up and say a few words, the pulpit is open.

(Larry Hanks, Ronald and Cynthia's son, who is also Corey's best friend, stands up and walks towards the pulpit. As he passes by the casket he looks down at Corey and it stops him in his tracks. Larry walks over to the casket, places his hands on the side, leans his head down, and begins to cry. He becomes so emotionally broken, that all he can do is shake his head in disbelief as his grief-stricken tears fall upon the chest of his best friend. Mr. Williams, who is sitting beside his wife gets up, walks over to the casket, and puts his arm around Larry.)

EARL WILLIAMS: I gotcha son, I gotcha.

(Mr. Williams slowly turns Larry around and walks him back to his seat knowing that he is far too upset to go up and talk. After about five minutes have passed, at the very back of the church, the sound of plush carpet being walked on begins to travel through the air. An individual, the last individual you would expect to see at Corey's funeral, is making their way to the pulpit. That individual is none other than Jacy Ellis. She slowly and hesitantly makes her way down the aisle, tightly clutching a gray sweatshirt in her hand. People are pointing at her and whispering, which is confirmation that she is not at all welcomed. After making what seemed like the longest walk of her life, Jacy reaches the pulpit. She wipes her eyes, takes a deep breath, and then looks up to find every pair of eyes in the church on her. In her mind, not only is she thinking about the evil and heinous looks that she's getting, but she also has to contend with the fact that her brother, her white brother, killed Corey. And she is the only white person in the entire church out of about four hundred and fifty black people. But because of the love she has for Corey, she is determined to speak her mind.)

JACY ELLIS: My name is Jacy Ellis.

(As soon as Corey's mother hears that name she looks up in amazement. She can't believe that Jacy is there.)

JACY ELLIS: I know that most of you think that I have no right to be here. And I know that most, if not all of you, blame me for what happened to Corey. I've heard the rumors.

(Shannon Kelly, the girl that stood up for Jacy when she was being harassed by the three black girls at school, shakes her head knowing that Jacy had nothing to do with Corey's death.)

JACY ELLIS: I'm not here to try and clear my name or change anybody's mind; you're gonna think what you want to think. God knows, I know, and Corey knows that I had nothing to do with what happened last Tuesday. My parents told me that it might not be such a good idea for me to come here today, but I had to. You see, I loved Corey just like the rest of you. I may not have known him as long as some of you, but I knew him long enough to know that the world has lost something special, something that can never be replaced. When I moved to this town almost two years ago, I could not believe what I was seeing. The hatred and separation here absolutely blew me away. I promised myself right then and there, that I would never allow my eyes to see what everybody else was seeing. I would never allow my eyes to see color. I promised myself never to see a nice black man, or a nice white man, but just to see a man. When I looked at Corey, I never saw his color. I saw an example; an example of love, of caring, of happiness, of honesty, and of sincerity. I saw an example of peace. In Corey, I also found a cure, a cure for gloom and sadness. No matter how bad of a day I was having, I always knew that seeing him would make me feel better. He always knew the right things to say and when to say them. He just knew how to take care of your heart.

(With tears in her eyes, Jacy smiles.)

JACY ELLIS: The things that made Corey so special are not things you're born with, they're things you're taught. Mr. and Mrs. Williams, you did an incredible job raising him. He was without a doubt, the gentlest gentleman I have ever known. And he loved both of you so very much. He talked about you all the time. He loved his mama and daddy. Corey loved everybody.

(Jacy, now finished, walks down to the casket. With tears in her eyes, she looks down at Corey and tries to figure out how something so bad, could happen to someone that was so good. In her right hand, Jacy is holding a sweatshirt. A sweatshirt that says, "CAROLINA LAW," on the front of it. Remembering that Corey wanted to go to the University of North Carolina to study law, Jacy went out and bought him the sweatshirt he never had a chance to earn on his own. She unfolds the sweatshirt, spreads it across his chest, smoothes out all the wrinkles, and whispers.)

JACY ELLIS: I'll always love you.

(With her face draped in tears, Jacy turns around to talk to Corey's parents)

JACY ELLIS: I'm so sorry.

(Mrs. Williams slowly looks up at Jacy.)

JEAN WILLIAMS: Who do you think you are coming here disrespecting my son?

JACY ELLIS: I meant no disrespect, I just...

(Mrs. Williams cuts her off in mid sentence.)

JEAN WILLIAMS: This is all your fault.

JACY ELLIS: Please don't say that.

JEAN WILLIAMS: It's your fault my son is lying in that casket.

JACY ELLIS: Mrs. Williams, please don't say that.

JEAN WILLIAMS: Get out.

JACY ELLIS: Mrs. Williams, please...

(Again she cuts Jacy off in mid sentence.)

JEAN WILLIAMS: Get out! Now!

(Mr. Williams leans forward and whispers to Jacy.)

EARL WILLIAMS: Maybe you should go.

(Now, feeling worst than ever, Jacy turns and walks away. As she walks down the aisle, she realizes that she's heavier going out than she was coming in. Not only does she carry the burden of Corey being gone, but because of what his mother said, she now carries the responsibility of his death, which feels like the weight of the world. At Corey's gravesite, the service has just ended and his parents are standing at his casket. His mother pulls a rose off of the arrangement on top of his casket. She kisses the casket and then heads for the family car. As Mr. Williams walks beside his wife holding her right arm, Cynthia Hanks is holding on to her left arm. In the very back, in a chair next to the aisle, Jacy has just sat down. As Corey's parents approach her on their way to the car, she looks down at the ground to avoid eye contact. She doesn't want to upset Corey's mom anymore than she already has. As they walk past Jacy, Mr. Williams drops a small piece of paper on her lap. Jacy looks at the paper, looks back at Mr. Williams, picks the paper up and unfolds it to see what it says. It reads, 'Thank you for making my son's last days his happiest. I know that what happened to my son was not your fault so don't blame yourself. I apologize for my wife. She's in a lot of pain and she's angry. Just give her time.' Jacy turns to look at Mr. Williams one more time as he continues on towards the car, never looking back at her. After most of the people have cleared out, Jacy takes a seat in the front next to the casket. A few feet away, Minister Ragland is talking to someone when he just happens to look across the cemetery toward the parking lot where he thinks he sees Jennifer Mundy's car. He leans his head a little to the left, squints his eyes, and realizes that it is Jennifer Mundy. Not wanting anybody to see her, Jennifer decides to leave as people are going to their cars. As Minister Ragland watches her drive off, he sees Jacy sitting in front of the casket by herself and decides to talk to her. He walks over and stands behind her.)

MINISTER: He was crazy about you.

(Jacy turns to see who is talking to her.)

JACY ELLIS: Who are you?

(He sticks out his hand for her to shake.)

MINISTER: Minister Joe Ragland.

JACY ELLIS: You're Minister Ragland?

(They shake hands.)

MINISTER: That's me.

JACY ELLIS: Corey told me a lot about you.

MINISTER: I hope it was good.

JACY ELLIS: Of course it was good. He always said nice things about you.

MINISTER: Yeah well, he was a good kid. May I sit down?

(Jacy moves over one seat.)

MINISTER: You know it takes a mighty brave person to do what you did today.

JACY ELLIS: You think me going to the funeral was a bad idea?

MINISTER: Not at all.

JACY ELLIS: I wish his mother saw it that way.

MINISTER: All she sees right now is life without her baby; she's in a lot of pain, Jacy. The loss of a child is a very painful thing you never get over. God has to teach you over time how to deal with the loss. Which in turn will teach you how to deal with the pain.

JACY ELLIS: Why do I feel like all of this is my fault?

MINISTER: It's not your fault, and you need to understand that. If you allow your mind or people, to convince you that this is your fault, the burden of it will break you down. It's too great. I know he wouldn't want you to blame yourself. Just pray for strength, and pray for his parents. God will take care of the rest.

(Minister Ragland pulls out one of his business cards.)

MINISTER: This is my card. If you want to talk or just need somebody to listen, give me a call. You can reach me on my cell phone at any time.

(Jacy takes his card.)

JACY ELLIS: Thanks.

MINISTER: I've got to run. Are you going to be all right?

JACY ELLIS: Yeah.

MINISTER: Are you sure?

JACY ELLIS: Yeah, I'm sure.

MINISTER: Okay. Call me if you need me.

JACY ELLIS: I will.

MINISTER: Take care.

JACY ELLIS: You, too.

(Minister Ragland gets up and heads for his car. Jacy has decided to stay a little longer. After sitting there for five or six seconds she gets up, walks over to the casket, and begins what she considers closure. She begins to talk to Corey as her tears helplessly fall on the pedals of red, yellow, and white roses that make up the beautiful flower arrangement on his casket. Back at Jacy's house, her dad is sitting at the kitchen table with the newspaper in front of him. Corey's funeral has made the front page. Jacy's mother walks into the kitchen to find him in a daze staring out of the window.)

KATHRINE ELLIS: Clint, what's the matter?

CLINT ELLIS: I'm thinking about the fact that those boys are going to prison, we're just as guilty as they are, and we slipped right through the cracks.

(She gently grabs his chin and turns his face towards her.)

KATHRINE ELLIS: We didn't throw any punches, and we didn't swing any bats. They did.

CLINT ELLIS: Kathrine, we've been swinging bats, and throwing punches for the last eighteen years honey. The only difference is, our son survived it.

(Clint gets up and walks away leaving her standing there. Now feeling worse because of what her husband has just said, she sits down at the table, only to look at the front page of the newspaper and find Corey's still brown eyes screaming back at her, Why? Why? Why?)

CHAPTER SEVENTEEN

(The next day, Minister Ragland decides it's time to take the ultimate risk. He's going to make another trip to Cary in hopes of getting through to Jennifer one last time. When he pulls up in the parking lot of her high school, she's getting into her car about to leave. After following her for about a mile, Jennifer pulls into the parking lot of a convenience store to put some air into her tire. Minister Ragland drives around the back of the store and comes out on the other side behind Jennifer's car. He gets out and nervously walks up behind her. Jennifer, not paying attention, doesn't see or hear him.)

MINISTER: How many people have to die before you tell the truth?

(After recognizing the voice, Jennifer stops what she's doing, stands up, and turns around.)

JENNIFER MUNDY: What are you doing here?

MINISTER: I'm here to let you know that a seventeen-year-old boy was killed and that more people are going to die if you don't do something soon.

JENNIFER MUNDY: Look, you had better leave me alone or I'm going to call the police!

MINISTER: Go ahead. I'm not breaking any laws; this is a public place. You're not being held here against your will; you can leave any time you want.

(Jennifer gets in her car and puts it in drive with all intentions of leaving.)

MINISTER: I saw you at the cemetery!

(Jennifer sits there for a second and then turns to face Minister Ragland. She's a little surprised that he saw her.)

MINISTER: You were friends, weren't you?

(Jennifer puts the car back into park.)

JENNIFER MUNDY: Yes.

MINISTER: Jennifer, I'm sorry about what happened to you, I really am. But that lie you told has turned an entire town upside down and now people are starting to die.

JENNIFER MUNDY: Don't you dare blame me for that! What happened to Corey was not my fault!

MINISTER: I know that! But the war that's about to break out in Swamp Fox will be, along with the tragedies that will come out of it. Jennifer, things were on edge before Corey was killed, and now it's only a matter of time before they really explode. You have to tell the truth!

JENNIFER MUNDY: I did tell the truth!

MINISTER: You did not tell the truth!

(Again, Jennifer puts her car in drive.)

JENNIFER MUNDY: I don't have time for this!

(Minister Ragland steps right up to Jennifer's door so that they're at eye level.)

MINISTER: Life, Jennifer! It's about life!

(Jennifer slams the gas pedal to the floor and speeds off. Later that same evening a nine-year-old white kid is riding his bike on the sidewalk on his way home. On that same street are three black guys looking for some pay back for what happened to Corey. After riding around for an hour or so, the passenger in the front seat, Tony Farmer, spots the little boy on his bike.)

TONY FARMER: Check it out!

(As he points, they all turn and look to their right.)

TONY FARMER: Pull up behind him.

(The driver turns the car around and slowly pulls up behind the little boy.)

TONY FARMER: Hand me the spray paint.

(One of the passengers in the back seat passes Tony the paint.)

TONY FARMER: Okay, pull ahead of him a little bit.

(The driver pulls ahead and Tony gets out.)

TONY FARMER: Excuse me, little man.

(The boy stops.)

TONY FARMER: Have you seen my dog? He's black and…

(Tony stops talking in the middle of his sentence and points.)

TONY FARMER: Oh, never mind there he is!

(The boy turns to look in the direction Tony is pointing, and when he does Tony grabs him, throws him on the ground, and begins to spray paint his face black as the little boy kicks and screams.)

TONY FARMER: Yeah, white boy! This is for my man, Corey!

(After the boys face is completely covered, Tony stands over him.)

TONY FARMER: Now go tell your cracker parents that, white boy!

(Tony slowly turns and walks to the car. The little boy, with paint burning his eyes, continues to roll around on the ground as he screams for help. The next morning, Minister Ragland stops by to see the Williams' and Cynthia answers the door.)

MINISTER: Hey, Cynthia.

CYNTHIA HANKS: Hey, Joe, come on in.

(Cynthia walks to the kitchen where she's doing dishes. Minister Ragland follows her and takes a seat at the kitchen table.)

CYNTHIA HANKS: Have you seen the front page of today's newspaper?

MINISTER: No.

CYNTHIA HANKS: Look on top of the refrigerator.

(Minister Ragland grabs the paper and sits down. What he sees on the front page causes him to take a deep breath as he shakes his head in frustration. The headline reads, "Nine Year Old Boy Attacked and Spray Painted Black While Riding His Bike".)

MINISTER: Now the children.

CYNTHIA HANKS: You know that somebody is sitting somewhere right now plotting revenge for what happened to that child. I don't know about you Joe, but just the thought of that scares me to death.

MINISTER: How are they doing?

CYNTHIA HANKS: I don't know. They've been locked up in their bedroom since yesterday.

(Minister Ragland shakes his head saddened by what Cynthia has just said.)

CYNTHIA HANKS: Tell me what's going on, Joe. I don't want the happy-go-lucky version; I want the real deal. What's going on?

MINISTER: Not too much. Right now nobody's saying anything.

CYNTHIA HANKS: And what does that mean?

MINISTER: That means that we are right back where we started. But it doesn't mean we should give up.

(Cynthia takes a seat at the table.)

CYNTHIA HANKS: Joe, I admire your determination, I really do. And your heart's in the right place. But let's look at the big picture. I'm a grown woman, I own my own home, and I can't even live there. People are being beaten to death with baseball bats, children are being attacked in the streets, the law is working against us, and the future of this town rest in the hands of a frightened seventeen-year-old girl. If we don't give up, what do we have to go on?

MINISTER: What did you just ask me?

CYNTHIA HANKS: I asked you what we have to go on.

MINISTER: You just answered your own question with your question. You ask what we have to go on. That's it. We have to go on. When Raymond is acting like a fool, we have to go on. When we are being threatened, we have to go on. Even when we lose our loved ones, we have to go on. Cynthia, since I've been here I've had my freedom taken away, my color degraded, and the name of my father in heaven cursed so many times I can't even count. The word of God says, "Be ye steadfast, immovable, always abounding in the work of the Lord, knowing that your labor is not in vain in the Lord." We've got to keep laboring no matter what the devil throws in our face. And to tell you the truth we shouldn't even be surprised. When you set out to do work for the Lord, you better expect the devil to show up; that's his job. To kill, steal, and destroy, but he will not destroy Joe Ragland. I'm like that tree planted by the rivers of living waters; I shall not be moved. So as far as the law, I'm not worried about them. I've already claimed the victory over that situation in the name of Jesus. So they're already defeated. The devil may be winning the battle Cynthia, but he will not win the war.

(Back at the station in Raymond's office, the father of the boy that was spray-painted is yelling and screaming. There are five other fathers there who also have young children that ride their bikes in that same area. They're all angry, they all want some answers, and revenge is the only solution they see.)

JOHNNY LEE: Raymond, I want something done and I want it done now!

RAYMOND CLETTER: Johnny, what do you want me to do? Without a positive description my hands are tied. Your son can't even give us the color of the car they were driving. Now you can't expect me just to go out and start arresting every black man I see. It doesn't work that way.

LUCAS HOLLY: It should, considering the fact that they all belong in a cage anyway.

RAYMOND CLETTER: Lucas, stay out of this! This has nothing to do with you!

LUCAS HOLLY: It has everything to do with me! My son rides his bike on the same sidewalk John, Jr. was riding on almost everyday. So until you can guarantee that some greasy fingered nigger won't grab my child, it has everything to do with me!

OLIVER MILLS: Same here.

WALLACE TILLEY: You let some nigger put his greasy hands on my child, you won't have to worry about me coming down here to talk to you. I'm just going to put a hole through his chest and string him from a tree.

RAYMOND CLETTER: All right, wait a minute! Wait one minute! Johnny, you're asking me to do the impossible. Without positive I.D., or some kind of description, all I can do is investigate, that's it!

JOHNNY LEE: Don't worry about it, Raymond. I'll handle it myself.

(Johnny grabs his coat and heads for the door.)

RAYMOND CLETTER: Johnny!

(Johnny stops and turns around to face Raymond.)

RAYMOND CLETTER: If you go out there and break the law, I'm going to arrest you.

(Johnny turns and walks out of the office as the others follow. Raymond, now completely frustrated, takes the pencil he's holding, breaks it, and throws it across the room. Later that same night, Minister Ragland, Cynthia Hanks, and her son Larry are driving out to Cynthia's house to get a few things.)

CYNTHIA HANKS: I never thought I'd feel weird going to my own house.

155

LARRY HANKS: Imagine how I feel. How long has it been for me, mom? Almost two years now?

CYNTHIA HANKS: Something like that.

(As they pull into the driveway they notice large black words painted on the house. When they finally stop the car, Minister Ragland leaves the head lights on so they can read the words. Someone has spray-painted, "You can't hide nigger. And "You're next to die" on the front of the house. Cynthia turns and looks at Minister Ragland as her eyes fill with tears. When they get out of the car they all stand and stare at the house in awe over what is before them. Larry puts his arm around his mother to comfort her as she cries, when all of a sudden the house explodes throwing all of them to the ground. Minister Ragland, in complete shock, sits up with his mouth wide open. Larry, who is only concerned about his mother, crawls over to her to see if she's okay when all of a sudden she jumps up and begins to yell over and over again. Thank you, Jesus! Thank you, Jesus! Thank you, Jesus! Now worried and confused, Larry calls out to his mom but she doesn't respond. He can't understand why she's thanking God after what has just happened. So he stands up, wraps his arms around her, and holds her tight as she continues to jump up and down yelling thank you Jesus. Minister Ragland gets up and walks over to where they're standing.)

MINISTER: Larry, I need for you to take the car and go back to the Williams's house!

LARRY HANKS: What's wrong with mama?

MINISTER: Don't worry about her. She's all right!

(Cynthia is still jumping and screaming.)

LARRY HANKS: She is not all right!

MINISTER: Larry, she's all right! Now I need for you to take the car and leave now!

LARRY HANKS: I'm not leaving mama here!

MINISTER: Larry, in about twenty minutes this place is going to be crawling with cops, one in particular. The reason Raymond has not been able to find me is because he's been looking for my Maxima. He has no idea I'm driving this rental car and I don't want him to know. That's why I need you to drive the car back to the Williams's and wait for us there!

LARRY HANKS: What about mama!

MINISTER: Larry, she's going to be fine, I promise. Please take the car and go.

(Larry looks at the Minister, looks at his mother, and then gives her a hug.)

LARRY HANKS: Mama, I love you.

(Still confused by his mother's behavior, Larry gives his mother one long, last hug as he begins to cry.)

MINISTER: Larry, you've got to go now!

LARRY HANKS: Please take care of her!

MINISTER: I will, I promise. We'll catch up with you at the Williams's house!

(Feeling completely uncomfortable with the idea of leaving his mother, Larry hesitantly lets go of her, gets in the car, and takes off for the Williams's. It's now two hours later and the fire has been put out. The fire trucks are wrapping up, preparing to leave, and the police are taking Cynthia's statement. Minister Ragland, who is standing beside Cynthia, pans around looking at all of the still smoldering wood and destruction that was once a beautiful home. All of a sudden, he sees Raymond leaning on his patrol car staring at him from across the yard, which causes chills to run up and down his spine. As the red light from one of the fire trucks repeatedly streaks across Raymond's face and the two of them make eye-to-eye contact, Raymond stands up straight, makes his hand into the shape of a gun and fires at Minister Ragland, reminding him of the ever-present danger that awaits him. Now completely covered in chill bumps, as if death was holding his hand, Minister Ragland shakes his head, turns around, and walks away as Raymond's cold, red eyes follow his each and every move. Later that night at the Williams's, everybody's sitting around in the living room. Jean Williams is sitting beside Cynthia Hanks with her arm around her.)

JEAN WILLIAMS: You all right, girl?

CYNTHIA HANKS: Yeah.

JEAN WILLIAMS: I'm so sorry about your house. You know you're welcome to stay here as long as you want.

(Cynthia hugs her.)

CYNTHIA HANKS: Thank you. Thank you for everything.

JEAN WILLIAMS: Don't even worry about it. I know if it were our house you would do the same for us.

(Jean gives her a kiss on the cheek and stands up.)

JEAN WILLIAMS: I'm tired. I'm going to bed. You guys make yourselves at home.

(As she heads towards the stairs she stops, leans over, and kisses Larry on his forehead.)

JEAN WILLIAMS: Don't worry about your mama, baby. We're going to take care of her. Good night.

(After they all say good night and Cynthia hears her bedroom door shut, she leans forward and whispers.)

CYNTHIA HANKS: Her birthday is in two days. We should throw her a surprise birthday party.

(Baffled by what his mom has just said, Larry looks at Minister Ragland, and then turns back to his mom.)

LARRY HANKS: A party? Mama, we just lost everything we had and you're talking about a party? What's wrong with you?

(Cynthia turns, takes a brief moment to look Larry in his eyes, and then breaks her silence by revealing to him a side of reality that he will never forget.)

CYNTHIA HANKS: Son, we have more now than we've ever had before. In the book of Genesis, there's a scripture that says, "You intended to harm me, but God intended it for good. To accomplish what is now being done, the saving of many lives." That bomb was planted to kill us, and those words painted on the house were there to hurt us. But God took one and defeated the other. If we had not stopped and read those words on the front of the house, where would we have been when that bomb went off?

(Now realizing her point, with tears wailed up in his eyes, Larry looks up at her as he answers her question.)

LARRY HANKS: Inside.

CYNTHIA HANKS: That's right son inside. If those awful words had not been there we would have gone inside and been killed, all of us. Tonight God has given us more than we've ever had before. He's given us a whole new understanding of faith. Once again He has proven His word to be true by allowing us to live. He took the enemy's evil intent, and used it to bless us. But that's not the best part. You know what the best part is?

(Larry looks up at his mother.)

CYNTHIA HANKS: The best part is that we didn't even deserve it. We did not deserve it, but He did it anyway. In spite of the sins we commit on a daily basis, in spite of the pain we cause other people, in spite of the things we do that displease him, He allowed us to live anyway.

(As a calm silence settles in the room, tears that celebrate life are falling from all eyes.)

CYNTHIA HANKS: We didn't deserve it, baby.

(Cynthia pauses as she wipes her eyes.)

CYNTHIA HANKS: To God be the glory for His grace and His mercy.

(Cynthia kisses her son good night and goes to bed. Leaving him to reflect on just how blessed he really is.)

CHAPTER EIGHTEEN

(It's now two days later and Mr. Williams is taking his wife out for a birthday dinner.)

JEAN WILLIAMS: Are you sure you don't want to go, Cynthia?

CYNTHIA HANKS: I'm positive. It's your birthday; go out and have a good time.

JEAN WILLIAMS: All right, just make yourself at home. I feel so bad about leaving you here.

CYNTHIA HANKS: You're not leaving me here. I don't want to go. Now get out of here.

EARL WILLIAMS: Honey, we really need to go or we're going to miss our reservations.

JEAN WILLIAMS: Cynthia, if you need anything, just call us.

CYNTHIA HANKS: Okay, mom.

(Mr. Williams finally gets her out of the door.)

EARL WILLIAMS: We'll see you, Cynthia.

(After he shuts the door, Cynthia runs over to the window and watches them walk down the driveway, get in the car, and leave. Once they are out of sight, Cynthia calls Minister Ragland on his cell phone.)

MINISTER: Hello!

CYNTHIA HANKS: Joe, they're gone!

MINISTER: We're on our way!

(Minister Ragland, along with twenty-five other friends and family members of the Williams' hop on the church bus. They leave their cars at the church so when Mr. Williams goes back home to get his wallet, she won't know they're there. Mr. Williams begins to slow the car down.)

JEAN WILLIAMS: Earl, what are you doing?

EARL WILLIAMS: I left my wallet back at the house.

(She shakes her head.)

JEAN WILLIAMS: What am I going to do with you?

(When they go back to the house he goes in to get his wallet leaving her in the car. After a few minutes he sticks his head out of the door and yells.)

EARL WILLIAMS: Jean!

(She rolls the window down.)

JEAN WILLIAMS: What is it?

EARL WILLIAMS: Can you help me find my wallet?

(As she gets out of the car she talks to herself.)

JEAN WILLIAMS: That poor man. First his hair goes and now his memory.

(As she approaches the front door everybody prepares to yell surprise. The door opens and they all jump out.)

EVERYBODY: Surprise!

(Startled by everybody jumping out and yelling, Mrs. Williams jumps back and places her hand over her heart. Her friends and family all pause waiting for her to respond. Cynthia walks up to her.)

CYNTHIA HANKS: Well, aren't you going to say something?

(A tear rolls down her face.)

CYNTHIA HANKS: Please tell me those are happy tears.

JEAN WILLIAMS: The happiest.

(Knowing now that everything is okay and she's not upset, Cynthia gives her a hug and then steps back so she can address the crowd.)

JEAN WILLIAMS: I don't know what to say. I can't believe this. Thank you for all of this, it couldn't have come at a better time. I've spent the last few days shut up in my room wondering how I'm going to go on. I don't have to wonder anymore. God just gave me about thirty different solutions. He gave me all of you.

(As the tears continue to fall, one at a time, people begin to give her hugs. Later on, as everybody is in the back yard having a good time, Minister Ragland pulls Larry aside.)

LARRY HANKS: What's up?

MINISTER: I need you to do me a favor.

LARRY HANKS: Name it.

MINISTER: I want you to talk to Jennifer.

LARRY HANKS: Do what?

MINISTER: I think if you talked to her it would do us some good.

LARRY HANKS: Minister Ragland, you're asking me to have a conversation with the same individual that destroyed my father's life and split up my entire family. I'm sorry, but I can't do that.

MINISTER: You can, but you won't.

LARRY HANKS: No, I won't. I'm sorry. I know you're trying to help my father and all, and I appreciate it, but I just can't do that. I wouldn't even know what to say to her.

MINISTER: You could tell her that you forgive her.

LARRY HANKS: But I don't.

MINISTER: But you should. Look, I know what she did was wrong; I'm not denying that for a second. But have you ever tried to look at all of this from where she's standing? If I was a seventeen-year-old girl, and somebody told me they we're going to kill me, I'd keep my mouth shut, too. Especially considering the unfortunate fact that in a court of law rape is hard to prove. Don't misunderstand me; I am not condoning the lie she told. That was wrong. All I'm saying is that if she was threatened, I can understand why she did it. I've counseled girls that have been raped by friends, family friends, aunts, uncles, and even their own parents. Most of the time these girls won't say anything because they've been threatened or somehow convinced that it was their fault. No woman, I don't care what she's wearing, how low cut her shirt is, how short her skirt is, or how much she flaunts and flirts. When it comes to rape, a woman is never the one to blame. "No", means "No", and that's it. Jennifer wants to talk to somebody, believe me she does. She knows the only way she can retain some peace of mind is by telling the truth.

(For the first time Larry is able to see both sides of the situation and not just his own.)

MINISTER: So what do you say? How about we take a trip to Cary tomorrow before you leave?

LARRY HANKS: All right.

(The next day Minister Ragland and Larry arrive at Jennifer's school. They park the car a couple of rows away from where she's parked so she can't see them. But they are still in clear view of her car so they can see her.)

LARRY HANKS: Are you sure this is a good idea?

MINISTER: Yes it is.

LARRY HANKS: Well then why am I so nervous?

MINISTER: There's nothing to be nervous about Larry, just relax.

(Minister Ragland looks up and sees Jennifer approaching her car.)

MINISTER: Okay there she is, go ahead!

(Larry gets out of the car and makes his way across the parking lot. Minister Ragland taps the horn and calls his name.)

MINISTER: Larry!

(Larry comes back to the car.)

LARRY HANKS: Yes.

MINISTER: Be nice, okay? Be nice.

(Larry shakes his head yes and makes his way over to Jennifer. As she's unlocking her car door, Larry quietly walks up and stands at the back of her car. With his stomach in knots, he calls her by a nickname his mother gave her when she was born.)

LARRY HANKS: Baby girl!

(Immediately she recognizes the voice and the nickname. Still standing with her back to Larry in shock, Jennifer quietly calls his name.)

JENNIFER MUNDY: Larry?

(Jennifer slowly turns around to face him.)

JENNIFER MUNDY: Larry!

(With a huge smile on her face, Jennifer takes off running towards her life long best friend for a hug. When she reaches Larry she wraps her arms around him squeezing him tight. With his emotions on a roller coaster, Larry doesn't hug her back. As Jennifer holds him with no intentions of letting him go, she begins to cry. Still standing there with his arms hanging by his side, Larry thinks back to all of the good times they had throughout the years. And it's those thoughts that eventually cause him to wrap his arms around Jennifer. After a minute or so goes by, they step back still holding hands.)

JENNIFER MUNDY: What are you doing here?

LARRY HANKS: I came to see you.

(Jennifer gives him another hug.)

JENNIFER MUNDY: I can't believe this! I thought you moved to Connecticut.

LARRY HANKS: I did. I just came back for a funeral. I'm leaving tomorrow.

(The smile that covered Jennifer's face suddenly disappears when Larry mentions the word funeral.)

LARRY HANKS: Corey's dead Jennifer.

(Jennifer takes a deep breath.)

JENNIFER MUNDY: I know, I heard. I'm sorry, Larry.

LARRY HANKS: Yeah, me too.

JENNIFER MUNDY: The three of us had a lot of fun when we were kids didn't we?

LARRY HANKS: Don't even talk about when we were kids. You two caused me to get more belts and switches put on my butt than I care to remember.

(Jennifer smiles thinking back to the times when they were children.)

JENNIFER MUNDY: We caused you? You caused us!

LARRY HANKS: You're crazy!

JENNIFER MUNDY: Don't even! What about the time you talked us into lighting those M-80s and throwing them into my parents' toilet? We almost flooded the whole house!

(Larry laughs.)

LARRY HANKS: That's nothing! What about the time you guys talked me into taking my dad's car out of gear? And I remember you specifically telling me that it wouldn't roll, yeah right. I ended up plowing over every bush in my yard. Not to mention old lady Jones' rose garden. That poor woman turned five shades of red and almost had a heart attack standing right there in her yard!

(Jennifer is tapping her leg as she laughs at Larry.)

LARRY HANKS: Oh, and let's not forget about the all time favorite hook up. The matches!

(Knowing exactly what he's talking about, Jennifer leans over, grabs her stomach, and completely loses it.)

LARRY HANKS: You and Corey did me dirty that day. You guys told me that you had some special matches. Matches that I could throw in the air and they wouldn't go out. Me, making the mistake of trusting yall, threw it in the air and the wind blew it back at me.)

(Jennifer is almost on her knees laughing when she reaches up to grab Larry's arm.)

LARRY HANKS: No, let go of me! It's not funny! The wind caught that match, blew it back, and my whole afro went up in flames. My whole head was just smoking.

(Jennifer at this point is laughing so hard she can barely breathe.)

JENNIFER MUNDY: Please stop! My stomach hurts!

LARRY HANKS: Good, I'm glad. That's pay back for you two rolling around on the ground laughing at me while I ran around in circles screaming my head off.

(As Jennifer breaks down to one knee laughing, Minister Ragland is looking at her with a look of absolute confusion. He just can't understand what's going on between the two of them to make her laugh so hard.)

JENNIFER MUNDY: Larry, please stop!

LARRY HANKS: I had to walk around for two months looking like one end of a black Q-tip with all those bandages on my head!

(As she continues to laugh she tries to talk.)

JENNIFER MUNDY: Please, please, please!

(Larry reaches down and helps her up.)

LARRY HANKS: Control yourself, woman.

JENNIFER MUNDY: You're so crazy, Larry! Oh, my goodness! I haven't laughed like that in a long time. Man, you're crazy! We did have some fun, didn't we?

LARRY HANKS: Yeah we did. Things were pretty good back then.

JENNIFER MUNDY: I heard what you called me when you walked up.

LARRY HANKS: What, baby girl?

JENNIFER MUNDY: Yes.

LARRY HANKS: What did you expect me to call you? That's the only thing my mom ever called you; you were her baby. You have a beautiful voice, baby; how's school, baby; you're so pretty, baby. Baby this, baby that, with all that baby going on I figured it was only a matter of time before you showed up at school wearing diapers.

(Jennifer chuckles.)

JENNIFER MUNDY: I miss those days. Good old Swamp Fox.

(Larry's smile slowly disappears.)

LARRY HANKS: You mean war zone Swamp Fox.

(Jennifer looks up at Larry as her smile also disappears.)

LARRY HANKS: There's nothing good about it anymore, Jen. It's not like it was before. Little kids are being attacked as they ride their bikes on the sidewalk, the same sidewalks we rode our bikes on. It's out of control, Jennifer. It was nothing to see little black and white kids playing together when we were growing up, now it's unheard of. Now their parents won't even let them talk to each other. It's a shame they have to miss out on so much.

(Jennifer is saddened knowing she's to blame.)

LARRY HANKS: Jennifer, every time I call home and talk to mama, I think about you. I wonder what you're up to, if you're doing okay. Then all of a sudden those feelings of concern for you start to fade away, and they're replaced by feelings I don't care to mention. I've often thought to myself that I had too much animosity towards you to ever speak to you again. But now that you're standing here in front of me all I can think about is how much I love and miss you.

(Jennifer reaches up and gently touches the side of his face.)

JENNIFER MUNDY: I see you're still the same old sweetheart you've always been.

LARRY HANKS: Why did you do it, Jen? My daddy loved you like you were his own daughter. There is nothing in this world he wouldn't have done for you.

(Feeling ashamed, Jennifer looks down at the ground. And as tears of regret begin to fall from her eyes she looks up at Larry.)

JENNIFER MUNDY: Look, I've gotta go. It was really nice seeing you again, Larry. You're looking good.

(Frustrated by the fact that Jennifer is running away and not answering his question, Larry can only shake his head as he looks away.)

JENNIFER MUNDY: Come on and give me a hug so I can go.

(As Jennifer asks for a hug, she begins to straighten his shirt because she's unable to look him in his eyes. Realizing that she's not going to answer his question, Larry decides to just give her a hug and let her go. As they hold each other tight Jennifer whispers in his ear.)

JENNIFER MUNDY: You'll always be my best friend, Larry. And I'll always love you.

(As Jennifer begins to cry, she let's go of Larry and gets in her car. She starts the engine and puts the car in reverse. But before she leaves she looks up at him one last time.)

JENNIFER MUNDY: Am I still your best friend Larry?

(Larry, who at the time is looking down at the ground, looks straight ahead over the top of Jennifer's car. And as his emotions get the best of him, he swallows the lump in his throat and answers her question as a tear falls from his face.)

LARRY HANKS: Always, baby girl.

(Jennifer reaches out and grabs his hand. Feeling it's best if she leaves, Jennifer slowly let's go of his hand, pulls out of her parking space, and drives off, leaving Larry standing there wondering why. The next day, Minister Ragland is on his way to the Medlin's where he's staying when his cell phone rings, it's Larry.)

MINISTER: Hello, hey Larry! You're on your way to the airport now? Okay, well listen. I appreciate what you did yesterday. I know that talking to Jennifer was a hard thing for you to do, but I do appreciate it. And Larry, don't worry about your mother; we're going to take care of her. All right, okay, I'll call you and keep you informed. Take care, bye.

(They hang up the phone just as Minister Ragland pulls into the Medlin's driveway. Chris, the Medlin's nine-year-old son, is in the yard messing around with his football. As Minister Ragland is walking across the yard towards the house, he sees that Chris is having a hard time putting the needle into his football to pump it up.)

MINISTER: You need some help, Chris?

CHRIS MEDLIN: Yes please!

(Minister Ragland walks over to Chris and he hands him the ball. As Minister Ragland is working the needle into the ball, he hears a machine of some sort. He looks up and sees a man on a bulldozer about twenty yards behind the Medlin's house clearing out trees. Not giving it much thought, Minister Ragland turns back to Chris.)

MINISTER: There you go Chris. Now all you have to do is pump it up.

(Chris begins to pump up the ball.)

CHRIS MEDLIN: Minister Ragland, can you throw with me for a little while?

MINISTER: Sure.

(Minister Ragland and Chris spread apart and begin to throw the ball.)

MINISTER: So you like football?

CHRIS MEDLIN: Yes sir.

MINISTER: What's your favorite position?

CHRIS MEDLIN: I like to play quarterback. But my favorite position is punter.

MINISTER: Really? So you like to kick?

CHRIS MEDLIN: Yes sir.

MINISTER: Let's see what you got.

CHRIS MEDLIN: You want me to kick it?

MINISTER: Yeah, go for it.

(Chris prepares himself, rears back, and kicks the ball clear over Minister Ragland's head into the woods.)

MINISTER: Goodness gracious! I see why you like to kick!

CHRIS MEDLIN: I can kick it further than that with my cleats on.

(As Minister Ragland squirms his way through briar patches and weeds to get the ball, a car passes by. Chris, who is watching the Minister at the time, turns to look at the car and is shocked by what he sees as he points.)

168

CHRIS MEDLIN: That's the car I saw!

(Minister Ragland, who is still making his way through the bushes to get the ball, responds to Chris not really paying attention to what he's saying.)

MINISTER: What was that Chris?

CHRIS MEDLIN: That's the car I saw in the woods!

MINISTER: It is?

(After finally reaching the ball and working his way out of the woods, still not giving a second thought to what Chris said about the car in the woods, Minister Ragland throws the ball back to him and they continue their game of catch.)

CHRIS MEDLIN: Man, I'm glad I wasn't in that car.

MINISTER: What are you talking about? What car?

CHRIS MEDLIN: The one that was parked in the woods on Wilson Road one night I was coming home. Everybody in the car was fighting.

MINISTER: Fighting?

CHRIS MEDLIN: Yes sir. Even the girl was fighting, but I don't think she won because she was the one doing all of the screaming.

(Chris mentioning a girl screaming has sparked the Minister's interest. After catching the ball that Chris has just thrown to him, Minister Ragland stands there for a second and then walks over to Chris with a very curious look on his face.)

MINISTER: You saw a girl in a car screaming?

CHRIS MEDLIN: Yes sir. I was coming home from my friend Craig's house and they were parked in the woods.

MINISTER: They? Who are you talking about when you say they?

CHRIS MEDLIN: I saw two men and a woman in a car in the woods fighting. But I couldn't see their faces.

MINISTER: Could you make out what she was saying?

CHRIS MEDLIN: She was screaming, "No, please don't," but they wouldn't listen to her. So she kept on screaming.

MINISTER: Chris, where does your friend Craig live?

CHRIS MEDLIN: Craig lives out on Murray Road, but that's not where I saw the car. I saw the car parked in the woods on the dirt road; on Wilson Road.

(Absolutely floored by Chris's answer, Minister Ragland stands there staring at Chris as he whispers to himself.)

MINISTER: Out of the mouths of babes.

CHRIS MEDLIN: What did you say?

MINISTER: Nothing. Chris, how do you know the car that just passed was the same car you saw in the woods that night?

CHRIS MEDLIN: It was white.

MINISTER: There are a whole lot of white cars around Chris.

CHRIS MEDLIN: Not with a shiny sticker on the back.

MINISTER: A shiny sticker?

CHRIS MEDLIN: Yes sir. It had a shiny star sticker on the back of it.

MINISTER: Chris, have you told anybody else about this?

CHRIS MEDLIN: No sir. My mama and daddy told me not to ride my bike on Wilson Road because people drive too fast and they could hit me. That's why I never said anything. I didn't want to get a whooping. You're not gonna tell on me are you?

MINISTER: No, I'm not. Hold on just a minute.

(Minister Ragland sticks his head just inside the front door to talk to Chris's parents who are sitting in the living room.)

MINISTER: I'm going to ride out for a little while. Is it okay if Chris rides with me?

BOBBY MEDLIN: Sure.

MINISTER: We'll be back shortly.

BOBBY MEDLIN: Take your time.

(Minister Ragland motions Chris to follow him. Once he catches up with Minister Ragland he begins to ask him questions.)

CHRIS MEDLIN: Where are we going?

MINISTER: I need to see who's driving that car.

CHRIS MEDLIN: Why are we taking this car? What's wrong with your other car?

MINISTER: Ahh, let's just say this one drives a little better.

CHRIS MEDLIN: Oh, you mean it's faster.

(A little surprised by the fact that Chris knew what he really meant, Minister Ragland looks down at him and he flashes the Minister a huge smile.)

MINISTER: You think you're smart, don't you?

CHRIS MEDLIN: Pretty much. But it's okay because I like to go fast.

(Chris and the Minister hop in the Maxima and take off. Minister Ragland, knowing he has to really drive fast to catch the car gets up to seventy-five in no time. Chris leans over towards Minister Ragland and looks at the speedometer to see just how fast they're going.)

CHRIS MEDLIN: Is driving seventy-five against the law?

(Minister Ragland looks over at Chris not wanting to answer the question.)

MINISTER: How about you just sit back and relax.

CHRIS MEDLIN: Okay.

(Chris sits back in his seat, rolls the window down, and sticks his arm out.)

CHRIS MEDLIN: Wooooooo...

(Minister Ragland looks at Chris; Chris looks at Minister Ragland, and flashes him a huge smile. After reaching a speed of eighty-five miles an hour, they spot the white car they're looking for up ahead. The car has just gone through an intersection after stopping at a stop sign. When Minister Ragland reaches the intersection, he stops, looks to his left, to his right, and then to his left again only to find trouble slowly approaching. To his left he sees Buck and Willie. As soon as Willie, who is sitting in the passenger seat sees Minister Ragland, he taps Buck on the shoulder and points at Minister Ragland's car. Buck immediately stops the truck right in front of Minister Ragland preventing him from going any further.)

MINISTER: Chris, hang on.

CHRIS MEDLIN: Are we gonna do eighty- five again?

MINISTER: No, only fifty this time.

(Disappointed by Minister Raglands answer, Chris slumps over forward in his seat.)

CHRIS MEDLIN: That stinks.

MINISTER: Backwards.

(Now excited Chris pops straight up in his seat as he smiles.)

CHRIS MEDLIN: Yeah!

(Minister Ragland throws the car in reverse and slams the gas pedal to the floor, thrusting Chris forward, causing him to laugh hysterically. At his first opportunity, Minister Ragland whips his car around and takes off with Willie and Buck in hot pursuit. After chasing the Minister a mile or so Willie works his way up beside him on the wrong side of the road.)

BUCK SANDERS: Willie, grab the rifle and take him out!

(Willie turns around and takes the rifle off of the gun rack. Once Buck is a little closer, Willie takes aim.)

WILLIE TAYLOR: We got you now, nigger! See you in hell, boy!

(As Willie takes aim and begins to squeeze the trigger, he hears a loud horn. It's the horn of an eighteen-wheeler that is coming around a blind corner. To avoid a head on collision with the semi, they are both forced off the road. Minister Ragland yanks his wheel to the right and ends up sliding sideways through a wet grassy opening, into a small patch of bushes, and coming to stop. After yanking his wheel to the left Buck drives down an embankment which causes him to lose control of his truck and hit a tree head on. With neither Buck nor Willie wearing seat belts, that tree would ultimately be the cause of their deaths. Buck dies instantly behind the wheel on impact. Willie is thrown through the windshield into the tree headfirst. He suffers massive head injuries and dies right there on the hood of the truck. The truck driver gets out and runs towards Buck and Willie. But he stops about twenty feet away from the truck when he sees Buck's blood soaked body draped across the hood. He then turns and looks across the street in the field at Minister Ragland as he puts his car in gear and pulls off leaving the scene of the accident. Later on, there are cops and paramedics everywhere at the scene. Deputy Durant is standing in the road moving traffic along, when out of nowhere comes that very same white car Minister Ragland was chasing. The mysterious white car pulls onto the shoulder of the road, the door opens, and shiny black cowboy boots step out.)

DEPUTY DURANT: How ya doing?

(It's Raymond. Raymond is driving the car that Chris saw in the woods.)

RAYMOND CLETTER: What in the world happened out here?

DEPUTY DURANT: Looks like a game of chicken gone bad. You see that fellow over there? He was driving the rig. He said when he came around the corner this truck was in one lane, and a car was in the other. These boys hit that ditch right there, lost control, and that's the end result.

(Raymond looks over at the truck and right away he knows whom it belongs to. He sees two white sheets over two dead bodies, shakes his head, and takes a deep breath.

RAYMOND CLETTER: This car you mentioned. Where is it and where's the driver?

DEPUTY DURANT: You're going to love this one. The truck driver said the car did a couple of doughnuts, came to a stop in that clearing over there, and then took off. Guess what color the car was.

(Raymond stands there for second in silence as his face turns fire red.)

RAYMOND CLETTER: Black.

DEPUTY DURANT: Guess what color the driver was.

RAYMOND CLETTER: Black.

DEPUTY DURANT: And guess what the license plate said.

RAYMOND CLETTER: John 3:3.

DEPUTY DURANT: You got it. And the truck driver said it was a Nissian Maxima. He recognized it the second he saw it. Said he bought his daughter a grey one just like it for graduation.

RAYMOND CLETTER: When you finish here, I want you and five other cars out looking for him. I don't care what you have to do, or whom you have to go through to do it! But I want you to find that nigger and deliver him to me today! Do you understand me?

DEPUTY DURANT: Yes sir.

RAYMOND CLETTER: Today, Durant!

DEPUTY DURANT: I heard you, Raymond.

(Now enraged with anger, Raymond turns around and walks away. Later that same night, Raymond is sitting in his office slowly rocking back and forth in his chair when he hears a knock on the door.)

RAYMOND CLETTER: Come in.

(It's Deputy Durant. He has just returned from a five-hour search for the Minister.)

173

RAYMOND CLETTER: Well?

DEPUTY DURANT: We couldn't find him.

RAYMOND CLETTER: What do you mean, you couldn't find him?

DEPUTY DURANT: We looked everywhere and we couldn't find him, Ray.

(Raymond stands up and begins to yell at Durant.)

RAYMOND CLETTER: He's one man! One man! There's no way he can just disappear into thin air, no way!

DEPUTY DURANT: He could with the right help. If people are helping him he could stay right here in Swamp Fox for a year and we'd never find him.

RAYMOND CLETTER: What about the car? That is the only black Nissan Maxima in this entire town! The only one and we can't find it!

DEPUTY DURANT: Look, I don't know what else to tell you Ray. We looked everywhere possible.

(Raymond sits down in his chair and sighs.)

RAYMOND CLETTER: All right! Just go on home and we'll get back out there in the morning.

DEPUTY DURANT: You sure?

RAYMOND CLETTER: Yeah. Just meet me here at seven a.m.

DEPUTY DURANT: You got it.

(Just before Durant walks out he turns to face Raymond.)

DEPUTY DURANT: Don't worry about it, Ray we'll get him.

RAYMOND CLETTER: Yeah.

DEPUTY DURANT: Good night.

(Raymond leans back in his chair and stares at the ceiling, confused by Minister Ragland's disappearance.)

CHAPTER NINETEEN

(After spending half of the next day looking for Minister Ragland's car and not finding it, Raymond decides to go see Ronald Hanks. He hopes Ronald will give him some information of the Minister's whereabouts. Raymond has requested that he see Ronald alone, just the two of them. So the guards take Ronald to a private room where Raymond is waiting. After they bring him in, they sit him down at a table across from Raymond and leave the room.)

RAYMOND CLETTER: How's it going, Ronald?

RONALD HANKS: What do you want?

RAYMOND CLETTER: What is it with you and your wife? I can never seem to get a decent greeting out of either one of you. I'm starting to get the impression that you two don't like me very much.

RONALD HANKS: If you ever lay one hand on my wife Raymond, I will kill you.

(Raymond rests his elbows on the tables and leans forward.)

RAYMOND CLETTER: That sounds like a threat to me. Are you threatening an officer of the law, boy?

RONALD HANKS: A threat? No, I'm making you a promise. If you harm her in any way, you will pay for it, Raymond. Some day, some way, I will find you, and I will make you pay.

RAYMOND CLETTER: I can't believe this. I do you a favor by driving all the way up here to let you know some very important information about your wife, and you threaten to kill me. I come up here to help you out, and all I get are death threats. That's a mighty strange way to show your appreciation, Ronald.

RONALD HANKS: What about my wife?

RAYMOND CLETTER: I just can't give it to you like that, that's not how it works. This is one of those you scratch my back, I'll scratch yours deal. You give me the information I need, and I'll give you the information you need. That's how it works.

RONALD HANKS: What information? What are you talking about?

RAYMOND CLETTER: I'm talking about the good Minister.

RONALD HANKS: What about him?

RAYMOND CLETTER: I need to know where he is. He may be responsible for the death of two men. A witness saw him leaving the seen of an accident yesterday where two men were killed and nobody's seen him since. My men have been looking for him since last night and they've come up with nothing. Now it's very important that I find him so we can straighten this whole thing out, and that's where you come in. Where is he?

(Ronald leans back in his chair and begins to laugh.)

RONALD HANKS: You've got a complete stranger, hiding in a town where you know everybody, and you can't find him? That's pathetic, Ray. Raymond you must be crazy to think that I would tell you where he is, absolutely crazy. Find him yourself.

(Ronald laughs in his face.)

RAYMOND CLETTER: You think that's funny? No, let me tell you what's funny. What's funny is that you are sitting here protecting the same man that's sleeping with you wife, you stupid nigger. That's what I came to tell you. While you're sitting in here rotting like an old piece of fruit, Minister Mack Daddy is taking your wife to the Promised Land.

(Ronald's smile slowly disappears from his face.)

RAYMOND CLETTER: Things aren't so funny now, are they?

RONALD HANKS: You're lying.

RAYMOND CLETTER: I'm lying? Think about it Ronald, since he's come into the picture how many times has she visited you alone? According to this logbook she's only been here once by herself. How often do you talk to her Ronald? What are your conversations like? Are they getting shorter and shorter? You've been replaced, my friend. Oh sure, they paint an innocent picture telling you he's going to get you out of here, but that's just a smoke screen. It's all a part of their plan.

RONALD HANKS: You're lying.

RAYMOND CLETTER: I know it hurts, Ronald, but what did you expect? You thought she was going to wait for you? Not with him around. He's got every black woman in town tripping over their own two feet trying to get at him. He's even got a few white ones chasing him. I mean he's the talk of the town.

(Ronald clinches his fist as Raymond's lie begins to take effect.)

RONALD HANKS: Shut your mouth, Raymond.

RAYMOND CLETTER: Hey, you may as well give credit where credit is due. For a nigger, he's not bad looking. And just sitting here looking at you I can clearly see why she's with him. Don't be surprised, Ronald, she's a woman; she has needs, needs you can't fulfill. But I wouldn't worry about that too much. I'm sure the handsome Holy one is taking care of that.

(By this time Ronald is raging inside.)

RONALD HANKS: You're pushing it, Ray. You're pushing it.

RAYMOND CLETTER: What do you think they are doing right now? Do you think they're trying to figure out a way to get you out of here? Or do you....

(Raymond stops talking and leans forward with a very serious look on his face.)

RAYMOND CLETTER: Did you hear that? Listen. You don't hear that? There it is again. I'm not one hundred percent sure, but I think I hear. There it is again.

(Raymond looks at Ronald with a straight face.)

RAYMOND CLETTER: I think I hear your wife screaming his name.

(At this point Ronald has had enough. He jumps up from his seat and attacks Raymond as he screams over and over.)

RONALD HANKS: I'm gonna kill you Raymond! I'm gonna kill you! I'm gonna kill you!

(The guards rush in and pull Ronald off of Raymond.)

GUARD: You all right Raymond?

RAYMOND CLETTER: Yeah, I'm fine.

GUARD: Looks like you just earned yourself seven days in the hole, boy.

(As the guards are taking Ronald away, he and Raymond make eye contact.)

RAYMOND CLETTER: I'll be sure to say hello to your wife.

(Knowing he's gotten to Ronald, Raymond begins to laugh as Ronald leaves the room kicking and yelling. Later that same night Raymond stops at the local bar to have a beer where he sees the Mayor sitting at the bar alone. Raymond walks in and sits down beside him never saying a word as he tries to figure out in his mind where Minister Ragland is. The Mayor can obviously see that he's a little stressed out and orders him a drink.)

HAYWOOD BURGESS: Ben, will you pour this man a double, please?

(The Mayor puts his hand on Raymond's shoulder.)

HAYWOOD BURGESS: Relax, Ray. You'll find him. Don't worry about it.

RAYMOND CLETTER: I just don't get it, Haywood. We can't find him, or his car. I just don't get it.

HAYWOOD BURGESS: Didn't I tell you to relax? My goodness, Ray, you're getting yourself all worked up over a questioning.

(Raymond turns and looks at the Mayor.)

RAYMOND CLETTER: What do you mean a questioning?

HAYWOOD BURGESS: I mean you're all stressed out because you want to question this guy and you can't find him; that's silly.

RAYMOND CLETTER: Question him? Haywood, when I find him I'm bringing him in.

HAYWOOD BURGESS: No you're not.

RAYMOND CLETTER: Yes I am.

HAYWOOD BURGESS: No, you are not. Ray, that truck driver said the Minister was on the right side of the road. It's those fools that were on the wrong side. He didn't do anything wrong, therefore, you can't arrest him. Now if you want to question him wherever you find him, fine. But you cannot arrest him.

RAYMOND CLETTER: What's your problem, Haywood? Why is it every time I try to deal with this guy you step in and interfere? Why are you protecting him?

HAYWOOD BURGESS: I'm not protecting him. I'm protecting us. I don't want anything to go wrong before his court date. We cannot have him going into that courtroom with something to hold over our heads. August 12th is our day, Raymond. Don't ruin it for us.

RAYMOND CLETTER: I can't believe this.

(The Mayor leans over and whispers in his ear.)

HAYWOOD BURGESS: You'll thank me on August 12th when you're escorting him to his cell for the next two years. I've got big plans for the good Minister.

(As the Mayor orders another round, Butch walks in. Butch is the man Minister Ragland saw clearing trees behind the Medlin's house when he was helping Chris put air in his football. Butch sits down beside Raymond at the bar.)

BUTCH RAEFORD: How's it going guys? Ben let me have a beer!

(Butch notices that something is wrong with Raymond.)

BUTCH RAEFORD: Who threw up in your cornflakes?

(With a frown on his face, Raymond looks at Butch.)

RAYMOND CLETTER: Not now, Butch. I'm not the mood.

(Butch leans forward and looks around Raymond to talk to the Mayor.)

BUTCH RAEFORD: What's his problem?

HAYWOOD BURGESS: He's impatient. Did you take care of those trees out behind Bobby's place?

BUTCH REAFORD: Yeah, I finished up yesterday. They're all gone.

HAYWOOD BURGESS: Good, I appreciate it, Butch. Just drop the bill off by my office tomorrow and Merna will cut you a check.

BUTCH RAEFORD: Okay. You know old Bobby seems to be doing pretty good for himself.

(Raymond turns, looks at Butch, and snickers.)

RAYMOND CLETTER: Good for himself, now that's funny. If it weren't for Haywood he'd still be living in that old shack on Luffy Road.

HAYWOOD BURGESS: That's not true, Raymond. Bobby has earned everything he has. He's worked for the town of Swamp Fox for almost twenty years now, and not once have I heard him complain or slack off. He's a hard worker and a good man that wanted better for his family. He fell on some hard times and needed some help, so I helped him.

BUTCH RAEFORD: Tell me something, Haywood. If I get a job with the town of Swamp Fox, will you buy me a house and a new car?

179

(Raymond looks at Butch and smiles as he is somewhat amused by Butch's comment.)

HAYWOOD BURGESS: That's pretty funny Butch, even for you. But for your information Bobby doesn't drive a car. He drives a truck. His wife drives a car, Mr. Funny Man.

BUTCH RAEFORD: Oh, that's his wife's car? It's nice.

RAYMOND CLETTER: What? That puke brown piece of junk she drives? You've got to be kidding.

BUTCH RAEFORD: Puke brown? I'm talking about that Black Maxima parked in the backyard.

(Raymond almost chokes on his drink when he hears Butch say Black Maxima. He turns and looks at Butch as if he had seen a ghost.)

RAYMOND CLETTER: Black Maxima? You saw a Black Nissan Maxima in their back yard?

BUTCH RAEFORD: Yeah I saw it yesterday when I was clearing out trees. It's as clean as a whistle.

(Raymond looks at the Mayor and smiles.)

BUTCH RAEFORD: Well, I've gotta get going. The warden gets worried if I'm not home by ten.

(Butch pulls money out of his pocket to pay for his beer.)

RAYMOND CLETTER: Put your money away, Butch, this one's on me. I owe you big time.

BUTCH RAEFORD: Owe me for what?

RAYMOND CLETTER: For being nosey.

BUTCH RAEFORD: Whatever. I'll see you guys later.

(Butch walks out and Raymond turns to the Mayor with a huge smile on his face.)

RAYMOND CLETTER: In the backyard. That's why we couldn't find him. We've got him now.

HAYWOOD BURGESS: No we don't. Now I told you Ray, you cannot bring him in. As a matter of fact, if you decide to drive out there and question him, don't go without me. Do you understand? Do not go without me.

RAYMOND CLETTER: I hear you.

HAYWOOD BURGESS: I mean it, Raymond.

RAYMOND CLETTER: I won't go without you, Haywood. I promise.

HAYWOOD BURGESS: Okay.

(The Mayor grabs his coat off of the back of his chair.)

HAYWOOD BURGESS: I'm gonna take off. Go home and get some rest, Ray, you look like crap.

RAYMOND CLETTER: I love you, too.

(The Mayor gives Raymond a pat on his shoulder as he walks out. With a smile on his face that stretches from ear to ear, Raymond orders another drink.)

RAYMOND CLETTER: Ben, pour me another double. I've got something to celebrate.

(Later on at approximately three in the morning, Minister Ragland is awakened by the sound of one of the trashcans in the backyard that has just been turned over. As he looks at the clock he hears the high pitch crash of another trash can hit the ground. Immediately he runs over to the window, looks to his left and sees Raymond running across the yard towards his patrol car that's parked across the street. After Raymond speeds off, Minister Ragland sits down on the bed and tries to figure out how Raymond found him.)

CHAPTER TWENTY

(The next morning around 9:00 a.m. Minister Ragland drives to the Mayor's office. He walks in and sees the Mayor's secretary sitting at her desk.)

MINISTER: Where's the Mayor?

MERNA JAMES: He's in his office.

MINISTER: I want to see him, now!

MERNA JAMES: You'll have to make an appointment.

(Minister Ragland turns and heads straight for the Mayor's office.)

MERNA JAMES: You can't go in there!

(Merna takes off behind Minister Ragland.)

MERNA JAMES: Hey, you can't go in there!

(Merna steps in front of Minister Ragland to stop him.)

MERNA JAMES: Did you hear what I said?

MINISTER: Excuse me!

(Minister Ragland side steps and walks around her right into the Mayor's office without knocking. The Mayor, who at the time is on the phone kicked back in his chair, stands up.)

MINISTER: I want to talk to you now!

(The Mayor cuts his phone call short.)

HAYWOOD BURGESS: Let me call you back.

(After hanging up the phone he puts his hands on his hips.)

HAYWOOD BURGESS: What do you think you're doing?

MERNA JAMES: I told him he needed to make an appointment. Do you want me to call Raymond?

MINISTER: Yes! Please do!

HAYWOOD BURGESS: No, Merna, don't call Raymond; I can handle this. Just shut the door behind you when you leave; everything's okay.

MERNA JAMES: Are you sure?

HAYWOOD BURGESS: Yes. Just give us a few minutes to talk.

(As Merna is walking out she gives Minister Ragland a very mean and nasty look only to receive a big huge smile from him that irritates her to no end.)

HAYWOOD BURGESS: You had better have a real good reason for busting up in my office.

MINISTER: Reason? Take a look out of that window behind you.

(After looking out of the window, the Mayor stands there with his mouth wide open.)

HAYWOOD BURGESS: Oh my goodness.

MINISTER: Is that a good enough reason for you?

(Minister Ragland's car has been spray-painted with white paint. On the hood it says, 'Nigger you're dead.' On the driver side it says, 'Leave now or die.' On the passenger side it says, 'I hate niggers.' And on the windshield it says, 'Go and live, or stay and hang.')

MINISTER: Now would you like to take a wild guess at who did it?

(The Mayor doesn't answer as he remembers Butch telling both he and Raymond where Minister Ragland's car was.)

MINISTER: I didn't think so. I tried to tell you that he was out of control but you wouldn't listen! I want to press charges, and I want to press them now! I want him arrested, and thrown in jail just like you would do anybody else.

HAYWOOD BURGESS: Did you actually see him do it?

MINISTER: At three o'clock this morning, I heard some noise behind the house where my car was parked. When I looked out of the window I saw Raymond staggering across the yard going to his patrol car across the street. So to answer your question, no, I didn't actually see him do it, but what else would he be doing in the backyard where my car is parked at three in the morning?

HAYWOOD BURGESS: Well, if you didn't see him do it then what exactly do you expect me to do about it?

MINISTER: I stopped by the station on my way here to take a look at his patrol car, and sure enough there was white paint on the floor in the back. How much more evidence do you need?

(Mayor Burgess takes a deep breath and then faces Minister Ragland.)

HAYWOOD BURGESS: All right let's go.

(They leave the Mayor's office and go to Raymond's house along with two other Deputies. Officer Durant knocks on the door and Raymond answers.)

RAYMOND CLETTER: What's all this? And what is he doing here?

HAYWOOD BURGESS: Raymond, I'm sorry and I hate to do this, but you're under arrest.

(Raymond chuckles.)

RAYMOND CLETTER: What?

HAYWOOD BURGESS: I've got to take you in, Ray.

RAYMOND CLETTER: You're joking, right?

HAYWOOD BURGESS: No I'm not. But if you'll just come with us, I'll explain everything.

RAYMOND CLETTER: You wake me up on my day off, you bring this freak to my house, you tell me I'm under arrest, you don't tell me why, and you expect me to go with you? Not without an explanation.

HAYWOOD BURGESS: Ray, just put your hands behind your back and let them put the cuffs on. I'll explain everything when we get to the station.

(Raymond stares at Minister Ragland.)

RAYMOND CLETTER: I'm gonna put on some clothes and go with you so we can straighten this whole thing out. But when I find out who's responsible for all of this, I'm gonna stomp the life out of them.

(When they get to the station they take Raymond out of the back seat in hand cuffs. People begin to stare and point as they walk him up the stairs.)

RAYMOND CLETTER: Now that you've embarrassed me in front of the whole town by parading me around in hand cuffs, how about telling me what's going on!

HAYWOOD BURGESS: Ray, you're under arrest for destruction of private property.

RAYMOND CLETTER: What are you talking about? What private property?

HAYWOOD BURGESS: The Minister's car. Last night it was vandalized.

RAYMOND CLETTER: And?

(The Mayor takes a deep breath.)

HAYWOOD BURGESS: Can you guys give us a minute please?

(Everybody standing around walks away so they can talk.)

HAYWOOD BURGESS: Why didn't you just leave him alone, Ray?

RAYMOND CLETTER: Haywood, I didn't do anything, I'm telling you. He's setting me up.

HAYWOOD BURGESS: Setting you up? Why would he trash his own car? That doesn't make any sense. Besides, he saw you run across the yard and get in your patrol car. And if that's not bad enough he's got witnesses that saw your car across the street from the house.

RAYMOND CLETTER: Haywood, you've got to believe me. I didn't touch that car.

HAYWOOD BURGESS: I believe you Ray, I believe you. But you're gonna have to let us take you through the procedure just to satisfy him. After we take his car to the body shop, I'll take him home and then I'll come back to get you.

RAYMOND CLETTER: You mean to tell me that you're going to lock me up in my own jail?

HAYWOOD BURGESS: I have to, Ray. Just until I can get rid of him.

(The Mayor gets up.)

HAYWOOD BURGESS: Durant, book him and lock him up.

(Raymond looks over at the Minister and mimes.)

RAYMOND CLETTER: You're dead.

(Minister Ragland gets up and follows the Mayor.)

HAYWOOD BURGESS: Deputy Collins, can you give us a ride back over to my office?

DEPUTY COLLINS: Sure.

HAYWOOD BURGESS: Minister Ragland, don't worry about your car. I'll make sure it gets painted. My friend owns a body shop across town. When we get back to my office we'll drop it off so he can get started.

MINISTER: Fair enough

(Deputy Collins drops Minister Ragland and the Mayor off at the Mayor's office.)

HAYWOOD BURGESS: Let me grab my keys and we'll go on down and drop your car off.

(Minister Ragland becomes even more frustrated as he looks at his car. The Mayor returns with his keys.)

HAYWOOD BURGESS: My car is parked in back. I'll pull around and you can follow me.

(Mayor Burgess heads for his car and Minister Ragland goes to his. As he waits for the Mayor he lays his head back and sighs. Mayor Burgess pulls up in front of his car and blows his horn. Minister Ragland looks straight ahead and what he sees sitting in front of him is like a dream come true. There before him sits a white Cadillac, a Cadillac that looks exactly like the one he was chasing the day Willie and Buck were killed. Not knowing for sure if it's the same car, Minister Ragland motions him to go ahead as if he's going to follow him. As the Mayor pulls forward Minister Ragland looks at his bumper and sees a Sheriff's Associations stickers with a shiny gold star on it. Exactly as Chris described it. Immediately Minister Ragland blows his horn, sticks his head out of the window, and yells to get the Mayor's attention.)

HAYWOOD BURGESS: What is it?

MINISTER: Is there any way we can do this a little later? I've got something very important that I have to do and it can't wait.

HAYWOOD BURGESS: Right now?

MINISTER: Yes. It can't wait. I really need to take care of it now.

(The Mayor looks at his watch.)

HAYWOOD BURGESS: Okay. Just meet me at my office around two this afternoon and we'll drop it off then.

MINISTER: I'll be there.

(Mayor Burgess makes a u turn and parks his car behind the building where it was. Minister Ragland, thinking he has it all figured out, drives back to the police station.)

MINISTER: I need to see Raymond!

DEPUTY STONE: Do what?

MINISTER: I need to speak with Raymond!

DEPUTY STONE: No, what you need to do is get out of here. You've caused enough trouble already!

MINISTER: I'm not here to start trouble! Now, it's very important that I talk to him. Five minutes, that's all I need!

DEPUTY STONE: I'll ask him. But I can almost promise you that he's not going to see you.

MINISTER: Just ask him, please.

(Deputy Stone is gone for about ten seconds and then he returns.)

DEPUTY STONE: Like I said, he does not want to see you.

MINISTER: Look, tell him the conversation I need to have with him could very well be the difference between me leaving and staying in this town.

DEPUTY STONE: What did I just tell you? He doesn't want to see you.

MINISTER: Just tell him what I said, please Deputy Stone.

DEPUTY STONE: I'll ask him but you're wasting your time.

(Again Deputy Stone leaves and comes back.)

DEPUTY STONE: You've got five minutes.

MINISTER: That's all I need.

(Minister Ragland walks back to Raymond's cell.)

RAYMOND CLETTER: Are you happy, preacher man? This is what you wanted right? You wanted me out of your way so you can reek havoc all over Swamp Fox. Well, congratulations.

MINISTER: I know who raped Jennifer Mundy!

(Raymond laughs.)

RAYMOND CLETTER: Here we go again. Okay Detective –know- it –all, I'll play along. Who raped Jennifer Mundy?

MINISTER: The Mayor.

(Raymond begins to laugh as he strolls over to his cot.)

RAYMOND CLETTER: Haywood raped Jennifer?

MINISTER: Yes.

RAYMOND CLETTER: You know you're something else; you really are. First you set me up, and now Haywood. You are some piece of work, but I'll be a good sport and play along. I'll entertain your little fantasy you have going on here. So how do you know he did it?

MINISTER: I know someone that saw his car, a white Cadillac, parked in the woods on Wilson Road the night Jennifer was raped. This person told me that he heard a girl in the car screaming, "no please don't, no please don't."

RAYMOND CLETTER: Oh yeah. And who is this so called person that saw all of this?

MINISTER: I can't say. But a few days ago this person saw the Mayor's car and instantly remembered seeing it in the woods that night. I followed that car down Creech Road the other day trying to see who was driving, but something happened and I lost him. A few minutes ago I was sitting in my car waiting for him to pull around so I could follow him to the body shop and there it is. The same white Cadillac with that same shiny gold star sticker on the bumper.

RAYMOND CLETTER: You were following me.

MINISTER: What?

RAYMOND CLETTER: You were following me. I was driving his Cadillac that day out on Creech Road. The same day you caused that accident and got those two boys killed. My car was in the shop so I used Haywood's Cadillac.

MINISTER: That accident was not my fault. They were on the wrong side of the road when that semi came around the corner, not me.

RAYMOND CLETTER: Innocent as always, right? If you think for one second that I believe this little theory of yours, you're crazy. Haywood is not a rapist. This is just another one of your little snow jobs. You go around setting everybody up so you can have a free for all. Well I'm here to tell you it's not going to work.

MINISTER: Setting everybody up? Let me give you a little advice, Raymond. When you set out to commit a crime and you drive your patrol car to do it, you're setting yourself up. When you plant a bomb to kill people and you drive your patrol car to do it, you're setting yourself up.

(Minister Ragland's accusations upset Raymond and he reaches out between the bars to grab him.)

RAYMOND CLETTER: I'm gonna to kill you! You're not going to pin that bombing on me!

MINISTER: I'm not trying to pin anything on you. Your patrol car was seen leaving Cynthia's yard that night about an hour before that thing went off!

RAYMOND CLETTER: You're lying! My car was parked at the station. I wasn't even working that night!

MINISTER: Oh yeah? Well then how do you explain this?

(Minister Ragland pulls an envelope out of his pocket.)

RAYMOND CLETTER: What is that?

MINISTER: This is a letter written by Cynthia's neighbor. A neighbor that says they saw your patrol car in Cynthia's yard that same night. I found it in the mailbox where I'm staying.

RAYMOND CLETTER: Let me see it!

MINISTER: So you can rip it to shreds? I don't think so.

RAYMOND CLETTER: Let me see the letter, I'm not going to do anything to it!

(He hands Raymond the letter.)

RAYMOND CLETTER: You got this out of your mailbox?

MINISTER: Yeah, the day after the bombing.

(Raymond slowly looks up at Minister Ragland after reading the letter.)

RAYMOND CLETTER: I didn't vandalize your car, Haywood did.

MINISTER: Excuse me.

RAYMOND CLETTER: Haywood painted your car and he planted that bomb.

MINISTER: Wait a minute, rewind, you lost me.

RAYMOND CLETTER: This is his handwriting.

MINISTER: How do you know that?

RAYMOND CLETTER: The man has been signing my paychecks for the last fifteen years. I know his handwriting when I see it. So that's why he insisted on parading me around in front of everybody today in those handcuffs. He did it so people will ask questions. He wants to make it known to everybody that I don't like you so when something happens to you, I'll look like the guilty one.

MINISTER: What about your car? I saw it sitting in front of the house at three a.m. this morning.

RAYMOND CLETTER: I'm the only one in Swamp Fox with keys to my patrol car right? Wrong, think about it. Out of all the people in this town, who is the one person that has access to every state owned vehicle in Swamp Fox?

(Minister Ragland's eyes grow wide as it all starts to make sense.)

MINISTER: The Mayor.

RAYMOND CLETTER: Exactly.

MINISTER: So let me get this straight. The Mayor thought I was on to him…

RAYMOND CLETTER: That's what he thought.

MINISTER: Okay, he thought I was on to him. So he planted the bomb to kill me and drove your car to do it, hoping that someone would see him and think that it was you?

RAYMOND CLETTER: You got it. See we've been looking for your car for the last three or four days but we couldn't find it. Haywood was out there two weeks ago right behind Bobby's house with a surveyor. He wanted some trees removed and that's when he saw your car. He knew exactly where you were and that's how you got the letter. If you remember anything about Cynthia's place, you'd know that she has no neighbors. Her closest neighbor is approximately a mile away. So there's no way anybody could have seen my car in her yard, not from mile away, especially at night.

MINISTER: Okay, so far I'm with you. But one thing I don't understand is how he knew when I was going to be at Cynthia's the night the bomb went off. How could he have known I was going to be there?

RAYMOND CLETTER: That, I don't know. But some…

(Raymond pauses in mid sentence.)

RAYMOND CLETTER: A bug.

MINISTER: On me!

(Minister Ragland begins to check himself to see if a bug is crawling on him.)

RAYMOND CLETTER: Not a crawly bug, a bugging device. When he trashed your hotel room he found...

(Not wanting to tell Minister Ragland he planted a bugging device in his hotel room, Raymond stops talking.)

MINISTER: What?

RAYMOND CLETTER: Nothing. Let me ask you something, when you decided to go to Cynthia's where were you?

MINISTER: At the Williams'. We were sitting in the living room.

RAYMOND CLETTER: That's how he knew when you were going to be there. He planted a bug somewhere in their house.

MINISTER: What? He bugged their house?

RAYMOND CLETTER: That's the only way he could have known.

MINISTER: Which means that thing is still in their house.

RAYMOND CLETTER: Considering he wants to keep up with you, I would say yes.

(Out of frustration, Minister Ragland rubs his forehead.)

MINISTER: We've got to do something.

RAYMOND CLETTER: We've got to find that bugging device. If we can find that bug, and then somehow get into his house and find the transmitter receiver, we can nail him to the wall. Now listen, he's going to be coming back here soon to pick me up and take me home. So you need to leave now. But make sure you leave angry.

MINISTER: What do you mean?

RAYMOND CLETTER: I mean we can't let anybody know what we're doing. We have to play it off so they'll think we're still at odds. I'm gonna start yelling, and I want you to follow my lead. As soon as Stone hears my voice he's going to come running through that door and we have to convince him that things are still bad between us. It's been a little too quiet back here.

MINISTER: Does this mean we're friends now?

RAYMOND CLETTER: Absolutely not. I still think you're a piece of garbage. But

I'm willing to put our differences aside long enough to nail this pervert. I'm still a cop, and I still have people to protect. So as far as you and I are concerned, nothing has changed. I want you out of my town. Now follow my lead.

(Raymond begins to yell at Minister Ragland causing Officer Stone to come running.)

RAYMOND CLETTER: I want him out of here!

(Minister Ragland plays along by yelling back.)

MINISTER: I'm not done talking to you!

DEPUTY STONE: Oh, yes you are, buddy, let's go!

(Deputy Stone grabs Minister Ragland by his arm and escorts him out of the building. After picking Raymond up from jail and dropping him off at home, Mayor Burgess heads home. Once he's out of sight, Raymond gets in his car and drives straight to the Williams's to meet Minister Ragland. After arriving at the Williams's house at almost the exact same time, they both walk up to the front door. Minister Ragland rings the doorbell and Cynthia answers. Immediately he puts his finger to his lips to keep her from talking in case the Mayor's listening. He then motions her to come outside. Once she's out of the house and the door is closed she begins to stare at Raymond.)

CYNTHIA HANKS: What's going on, Joe? And what is he doing here?

MINISTER: I'll explain in a few minutes. For right now, I need for you to go inside, and bring everybody outside.

CYNTHIA HANKS: Joe, what is going on?

MINISTER: Cynthia, I'll explain everything when you come back. Now will you please go inside and bring them out?

(Cynthia stands there for a second, looks at Minister Ragland, looks at Raymond, and then turns to go inside.)

MINISTER: Cynthia.

(She turns to face him.)

MINISTER: Make sure when you talk to them you're not standing anywhere near the living room.

CYNTHIA HANKS: Joe, you're scaring me.

MINISTER: Don't be, just go get them.

(Feeling very uncomfortable, Cynthia finally goes inside and returns with Mr. and Mrs. Williams.)

CYNTHIA HANKS: Okay we are all out here. Now what's going on?

MINISTER: We think we may have found out who raped Jennifer.

(Cynthia covers her mouth as she starts to cry.)

CYNTHIA HANKS: What! You know who raped Jennifer?

MINISTER: We think so.

CYNTHIA HANKS: Who was it?

(Minister Ragland looks at Raymond and then turns back to Cynthia.)

MINISTER: We think it was the Mayor.

(The three of them can't believe what they're hearing.)

JEAN WILLIAMS: Why do you think it was him?

MINISTER: You remember that letter I told you about that mysteriously showed up in the mailbox?

CYNTHIA HANKS: Yeah.

MINISTER: I showed it to Raymond and he recognized the handwriting. Haywood wrote that letter.

CYNTHIA HANKS: And?

MINISTER: Look, right now is not the time to talk about this. There's something much more important that we have to do.

CYNTHIA HANKS: What do you mean now is not the time? Now is the perfect time! Anything else can wait, Joe.

RAYMOND CLETTER: No it can't.

(Cynthia, Mr. Williams, and Mrs. Williams are surprised by the fact that Raymond has spoken up. His response has caused them to all turn and look at him at the same time.)

CYNTHIA HANKS: I don't know if you're aware of it or not, but you're in no position to give any kind of demands around here!

(Cynthia's comment has caused a moment of silence as she and Raymond lock eyes.)

CYNTHIA HANKS: Now, as I was saying, everything else can wait.

MINISTER: It can't wait, Cynthia! We've got to search the house now!

EARL WILLIAMS: Wait a minute, search the house? Why do we need to search the house?

RAYMOND CLETTER: We think Haywood may have planted a listening device somewhere near your living room.

EARL WILLIAMS: What?

JEAN WILLIAMS: What listening device? Earl what is he talking about?

EARL WILLIAMS: Why would he plant it in our house? And when could he have gotten into our house?

RAYMOND CLETTER: We think he may have planted a listening device in your house so he could keep up with Joe. And he probably did it the day of your son's funeral. He knew that you guys and your neighbors would be gone for a while.

JEAN WILLIAMS: All right wait a minute, stop it! I want somebody to tell me what's going on!

RAYMOND CLETTER: Mrs. Williams, when Joe made the decision to go out to Cynthia's he was standing in your living room. Now we're almost positive that Haywood planted that bomb in hopes of killing Joe. But think about it, how could he have known when Joe was going to be there? He wasn't in your living room when they were talking about it. He got the information he needed by bugging your house. There is a listening device planted somewhere near your living room.

JEAN WILLIAMS: Are you telling me that since the day of Corey's funeral, that man has been listening to every word we've been saying?

RAYMOND CLETTER: If it's in there, yes.

(Mrs. Williams, feeling violated, all of a sudden turns and starts walking towards the house.)

MINISTER: Where are you going?

JEAN WILLIAMS: I 'm going to get that thing out of my house!

MINISTER: Jean, you can't do that!

JEAN WILLIAMS: You watch me!

MINISTER: Earl, please stop her!

EARL WILLIAMS: Jean!

JEAN WILLIAMS: I want it out of my house, Earl!

(Realizing that she's not going to stop, Mr. Williams takes off after her.)

MINISTER: Jean, it's the only evidence we have!

(Fully intent on finding the bug, Mrs. Williams continues to walk towards the house. So Raymond says something that is guaranteed to change her mind.)

RAYMOND CLETTER: Without that bug we can't save Ronald!

(Mrs. Williams immediately stops walking as she's still facing the house.)

RAYMOND CLETTER: We're going to need all the evidence we can get and that bug is the perfect start.

(She turns around, looks at Cynthia Hanks, and then takes a seat on her porch step. Cynthia, feeling her pain, sits on the same step and puts her arm around Mrs. Williams to comfort her. Raymond and the Minister walk over to join the rest of them at the porch.)

RAYMOND CLETTER: All we need to do is find that bug, and then somehow get into his house and find that receiver. If we do that, we'll have enough evidence to summons a warrant and get him into court. Without proper authorization, planting a bugging device is an illegal procedure.

JEAN WILLIAMS: So basically, we have to live with this thing until you find a way to get into his house, right?

RAYMOND CLETTER: Yes.

CYNTHIA HANKS: What about the rape? Can you get him for that too?

RAYMOND CLETTER: Well I'm thinking that with this bugging device, if we can find it, we'll have a little something to play with. We can play a little reverse psychology on him and make him tell on himself. But first we've got to find that bug. Do you guys have a stereo near the living room?

EARL WILLIAMS: Yeah.

RAYMOND CLETTER: Good, when we all get inside, Earl, I want you to turn on the radio so he won't suspect anything if he's listening. Cynthia, Jean, I want you two to look around in the kitchen. I'll look around in the dining room, Joe you look around in the living room. What we're looking for is a small circular shaped device about the size of a nickel with no wires attached to it. If you see it, don't

195

touch it. Just raise your hand and I'll take it from there. And please no whispering. If he's listening, he'll hear every word you say. Those things are super sensitive. Does everybody understand?

(They all say yes.)

RAYMOND CLETTER: Let's do it.

(Once they're all inside and Mr. Williams turns on the radio, they all begin to search for the bug. After about five-minutes Raymond crawls under the dining room table which is exposed to the living room. He carefully looks around and sees nothing. The glass top of the table is sitting on a stand that looks like an old wooden log. He pulls a little flashlight out of his pocket and checks the inside of the stand that is hollowed out, and there it is. Raymond immediately gets up and motions everybody to go back outside.)

RAYMOND CLETTER: I found it. It's in the center of your table stand.

EARL WILLIAMS: So what do we do now?

RAYMOND CLETTER: We find a way to get into his house with a video camera and get that receiver on tape. Then in court it's not his word against ours.

CYNTHIA HANKS: How are you going to get into his house?

RAYMOND CLETTER: Getting in is the easy part. Getting in legally, that's the hard part. We've got to do this the right way so if we do get him into court, he won't have anything against us.

MINISTER: No judge in this town is going to give you a warrant to search his house. And if they do, you know they'll tell him.

RAYMOND CLETTER: Yeah, I know.

(Raymond looks at his watch.)

RAYMOND CLETTER: Well, look I'm going to head on home and make some phone calls to see what I can come up with. When I find out something I'll give you a call Joe.

JEAN WILLIAMS: What about us? What do we do in the house?

RAYMOND CLETTER: Just carry on like you normally do. I know it's going to be a little strange, but just keep in mind what we're trying to do here. And remember no whispering. If he hears you whispering he'll know we're on to him. Joe, I'll call you later.

(Raymond heads for his car.)

CYNTHIA HANKS: Joe, are you sure we can trust him?

(As he watches Raymond walk away, Minister Ragland takes a deep breath.)

MINISTER: Yeah. We can trust him.

EARL WILLIAMS: How can you be so sure?

MINISTER: Because I see God on the move. Raymond is changing and he doesn't even know it. We can definitely trust him.

CHAPTER TWENTY-ONE

(The next day, Cynthia decides to go see her husband at the prison to let him know what's going on. As Ronald enters the room, she immediately senses that something is wrong with him. The lies Raymond told him about his wife and Minister Ragland having an affair have taken effect.)

CYNTHIA HANKS: What's wrong?

RONALD HANKS: Nothing.

(Cynthia pauses.)

CYNTHIA HANKS: Baby, what's wrong?

RONALD HANKS: Nothing, I'm fine.

CYNTHIA HANKS: Okay. Guess what, Joe may have found out who raped Jennifer.

RONALD HANKS: Really, that's good.

(Knowing full well that something is wrong, Cynthia sits back in her chair and crosses her arms.)

CYNTHIA HANKS: Ronald, I've been married to you for twenty-four years, and I know when something's bothering you. Now tell me, what's wrong?

RONALD HANKS: So how's Joe?

CYNTHIA HANKS: He is fine. Now tell me what's wrong with you?

RONALD HANKS: How often do you see him?

CYNTHIA HANKS: I see him everyday. Now, will you please answer my question? I have to leave soon.

RONALD HANKS: And why is that, Cynthia?

CYNTHIA HANKS: Joe thinks that it's best if I stay closer to the home. He said it's not a good idea for me to be out driving by myself.

RONALD HANKS: Is that right, well I tell you what. To make Joe happy why don't you leave now? And to make him really happy, don't ever come back.

(Cynthia leans forward.)

CYNTHIA HANKS: What did you say?

RONALD HANKS: You heard me. I said stay away from me. I don't ever want to see you or your little boyfriend again. Don't ever come back here; I mean it!

(As her mind searches for understanding, Cynthia begins to cry.)

RONALD HANKS: And now comes the fake tears. Do me a favor Cynthia, save the drama for the stage. Guard! Guard!

(The guard comes in and escorts him back to his cell, leaving Cynthia sitting there in tears. Back at Raymond's office, Minister Ragland is standing at the back door of the police station. He knocks on the door expecting Raymond to answer, but instead Deputy Durant answers. Raymond told Minister Ragland that he would answer the door so that nobody would know they're working together.)

DEPUTY DURANT: Come on in, he's in his office.

(As he tries to figure out why Deputy Durant answered the door, Deputy Durant escorts him to Raymond's office.)

RAYMOND CLETTER: Thanks Durant.

(Deputy Durant shuts the door as he leaves.)

MINISTER: Is this your way of hiding what we're doing Ray? Sending him to answer the door? What's wrong with you, Ray?

RAYMOND CLETTER: You don't have to worry about Durant, he's okay. Now listen, I think I may have found a better way to get Haywood.

MINISTER: How?

RAYMOND CLETTER: Being in law enforcement as long as I have, I've had to deal with rape cases before. I've sat down and talked with men that have raped women and they all seem to thrive on the same thing. When a man rapes a woman, it's not the sex that drives him; it's the domination. Having power over that woman. To hear her scream and beg him to stop is what they like. You would think that when a man is raping a woman, he's angry; but he's not. The only time he gets angry is when she gives in and stops fighting. It takes all of the fun out of it. Now I know that's sickening, but that's how they operate.

MINISTER: What's your point, Ray?

RAYMOND CLETTER: My point is why not beat him at his own game? Why don't we set him up?

MINISTER: How?

RAYMOND CLETTER: We know that night Jennifer was raped she was picked up in front of the church, right?

MINISTER: Yeah.

RAYMOND CLETTER: But what we don't know is did she get into the car on her own, or was she forced in.

MINISTER: Where are you going with this, Ray?

RAYMOND CLETTER: I'm going to the refrigerator to get a piece of cheese, put it on the trap, and wait for the rat to take the bait.

MINISTER: What is that, Ebonics for cops? What are you talking about?

RAYMOND CLETTER: Look. Every Thursday night, at the same time, Haywood, Pete, and myself have dinner at Sally's. We usually finish around ten and we're out of there by ten fifteen. Only this time, instead of me leaving at ten fifteen, I'll leave at ten and meet you at my patrol car, which will be parked behind Pete's store.

MINISTER: Meet me there for what, Ray?

RAYMOND CLETTER: To catch the mouse taking the cheese. Every Thursday, just before we leave, Haywood always uses the bathroom, always. This Thursday when he goes to the bathroom, I'll get Pete to call me on his cell phone so we'll know when to send her to the corner of Miller and Main. The very road Haywood takes to go home. If all goes well, Haywood will stop and offer her a ride, which she'll refuse of course. Now if he is a rapist and he wants her bad enough, he'll force her into the car. And that's where we come in. From behind Pete's store we'll have a clear view of that corner. We can be out of my car and into his in about fifteen seconds if he tries anything.

(After explaining everything they both sit in silence staring at each other.)

RAYMOND CLETTER: Well, what do you think?

MINISTER: I think that you have finally lost your mind, that's what I think.

RAYMOND CLETTER: What?

MINISTER: You can't put some poor woman's life in danger like that, Ray! What's wrong with you?

RAYMOND CLETTER: What danger? There is no danger. There's not a whole lot he can do in fifteen seconds, Joe. It's a full proof plan, I'm telling you.

MINISTER: I don't trust it, Ray. I just don't trust it; sounds a little too risky to me. Besides, where are you going to find a woman crazy enough to take a chance like that anyway?

(Raymond gets on his intercom.)

RAYMOND CLETTER: Durant.

DEPUTY DURANT: Yeah.

RAYMOND CLETTER: Send her in.

(Raymond lets go of the intercom button and sits back in his chair.)

MINISTER: You're joking, right?

RAYMOND CLETTER: No.

MINISTER: You mean to tell me, that you actually found a woman that's willing to go along with that crazy plan?

RAYMOND CLETTER: I sure did.

MINISTER: And you told her exactly what you told me, the whole thing?

RAYMOND CLETTER: Yes.

MINISTER: And she still wanted to do it?

RAYMOND CLETTER: Yes she did.

MINISTER: Unbelievable. I've got to hand it to you Ray, you're good. A little twisted, but you're good. So who is she?

(The girl knocks on the door and Raymond motions her to come in. Minister Ragland can't see her because his back is to the door. So he waits for her to walk in instead of turning around to see who she is. She walks in and stands beside Minister Ragland. He looks up, and to his surprise, there stands the last person he ever expected to see.

There beside him stands Jacy.)

MINISTER: No way! No way! No way! No way!

RAYMOND CLETTER: Joe, just listen!

MINISTER: No way, Ray! You can forget it! This is not going to happen, not with her!

RAYMOND CLETTER: Why not? I explained everything to her and she's okay with it!

MINISTER: But I'm not, Ray! She is a seventeen-year-old child. You cannot do this!

RAYMOND CLETTER: Fine, Joe. We'll just handle it ourselves.

(Minster Ragland turns to Jacy who is now sitting in the chair next to him.)

MINISTER: I can't let you do this.

JACY ELLIS: It's too late.

MINISTER: No it's not! You can get up and walk out of here right now and forget about this whole thing!

JACY ELLIS: Why? So he can rape somebody else? I'm doing it.

(Minister Ragland looks at Raymond.)

MINISTER: See what you've done, this is your fault Ray. She's going to end up in the hands of a rapist, she's going to get hurt, and it's going to be your fault. I don't want to have anything to do with it.

RAYMOND CLETTER: Joe, she's not going to get hurt. I've thought this whole thing through a million times. There is no danger!

JACY ELLIS: Minister Ragland.

(He turns to Jacy.)

JACY ELLIS: Did you or did you not tell Corey to always stand up for what he believed in?

MINISTER: Yes, I told him that, but this is a totally different situation.

JACY ELLIS: No, it's not. I want to do this because I believe it's the right thing to do. Somebody's got to do something before he rapes again. Now I would really like for you to be there when this happens. For me, please.

(Minister Ragland takes a deep breath.)

MINISTER: I'm sorry I can't; I just can't do it. If something went wrong and you got hurt it would haunt me for the rest of my life.

RAYMOND CLETTER: Joe, look at me. Look at me, Joe!

(Minister Ragland turns to face Raymond.)

RAYMOND CLETTER: Do you really think that I would purposely put her life in danger? Do you really believe that?

(Minister Ragland pauses and takes a deep breath before answering.)

MINISTER: No, I don't.

RAYMOND CLETTER: Then trust me; I know what I'm doing. When I put this whole thing together I had no plans of doing it on my own. I'm going to need your help, Joe. Are you with me?

(Minister Ragland looks at Jacy, looks at Raymond, and then shakes his head as he answers.)

MINISTER: I must be absolutely crazy for agreeing to this.

RAYMOND CLETTER: So you're with me?

MINISTER: Yeah, I'm with you Ray. But I'm telling you now, if at any time at all I feel that something's not right, this whole thing is over.

RAYMOND CLETTER: Fair enough.

MINISTER: I mean it Ray, it's over!

RAYMOND CLETTER: You have a deal.

(Jacy gets up and hugs Minister Ragland.)

JACY ELLIS: I'm so glad you're going to help us!

RAYMOND CLETTER: Okay Jacy, let's go over this one more time. Now tomorrow when you go to his office....

(Minister Ragland interrupts.)

MINISTER: Wait a minute what do you mean when she goes to his office! Why is she going to his office?

RAYMOND CLETTER: Joe!

MINISTER: I'm just asking.

RAYMOND CLETTER: No, you're just freaking out. Now will you relax and let me handle this?

MINISTER: Fine. But I hope you know what you're doing Ray!

RAYMOND CLETTER: I know exactly what I'm doing. So let me do it, my way.

MINISTER: It's your show.

(Later that same afternoon Minister Ragland drives over to the hotel where he was staying to find out if anybody saw anything the night his room was trashed. As he pulls up into the parking lot he sees a sixty five year old gray haired black woman walking on the second floor balcony. Minister Ragland gets out of his car and yells up to her.)

MINISTER: Excuse me!

(The old woman stops and looks over the balcony to see who's yelling.)

MINISTER: Can I please talk to you for just a minute? I'll come up there!

(Minister Ragland walks up to the second floor. As he approaches Hattie, she begins to gawk and check him out from head to toe.)

MINISTER: I'm sorry to bother you, but if you could spare me about five minutes of your time I sure would appreciate it. My name is...

(Hattie interrupts him as he sticks out his hand for her to shake.)

HATTIE EVANS: I know who you are.

MINISTER: You do?

HATTIE EVANS: Yes I do. You're that fine young thang running around here causing all kinds of trouble.

MINISTER: What's your name?

HATTIE EVANS: My name is Hattie, Hattie Evans. But you can call me anything you want to baby.

MINISTER: Nice to meet you Miss Hattie.

HATTIE EVANS: I've heard all about you.

(Hattie takes one step back and checks him out again from head to toe.)

HATTIE EVANS: My friend lied to me again.

MINISTER: Beg your pardon?

HATTIE EVANS: My friend Tracy Carter told me you were handsome; she lied. You're just flat out fine. And if I was twenty years younger, I'd mess your world up young buck. You'd be ready to marry old Hattie when I got through with you.

(Minster Ragland laughs at the fact that he's being hit on by a sixty five-year-old woman.)

MINISTER: Thanks for the compliment. I appreciate it, I think.

HATTIE EVANS: Is there something old Hattie can do for you baby?

MINISTER: Yes there is. I'm trying to find out who destroyed my room that night. I have to go to court for that soon and if I don't find out who did it they're going to lock me up.

HATTIE EVANS: I was on call that night but I didn't see anything.

MINISTER: So you were here that night?

HATTIE EVANS: I'm always here baby. I've been working here for thirteen years.

MINISTER: You didn't happen to see the Mayor here that night did you?

HATTIE EVANS: Not that night I didn't. Are you married, baby?

(With a smile on his face he answers.)

MINISTER: No, I'm not. So you've seen the Mayor here before?

HATTIE EVANS: Have I seen him here before? I see him here at least once a month. He's always coming around here at two and three o'clock in the morning with some little old young gal. Most of them don't look any older than seventeen or eighteen.

MINISTER: Isn't he married?

HATTIE EVANS: Let me tell you something-pretty eyes. That man does more dirt than glad do trash bags you hear me? He don't care about no marriage.

(Hattie leans forward a little closer to Minister Rgaland.)

HATTIE EVANS: So, do you have a girlfriend sweet baby?

(Again Minister Ragland laughs.)

MINISTER: No, I don't. These young girls you've seen him with, have you ever seen him get rough with any of them? Like forcing them into a room or anything?

HATTIE EVANS: No, they come up here on their own. He's probably giving them money or something. So how long are you in town, Mr. Pretty eyes?

MINISTER: I'm not really sure.

HATTIE EVANS: You know now that I think about it, I did see something strange. I saw Raymond's police car in the parking lot that night. I don't know what he was doing here but I did see his car. If I were you I'd check him out. Cause if there was ever a low down snake in the grass heathen, it's Raymond.

MINISTER: You saw Raymond's patrol car here? Do you remember what time it was?

HATTIE EVANS: Between one and two in the morning.

MINISTER: Between one and two, okay. Well, Miss Hattie, I do thank you for talking to me.

(Minister Ragland sticks out his hand for her to shake, and as if she were standing at the alter about to get married, Hattie gently grabs his hand and just stands there not saying word. Minister Ragland looks down at his hand and then looks up at Hattie.)

MINISTER: Miss Hattie, can I have my hand back?

HATTIE EVANS: I'm sorry baby. Miss Hattie couldn't think straight there for a minute.

(Hattie begins to fan her face with her hands.)

HATTIE EVANS: Boy you got Miss Hattie sweating up here on the second floor today.

(Minister Ragland laughs.)

MINISTER: Miss Hattie you take care of yourself. And don't you let'em work you too hard, you hear me?

HATTIE EVANS: I hear you.

MINISTER: Take care.

HATTIE EVANS: You too, with your fine self.

(As Minister Ragland is walking away headed for his car Hattie locks in on his butt.)

HATTIE EVANS: Boy, Duncan Hines aint got nothing on them cakes right there.

(Later that same afternoon Raymond drives over to Pete's store to fill him in on the game plan. After telling him all the details, Pete is left speechless.)

RAYMOND CLETTER: So what do you think?

PETE WILSON: I think you need to go on down to old Jeff Lee's office, lay back on that leather couch, and get you some help because you're going crazy.

RAYMOND CLETTER: I knew it. I knew you wouldn't believe me.

PETE WILSON: What do you expect, Ray? You come in here telling me that you think Haywood raped Jennifer because of what some nigger told you, give me a break. If anything we should be trying to put him away. He's the enemy, not Haywood!

RAYMOND CLETTER: Pete, this has nothing to do with Joe. You think I'm just making this entire thing up? I didn't want to believe it either. But after piecing everything together it was obvious who the guilty one was, and it's Haywood.

PETE WILSON: Raymond, friends don't set friends up. That's not how it works.

RAYMOND CLETTER: What are you afraid of, Pete? What does he have on you? In all the years I've known you I've never seen you stand up to him.

PETE WILSON: He doesn't have anything on me! And I'm not afraid of him. Haywood is my friend, through good and bad he's been my friend. Now, if I do what you're asking me to do, what kind of friend am I? Friends don't set friends up, Ray; it is wrong!

RAYMOND CLETTER: It's wrong? It's wrong? What about all the things he took from Jennifer? Was that wrong, Pete? Whether a little or a lot, that girl is going to be scared mentally and emotionally for the rest of her life!

PETE WILSON: Raymond, you're assuming. You don't know for sure if he did it!

(Raymond reaches his boiling point and begins to yell.)

RAYMOND CLETTER: He did it! There is no assumption! Haywood Burgess is guilty of rape and I know it!

(Raymond's yelling is making Pete a little nervous. Knowing he's wrong for yelling, Raymond puts his head down and takes a deep breath.)

RAYMOND CLETTER: Look, I'm sorry for yelling at you Pete. I know none of this makes any sense to you, but I'm right on this one, I know it. And if you'll just do this one thing for me you'll see that I'm right. Just one quick phone call when he goes to the bathroom, that's all I ask.

(Pete pauses.)

PETE WILSON: Just a phone call?

RAYMOND CLETTER: That's it.

PETE WILSON: I'll help you Ray, on one condition.

RAYMOND CLETTER: What's that?

PETE WILSON: No matter what happens, whether you guys end up in court or whatever, my name never gets mentioned. Keep me out of it.

RAYMOND CLETTER: Deal.

PETE WILSON: I'm serious Ray. You can never tell him I had anything to do with this!

RAYMOND CLETTER: No one will ever know a thing.

PETE WILSON: Nobody but Minister loud mouth. What are we going to do about him? I don't trust him Ray!

RAYMOND CLETTER: I know Joe is a little hard to take, and he's stubborn as a mule. But now that I'm on the outside looking in, I can see that his heart is in the right place. He doesn't want to hurt anybody; he just wants to help. His methods aren't always up to par, but his intentions are good.

PETE WILSON: He better be Ray. He better be.

(Later that evening around 7:00 p.m., after running around all day, Raymond finally gets home. He walks in the front door, takes his shoes off, drops his keys on a small table sitting near the door, and walks upstairs to his bedroom. As Raymond hangs his jacket in the closet, a brown and white book, which is sitting on the top shelf catches his eye. Raymond stands motionless staring at the book. After about thirty seconds of contemplating, Raymond grabs the book, sits on the bed and opens it up. The first thing he sees is a newspaper clipping about the accident that killed his daughter, wife, and mother. He looks at it for a second, puts it back on the shelf, walks out of his room, and into his daughter's room. Before he walks in Raymond closes his eyes, leans his head on the door, takes a deep breath, and then enters the room. Everything in her room is exactly as she left it. Even her dingy little socks are still on the floor next to her bed. Raymond slowly enters the room looking at everything as if it were his first time being there. He walks over to a small shelf on the wall where her ballet trophies are and picks one of them up. He wipes the dust off, looks at it for a few seconds, and then puts it back on the shelf. As he begins to pan around the room, he spots some stuffed animals on her bed, but there is one in particular that stands out from the rest. It's a little black teddy bear with a cowboy hat, a vest, and a little pair of chaps that he and his daughter named Justice. Raymond walks over to the bed, sits down, grabs Justice, and plays back in his mind the smile that little bear generated when his daughter saw it for the first time. Still sitting on the bed, Raymond looks across the room to his left and sees a picture of him, his wife, his daughter, and his mother. As he zeroes in on the picture, his emotions begin to churn, creating a huge lump in his throat. Raymond walks over to the desk where the picture is sitting. He grabs the picture, looks at it, smiles, and then breaks down crying as he is reminded of the huge void they all left in his life. Raymond pulls his daughter's little plastic chair from under her desk, sits down in it, grips the picture with both hands, and presses it against his forehead as he cries.)

RAYMOND CLETTER: I'm so sorry. I'm so sorry. It should have been me baby.

(As his tears splatter on the glass that covers the picture, he continues to talk to the still eyes that stare back at him.)

RAYMOND CLETTER: You were supposed to bury me first. You were my world. Now I have nothing.

(Raymond looks up towards heaven and begins to scream at God as the tears continue to stream down his face.)

RAYMOND CLETTER: And you call yourself a loving God! Love does not burn women and children alive! You're not love! And there's nothing good about you! You're evil! You let three of the sweetest people on this earth die a horrible death! You are evil!

(After getting his emotions somewhat under control, Raymond looks down at the picture one last time, wipes his eyes, takes a deep breath, gently kisses the picture, and then places it back on her desk. As he looks around, he realizes being in that room is just too hard to handle. As he opens the door and is about to walk out, he looks around the room one last time. Just before he closes the door, he steps back in, grabs her little teddy bear Justice, and walks out closing the door behind him. It's now seven thirty the next day and Raymond is on his way to the restaurant to meet Pete and the Mayor. He parks his car behind Pete's store and walks over to the restaurant. After eating dinner they sit and talk for a little while and then Raymond looks at his watch.)

RAYMOND CLETTER: Well fellows, I'd love to stay and chat but I've gotta get going.

HAYWOOD BURGESS: Where are you going in such a hurry?

RAYMOND CLETTER: I've got places to go and people to see.

(Pete plays along.)

PETE WILSON: Translation. He's got a date.

HAYWOOD BURGESS: Ohhh. Who's the unlucky woman?

RAYMOND CLETTER: Very funny. I don't have a date, and if I did I surely wouldn't tell you two about it.

HAYWOOD BURGESS: Take it easy my friend.

(After Raymond leaves the table they both turn, look at each other, and at the same time say.)

PETE, HAYWOOD: He's got a date.

(When Raymond gets to his car he sees Jacy and Minister Ragland standing behind it. Minister Ragland parked his car at the police station and they walked to Pete's store. Raymond opens the doors and they all get in.)

RAYMOND CLETTER: All right, let's go over this one more time. Jacy, if he does stop and offer you a ride, under no circumstances are you to get in the car. Do you understand that?

JACY ELLIS: Yes. But what if...

(Minister Ragland cuts her off in mid sentence.)

MINISTER: There is no what if! Do not get in the car! It's that simple.

JACY ELLIS: If he doesn't try to force me into the car then how are we going to get him? Think about it, if I get in the car on my own, more than likely he's going to try something. And when he does, that's when you guys show up and arrest him.

(Minister Ragland goes into instant panic mode.)

MINISTER: Oh my word. Ray, will you please talk to her.

RAYMOND CLETTER: Jacy, please. You're going to give this man a heart attack. Just stay out of the car, okay?

JACY ELLIS: You're the boss.

(Raymond's cell phone rings.)

RAYMOND CLETTER: That's probably Pete.

(Raymond answers the phone.)

RAYMOND CLETTER: Hello, all right, I appreciate it. I'll call you later to let you know what's going on.

(Raymond hangs up.)

RAYMOND CLETTER: Okay, we're on. Pete said he just went to the bathroom. Jacy, don't worry about a thing. If he tries anything at all we'll be right there.

JACY ELLIS: I'm not worried.

MINISTER: Well I am.

RAYMOND CLETTER: All right it's show time. Jacy, you need to head for the corner.

(Jacy gets out of the back seat and starts walking towards the corner.)

RAYMOND CLETTER: Hey, Jacy!

(She stops and turns around.)

RAYMOND CLETTER: Do not get in the car!

JACY ELLIS: I know.

(Once Jacy reaches the corner, Minister Ragland gets extremely fidgety.)

RAYMOND CLETTER: The trap is set.

(Minister Ragland begins to bounce his leg up and down shaking the whole car.)

RAYMOND CLETTER: Will you give me break with that shaking!

MINISTER: I can't help it. This whole thing is driving me nuts.

RAYMOND CLETTER: You're stressing over nothing, Joe. Nothing is going to happen to her.

(Raymond sees headlights coming down the street.)

RAYMOND CLETTER: Okay, here we go, that might be him.

(Raymond leans forward to get a better look.)

RAYMOND CLETTER: Yep, that's him. This is it!

(Minister Ragland turns and looks at Raymond.)

MINISTER: I think I feel myself aging.

(Raymond laughs at him.)

RAYMOND CLETTER: You're not aging. You're just overreacting; relax.

(The Mayor drives by and does not stop.)

RAYMOND CLETTER: There he goes. See he didn't even stop. And to think, you aged twenty years for nothing.

MINISTER: That's not funny, Ray.

(Raymond laughs.)

RAYMOND CLETTER: I'll go get her.

(As Raymond is walking towards the corner to get Jacy he sees the Mayor turn around. So he makes a mad dash back to the car.)

MINISTER: What are you doing, Ray?

RAYMOND CLETTER: Haywood turned around!

MINISTER: What!

RAYMOND CLETTER: He turned around!

(Minister Ragland, now stressed out all over again, grabs Raymond by the arm. Raymond turns and looks at him.)

MINISTER: I think I'm aging again.

RAYMOND CLETTER: Will you please let go of my arm, Joe, and relax! You're making me nervous!

(The Mayor pulls up along side of the curb in front of Jacy, shuts the car off, and gets out.)

HAYWOOD BURGESS: How are you doing?

JACY ELLIS: I'm fine, how are you?

HAYWOOD BURGESS: I'm good. Aren't you Ray's new assistant?

JACY ELLIS: Yeah.

HAYWOOD BURGESS: What are you doing out here this late?

JACY ELLIS: I'm waiting for my ride.

HAYWOOD BURGESS: Don't you think it's a little dangerous to be out here by yourself?

JACY ELLIS: No, I'm fine.

HAYWOOD BURGESS: Would you like a ride somewhere? I could drop you off where ever you need to go.

JACY ELLIS: No, I'm going to wait here but thanks anyway.

HAYWOOD BURGESS: Are you sure?

JACY ELLIS: Yeah, I'm sure.

HAYWOOD BURGESS: Okay. You be careful.

(The Mayor gets in his car and starts the engine. Just as he's about to pull off, Jacy stops him.)

JACY ELLIS: Hey wait!

(He leans his head down to look out of the passenger side window.)

HAYWOOD BURGESS: Did you say something?

JACY ELLIS: Maybe it is a little too dangerous for me to be out here by myself. Does the offer still stand?

HAYWOOD BURGESS: Sure.

(He gets out and walks around to the passenger side.)

RAYMOND CLETTER: Here we go! He's gonna do it!

MINISTER: Well let's go!

RAYMOND CLETTER: We have to wait until he grabs her.

(The Mayor opens the door for Jacy and she gets in.)

RAYMOND CLETTER: No don't! Don't get in the car, Jacy!

MINISTER: What is she doing?

(Jacy gets in, the Mayor shuts her door, and they drive off.)

MINISTER: Let's go, let's go! We can't lose them!

RAYMOND CLETTER: All right calm down, I'm going!

(Raymond tries to start the car and gets nothing.)

MINISTER: What are you doing, let's go!

RAYMOND CLETTER: It won't start!

MINISTER: What do you mean it won't start!

(Raymond jumps out of the car and takes off running.)

MINISTER: Where are you going!

RAYMOND CLETTER: To the station to get another car. I'll be right back!

(Minister Ragland looks up towards heaven and closes his eyes.)

MINISTER: Lord, please don't let anything happen to her.

(When Jacy looks in her side mirror and doesn't see headlights following her, she starts to get a little nervous. She then turns around and looks out of the back window.)

HAYWOOD BURGESS: What's the matter? What are you looking for?

JACY ELLIS: Nothing. Hey you know what, I changed my mind. I think I'll go back and wait for my ride.

HAYWOOD BURGESS: You don't want to do that; it's too dangerous. I don't mind giving you a ride.

JACY ELLIS: I know and I appreciate it. But I'd rather go back and wait.

HAYWOOD BURGESS: Don't be silly. If I dropped you off on that corner and something happened to you I'd feel just terrible.

JACY ELLIS: Please take me back.

HAYWOOD BURGESS: I can't do that.

JACY ELLIS: Why not?

HAYWOOD BURGESS: Because if I take you back, then how are we going to enjoy that fine little body of yours?

(Jacy looks at him.)

JACY ELLIS: Look, you're really starting to scare me. I want to go back and I want to go back now.

(The Mayor reaches over and tries to play with her hair, so Jacy leans over out of his reach.)

HAYWOOD BURGESS: Scare you? There's nothing to be scared about, honey. I'm not going to hurt you. As a matter of fact, when we get through with you, you're gonna feel real good.

JACY ELLIS: What are you talking about? Who is we?

HAYWOOD BURGESS: We, is me and an old friend of mine. Now, as far as what we are going to do to you. Well, let's just say we're going to give you something that dead nigger could never give you.

(Jacy opens the door.)

JACY ELLIS: Stop this car now or I'm jumping out!

(He quickly reaches over and grabs a hand full of her hair.)

HAYWOOD BURGESS: Shut that door or you won't have to worry about jumping out!

(In fear that he would really push her out Jacy shuts the door.)

HAYWOOD BURGESS: You pull another stunt like that and I'll kill you, so help me. Now I suggest you sit back, relax, and save your energy, you little whore. You're gonna need it.

JACY ELLIS: Please don't do this!

(He backhands her across the face.)

HAYWOOD BURGESS: Shut your mouth!

(With blood trickling from her mouth and pain ricocheting across her face, Jacy leans forward as she cries. While Raymond and Minister Ragland are driving around looking for the Mayor, Raymond decides to call Pete.)

PETE WILSON: Hello?

RAYMOND CLETTER: Pete, its Raymond.

PETE WILSON: What happened?

RAYMOND CLETTER: Everything went wrong, Pete.

PETE WILSON: What do you mean everything went wrong? Don't give me bad news, Ray!

RAYMOND CLETTER: She got in the car.

PETE WILSON: On her own?

RAYMOND CLETTER: Yeah.

PETE WILSON: Okay. And now you guys are following them, so what's the problem?

(Raymond doesn't answer.)

PETE WILSON: What's wrong Ray?

RAYMOND CLETTER: We're not following them.

PETE WILSON: Why not!

RAYMOND CLETTER: My car wouldn't start and they got away.

PETE WILSON: Great, that's just great! Maybe they'll let us be cellmates, Ray, what do you think?

RAYMOND CLETTER: Cellmates? What are you talking about?

PETE WILSON: Do you know what the law says about using a minor for police operations without written consent from the legal guardian or parent of that minor? It says don't do it Ray! It's against the law.

RAYMOND CLETTER: Don't blame me! If she had followed directions none of this would be happening!

PETE WILSON: It was your bone-headed plan, Ray!

RAYMOND CLETTER: Pete, right now it doesn't matter who's at fault! What matters is that we find that white Cadillac! So just stay by the phone and I'll call you when we come up with something!

PETE WILSON: Stay by the phone? You must be crazy if you think I'm just going to sit here and do nothing. I'm going to look for that Cadillac!

RAYMOND CLETTER: He's gonna figure out you're involved Pete, what about that?

PETE WILSON: Forget him! I'm not thinking about him; I'm thinking about the girl!

RAYMOND CLETTER: All right, fine. If you want to help us look, that's up to you. But if you happen to find them, don't do anything. I want you to call me the second you see them so don't forget your cell phone.

PETE WILSON: I've got it in my hand.

RAYMOND CLETTER: I'll be in touch.

(After hanging up the phone Raymond looks at Minster Ragland who is looking straight ahead.)

RAYMOND CLETTER: We'll find her Joe, don't worry.

MINISTER: I promised her Ray. I gave her my word that I wouldn't let anything happen to her.

RAYMOND CLETTER: Joe, you can't blame yourself. We told her not to get in the car.

216

MINISTER: She's a child, Ray. A seventeen-year-old kid; we should have kept her out of it.

(Again Ray sighs as he realizes that he may have made the ultimate mistake. As Jacy and the Mayor continue to travel the long dark country roads, Jacy, feeling that she's in a no win situation either way, decides to ask the Mayor about Jennifer.)

JACY ELLIS: You raped Jennifer didn't you?

(The Mayor looks at her, and then put his eyes back on the road never saying a word.)

JACY ELLIS: Didn't you?

HAYWOOD BURGESS: Shut up.

JACY ELLIS: You think you're so tough, walking around here like you're the king of the world. Well I hope you enjoyed your reign, because when this is all over, you're going to jail. Raymond knows about everything that happened that night on Wilson Road. And now this, you're going down.

(The Mayor slams on the brakes and pulls off the road. While on the side of the road, still looking straight ahead and holding onto the steering wheel as tight as he can, Mayor Burgess turns to face her.)

HAYWOOD BURGESS: You know what your problem is you little nigger loving whore?

(Jacy slowly turns to face him.)

HAYWOOD BURGESS: You talk too much!

(As soon as he gets his last word out he reaches over, grabs a hand full of her hair, and slams her head against the passenger window knocking her out cold. He then pulls back on the road and continues on feeling no regret whatsoever for what he's just done. After driving another eight miles or so, the Mayor reaches his destination. He pulls in the driveway and parks his car in the backyard so it can't be seen from the road. After turning off the engine and walking around to the passenger side of the car, he opens the door to find Jacy still unconscious in the front seat.)

HAYWOOD BURGESS: Hey! Hey!

(He gets no response so he reaches in the car and shakes her.)

HAYWOOD BURGESS: Wake up!

(Still getting no response, the Mayor sits her up straight and smacks her across the face. Jacy wakes up gasping for air.)

217

HAYWOOD BURGESS: Let's go!

(Before Jacy fully comes to he grabs her by the arm, pulls her out of the car, and literally drags her across the backyard.)

HAYWOOD BURGESS: Stand up and walk!

(Jacy finally gets on her feet and begins to walk. As they approach the house Jacy gets her second wind and decides to fight back. She yanks her arm away, punches him in the stomach, and tries to run but her efforts are short lived. Again he grabs her by her hair, puts his other hand around her throat, and slams her against the wall of the house.)

HAYWOOD BURGESS: Look, I've had just about enough of you!

(He pulls out his gun and places it on her temple.)

HAYWOOD BURGESS: Settle down, shut up, or you die! Do you understand me?

(With tears streaming down her face Jacy nods her head yes. After finally getting Jacy under control, he rings the doorbell but gets no response. After ringing the bell for a second time he hears footsteps walking towards the door. While waiting for his friend to answer the door he checks Jacy out from head to toe.)

HAYWOOD BURGESS: Oh yeah, sweetheart. We've got big plans for you.

(As the Mayor holds Jacy by the back of her neck the door opens.)

HAYWOOD BURGESS: So what do you think? Is she ripe enough for you?

(As the Mayor's friend stands there with a smile on his face, Jacy with all her might lunges forward and tries to kick him.)

JACY ELLIS: You liar!

(The Mayor has to pull Jacy back and hold her extra tight as she squirms to get a loose. Jacy wants to get her hands on the Mayor's friend not only because she's afraid of what he's going to do to her, but also because he betrayed her. The man standing in the doorway with a smile on his face and evil in his eyes is none other than Pete Wilson. Pete is in on the whole thing. He's also the mysterious second man Chris Medlin saw in the Mayor's car that night on Wilson Road. He too, is guilty of raping Jennifer Mundy.)

PETE WILSON: She's ripe enough for me.

HAYWOOD BURGESS: Have they called?

PETE WILSON: Yeah Raymond did.

HAYWOOD BURGESS: And?

PETE WILSON: There's nothing to worry about. They have no idea where you are.

HAYWOOD BURGESS: Now, this guy you paid to sabotage Raymond's car, he will keep his mouth shut, right?

PETE WILSON: Oh yeah. I've used him quite a few times.

JACY ELLIS: You were supposed to help us, you jerk!

(Again Jacy lunges forward as she attempts to grabs Pete.)

PETE WILSON: You're a feisty little thing aren't you? Come on in, Haywood.

(Once they're inside Pete stands face to face with Jacy.)

PETE WILSON: You ready to party, sweetheart?

HAYWOOD BURGESS: Pete, are you sure they won't come by here?

PETE WILSON: I'm positive.

(At that very moment Pete's cell phone rings. He picks it up and checks the caller I.D.)

PETE WILSON: It's Raymond. Take her into my bedroom, shut the door, and keep her quiet.

(The Mayor pulls Jacy down the hall to the bedroom and shuts the door.)

PETE WILSON: Hello?

RAYMOND CLETTER: Pete, its Raymond. Have you had any luck?

PETE WILSON: Not yet.

RAYMOND CLETTER: Where are you?

PETE WILSON: I'm out on McKenzie Road.

(As Pete answers Raymond's question, a high pitch scream rings out from the bedroom where the Mayor is holding Jacy.)

RAYMOND CLETTER: What was that?

PETE WILSON: I accidentally hit the volume on the radio.

RAYMOND CLETTER: Oh. Look, if you come up with anything, call me.

PETE WILSON: You got it.

RAYMOND CLETTER: We're going out to Grant Lake to see...

(Again Jacy manages to belt out another cry for help.)

RAYMOND CLETTER: Now what was that?

PETE WILSON: That was my volume again, sorry. You know my volume control is on my steering wheel.

RAYMOND CLETTER: It's kind of sensitive, isn't it?

PETE WILSON: It happens, what can I say.

RAYMOND CLETTER: Anyway. Just call me if you come up with something.

PETE WILSON: All right.

(Realizing just how close they came to getting caught, Pete takes a deep breath and storms off to his bedroom to deal with Jacy.)

PETE WILSON: I thought I told you to keep her quiet!

HAYWOOD BURGESS: I tried to. I covered her mouth and she bit my hand!

(Pete walks over to Jacy and grabs her by her hair.)

PETE WILSON: So you like to scream?

(Jacy doesn't answer so he pulls her hair even harder.)

PETE WILSON: I asked you a question you whore! Do you like to scream?

(Jacy at this point is so upset she can barely talk.)

JACY ELLIS: Please don't hurt me!

PETE WILSON: Oh, I like that. Say it again!

JACY ELLIS: If you let me go I promise I won't say anything to anybody, I promise!

PETE WILSON: You want us to let you go?

JACY ELLIS: Please!

PETE WILSON: And you promise you won't say anything?

JACY ELLIS: I promise!

PETE WILSON: Haywood, what do you think? Should we let her go?

HAYWOOD BURGESS: Yeah, why not. Let her go.

JACY ELLIS: Thank you so much, thank you. I promise I won't tell anybody!

(Jacy begins to get excited about being set free.)

PETE WILSON: All right calm down. We're gonna let you go, but before you leave you have to do something for us.

JACY ELLIS: I'll do anything, just let me go.

PETE WILSON: Before you leave, you have to scream, "please don't rape me."

(Jacy looks at the Mayor and then turns back to Pete.)

JACY ELLIS: And you'll let me go?

PETE WILSON: We'll let you go.

(Again Jacy looks at the Mayor and then turns back to Pete.)

JACY ELLIS: That's all I have to do?

PETE WILSON: That's it.

JACY ELLIS: Please don't rape me!

PETE WILSON: What do you think, Haywood? Is that what we're looking for?

HAYWOOD BURGESS: I don't think so.

PETE WILSON: You're gonna have to try again.

(Jacy sighs and looks at Pete.)

JACY ELLIS: Do I have to?

PETE WILSON: If you want to leave, yes you do.

JACY ELLIS: Please don't rape me!

PETE WILSON: That's still not it.

(All of a sudden Pete reaches out, grabs Jacy by her throat, and smacks her across the face causing her to scream.)

PETE WILSON: That's it! That's the scream I'm looking for!

(He pushes her over to the Mayor.)

JACY ELLIS: No, please!

PETE WILSON: There you go! That's what I want to hear!

(Pete puts one of his hands on each side of Jacy's face and pulls her towards him trying to kiss her. Having no success, he then tries to kiss her on her neck, but she's squirming around and he can't do it.)

PETE WILSON: You sure are a wild one! Haywood what do you say we help her burn off a little bit of this energy she's got?

HAYWOOD BURGESS: I thought you'd never ask.

(Pete grabs Jacy's shirt collar, rips her shirt open, and then throws her on the bed.)

PETE WILSON: You know what Haywood, because I'm such a nice guy, I'm gonna let you have first dibs!

HAYWOOD BURGESS: You are the man.

(The Mayor begins to undress. As he's taking off his belt Jacy screams for help.)

JACY ELLIS: Somebody help me, please!

(Angered by Jacy's screaming, the Mayor begins to whip Jacy across her legs with his belt.)

HAYWOOD BURGESS: Shut your mouth and take off your clothes!

JACY ELLIS: Please don't do this!

(Pete gets angry, walks over to the bed, and begins to forcefully take her pants off as she kicks and screams. After being kicked three or four times he finally gets them off.)

JACY ELLIS: No, don't do this!

(The Mayor gets down to his boxers and walks over to the bed. He puts one knee on the bed and leans forward to kiss her.

HAYWOOD BURGESS: Come on, honey. How about a little foreplay?

(The Mayor grabs her legs and pulls her closer as he attempts to kiss her again. Realizing that's not going to work, he throws her on the bed and gets on top of her.)

HAYWOOD BURGESS: I'm willing to forget about the foreplay if you are?

(Just as he grabs the waistband of his boxers to pull them down he feels a cold piece of metal on the side of his face that stops him immediately.)

RAYMOND CLETTER: Can you see it Haywood? Can you see the headline? "Man Dies From Gun Shot Wound To The Head While Raping Young Girl, Brain Stem Found In Corner Across Room." Can't you see it?

(The cold piece of metal on his face is the barrel of Raymond's pistol. When Raymond called Pete earlier and Pete said he was out on McKenzie Road looking for the Mayor, Raymond knew he was lying because McKenzie Road is completely shut down for construction. And then when he heard the screams in the back ground not once, but twice, he knew something was going on.)

HAYWOOD BURGESS: Take it easy, Ray.

RAYMOND CLETTER: Shut up and get on your feet.

(Raymond snatches the Mayor up off the bed, puts his hands around his throat, and slams him into the corner never letting him go.)

RAYMOND CLETTER: Jacy, you all right?

(Jacy sits on the bed shaking and crying, as she slowly nods her head yes.)

RAYMOND CLETTER: Why don't you go to the bathroom and put your clothes on.

JACY ELLIS: He ripped my shirt.

(With the barrel of his gun planted in the Mayor's temple, Raymond carefully takes his jacket off and throws it to Jacy.)

RAYMOND CLETTER: Here, take this.

(Jacy puts the jacket on to cover her upper half, and grabs a blanket to cover her lower half, as her slumped over exhausted body crosses the floor. Once she's out of the room Raymond gets back to business.)

RAYMOND CLETTER: You got him, preacher man?

MINISTER: I got him, baby!

(Minister Ragland is standing near the door holding Pete in a full nelson.)

RAYMOND CLETTER: So you were gonna set me up to take the fall? After all these years of bending over backwards to help you out when you needed it, you were just gonna stab me in the back?

HAYWOOD BURGESS: I had no choice, Ray, he was getting too close. And prison is somewhere I refuse to go.

RAYMOND CLETTER: Oh, you can't go, but I can?

223

HAYWOOD BURGESS: It doesn't matter now, Ray. But what does matter, is you saving your own tail.

RAYMOND CLETTER: Me saving my own tail. And what does that mean?

HAYWOOD BURGESS: Do you really think I'm going to go to prison for any of this?

RAYMOND CLETTER: Oh you're going, trust me.

HAYWOOD BURGESS: No I'm not Ray. I'm not going anywhere. I'm Haywood Burgess. Haywood Burgess, friend of the Governor, Haywood Burgess, friend of the D.A., Haywood Burgess, friend of every judge on the bench from here to Georgia, and do you know what that means? That means I'm untouchable, so untouchable that not even an enraged tough son of a gun like you can stop me. So why don't you take that gun, that attitude of yours, your little nigger partner over there, and get out of here we can finish what we started. That is, unless you guys would like to stay and watch. You never know, we may even give you a turn if you behave.

(Raymond begins to laugh.)

RAYMOND CLETTER: You know, Haywood, you're right. You are untouchable. And if I take you in, book you, and throw you in jail it won't matter because you'll just get off anyway.

HAYWOOD BURGESS: You're not as dumb as you look Ray.

RAYMOND CLETTER: You're right I'm not dumb. But I am crazy.

(Raymond has a look in his eye that causes the Mayor's smile to disappear.)

RAYMOND CLETTER: Have you ever been raped Haywood?

HAYWOOD BURGESS: What do you think?

(Raymond punches him in the mouth with every ounce of strength he has causing his nose to bleed profusely. Then Raymond puts his gun on the Mayor's forehead)

RAYMOND CLETTER: If you don't answer my question, I'm gonna pull this trigger and split your face right down the middle.

(Minister Ragland sees that Raymond is losing his cool.)

MINISTER: Raymond, read him his rights and let's get out of here!

RAYMOND CLETTER: Answer the question!

HAYWOOD BURGESS: No.

RAYMOND CLETTER: Then that means you don't know what it's like to have your peace of mind taken away, right?

(The Mayor doesn't answer right away so Raymond draws back as if he's going to hit him again.)

RAYMOND CLETTER: You better answer!

HAYWOOD BURGESS: No!

RAYMOND CLETTER: Which means you don't know what it's like to have your body violated, right?

HAYWOOD BURGESS: No.

RAYMOND CLETTER: Well, guess what my friend, today is your lucky day. Open your mouth.

(The Mayor's eyes grow wide as the reality of what's about to happen sets in.)

HAYWOOD BURGESS: What?

MINISTER: Ray, what are you doing?

RAYMOND CLETTER: Open your mouth.

MINISTER: Ray, what are you doing?

(Raymond begins to yell.)

RAYMOND CLETTER: I said open your mouth!

(The Mayor, after all of his tough talk, breaks down and cries like a little baby as he slowly opens his mouth.)

MINISTER: Raymond, read him his rights and let's go!

RAYMOND CLETTER: He doesn't have any rights! He gave up his rights when he decided to rape Jennifer! You raped her, didn't you?

(The Mayor is crying so hard that he can't even answer the question. So Raymond punches him again and screams.)

RAYMOND CLETTER: Didn't you?

HAYWOOD BURGESS: Yes.

RAYMOND CLETTER: And you were going to rape Jacy, weren't you?

HAYWOOD BURGESS: Yes!

RAYMOND CLETTER: Now do you see what I'm talking about Joe? He has no rights!

RAYMOND CLETTER: I thought I told you to open your mouth!

(The Mayor hesitantly opens his mouth as he continues to cry. Once he does, Raymond sticks his gun in as far as he can almost causing him to gag.)

MINISTER: Raymond, give me the gun now!

RAYMOND CLETTER: I'm sending you to hell tonight Haywood!

MINISTER: Raymond, give me the gun!

RAYMOND CLETTER: Shut up! He's got to die!

MINISTER: That is not your decision Ray. You are not God!

(Raymond turns and points his gun at Minister Ragland.)

RAYMOND CLETTER: I told you to shut up!

MINISTER: Ray, if you shoot him, your life as you know it is over!

RAYMOND CLETTER: My life has been over!

(Raymond turns the gun back to the Mayor as he begins to cry.)

RAYMOND CLETTER: My life ended when I lost my family, it's not fair! I went to church, I prayed, I helped people whenever they needed it and I lived a clean life! And what did I get in return? A family that was burned so bad they had to be identified by their dental records! They never hurt anybody, and here you have this sick pervert raping every woman he sees and will probably live to be a hundred. It's not fair!

(Raymond forcefully shoves the gun into the Mayor's mouth chipping his tooth.)

RAYMOND CLETTER: This is for Jennifer, and every woman that's ever been violated by people like you.

(In hopes of stopping Raymond, Minister Ragland yells one last time.)

MINISTER: Raymond, no!

(Raymond cocks the hammer of the gun back and pulls the trigger.)

MINISTER: Ray, no!

(Unfortunately, Minister Ragland's plea is ignored and Raymond pulls the trigger. But just before the gun goes off, a hand appears out of nowhere; it's Jacy. She grabs the gun on top and places her thumb in front of the hammer so it won't fire. With tears in his eyes, Raymond is shaking almost out of control. He slowly turns and looks at her. With black mascara filled tears covering her face, Jacy and Rayond make eye contact. With one last plea, Jacy softly says.)

JACY ELLIS: No more killing.

(As Raymond watches a tear slowly fall from her beautiful brown eyes, she again softly pleads with him.)

JACY ELLIS: If you kill him, you become him.

(Raymond turns, looks at the Mayor, and then looks at Jacy.)

JACY ELLIS: Please.

(Again Raymond looks at the Mayor and then turns back to Jacy.)

JACY ELLIS: Corey was enough, Raymond. Let me have the gun please.

(Realizing that killing the Mayor is not the right thing to do, Raymond slowly lets go of the gun. Once Jacy has possession of it, Minister Ragland breathes a sigh of relief as she hands it to him. Minister Ragland pushes Pete over to the bed to sit down and Raymond does the same to the Mayor. After they're both on the bed and sitting down, Raymond begins to read them their rights.)

CHAPTER TWENTY-TWO

(It's now one month later and the trial "Ellis versus Burgess and Wilson," is well under way. The Mayor has hired three of the best lawyers on the East Coast to represent both he and Pete. As they get the third session of this case under way, Jacy's lawyer is about to call his next witness.)

JACY'S LAYWER: Your honor, I would like to call Miss Jacy Ellis to the stand.

(For the first time since the trial started, Jacy is called to the stand to testify. As she nervously walks across the courtroom and sits down on the witness stand, the bailiff approaches her with a bible to swear her in. Once she's sworn in, her lawyer, who is the prosecution, begins to question her.)

JACY'S LAWYER: Miss Ellis in this written statement, which the defense has read. You said the only thing you remember about the night of September thirteenth is getting in Mr. Burgess' car and then waking up in Mr. Wilson's backyard, is that correct?

JACY ELLIS: Yes.

JACY'S LAWYER: Miss Ellis can you please tell the court what happened after that.

(Before answering, Jacy looks over at Minister Ragland for a little comfort and support as her stomach ties up in knots. He casually smiles, raises his hand to chest level, gives her a thumbs up, and mimes to her.)

MINISTER: You can do it.

(Now feeling a little bit more comfortable, Jacy takes a deep breath and begins to explain what happened.)

JACY ELLIS: Well, after he pulled me out of the car he told me that if I didn't settle down and stop fighting him he was going to kill me.

JACY'S LAWYER: Miss Ellis, you said "he". Can you please tell the court exactly to whom you're referring?

JACY ELLIS: Mr. Haywood Burgess.

JACY'S LAWYER: Thank you Miss Ellis. What happened next?

JACY ELLIS: When we got in the house...

(In mid sentence, Jacy begins to cry as she talks about that horrible night.)

JACY ELLIS: When we got in the house, Mr. Burgess took me back to Mr. Wilson's bedroom and held me there to keep me quiet. They didn't want me in the living room because the phone rang and they thought it was Raymond Cletter who was out looking for me.

JACY'S LAWYER: What happened when Mr. Wilson entered the room, Miss Ellis?

JACY ELLIS: He was very angry because while he was on the phone I was screaming and he said Raymond almost heard me.

JACY'S LAWYER: You actually heard Mr. Wilson say Raymond almost heard you?

JACY ELLIS: Actually he said Raymond did hear me.

MAYOR'S LAWYER: Your honor I object! This witness has just given two different answers for the same question.

JUDGE: Sustained. Miss Ellis, try to be clearer with your answers by giving us only the facts.

JACY ELLIS: Yes sir.

JUDGE: Counsel, you may continue.

JACY'S LAWYER: Miss Ellis, after coming into the room, did Mr. Wilson touch you at any time?

JACY ELLIS: Yes.

JACY'S LAWYER: What about Mr. Burgess? Did he touch you at any time while you were in the bedroom?

229

JACY ELLIS: Yes.

JACY'S LAYWER: Can you please explain to the court exactly what happened?

(Jacy takes another deep breath.)

JACY ELLIS: Mr. Wilson grabbed my hair and yelled at me for screaming.

JACY'S LAWYER: Is that the only time he touched you?

JACY ELLIS: No. He tried to kiss me. And when I resisted he got mad and forced me to kiss him.

JACY'S LAWYER: Miss Ellis can you tell the court where Mr. Burgess was when all of this was going on please?

JACY ELLIS: He was holding my arms.

JACY'S LAWYER: Your honor I have no further questions.

JUDGE: Would the defense like to question the witness?

MAYOR'S LAWYER: Yes your honor.

(The Mayor's lawyer stands in front of Jacy.)

MAYOR'S LAWYER: Miss Ellis, you stated earlier that you do remember getting into Mr. Burgesses' car, correct?

JACY ELLIS: Yes.

MAYOR'S LAWYER: But you don't remember anything after that except waking up in Mr. Wilson's back yard, right?

JACY ELLIS: Yes.

MAYOR'S LAWYER: Miss Ellis, did you get into Mr. Burgess' car on your own, or were you forced into the car?

JACY ELLIS: I got in on my own.

MAYOR'S LAWYER: And you don't remember anything after that except waking up in Mr. Wilson's back yard?

JACY ELLIS: That's right.

MAYOR'S LAWYER: Miss Ellis, can you please tell the court how your lipstick got on the collar of Mr. Burgess's shirt?

(Jacy is caught off guard by the question.)

JACY ELLIS: I don't know.

MAYOR'S LAWYER: Oh, I forgot! He put something in the drink he gave you.

JACY ELLIS: He didn't give me a drink.

MAYOR'S LAWYER: So what was it that caused you to all of a sudden pass out?

JACY ELLIS: I don't know.

MAYOR'S LAWYER: So is it possible that you don't remember willfully engaging in a kiss with Mr. Burgess?

JACY ELLIS: No, it's not possible.

MAYOR'S LAWYER: Miss Ellis, if you don't remember anything, how can you determine whether you did or did not willfully kiss Mr. Burgess?

JACY ELLIS: Because I know!

MAYOR'S LAWYER: Your honor I have no further questions.

(The Mayor's lawyer walks back to his seat.)

JUDGE: Miss Ellis you may step down.

(Jacy walks back to her seat. When she sits down her lawyer leans over towards her.)

JACY'S LAWYER: Good job.

(Although Jacy doesn't quite agree with him, she nods her head yes and the trial goes on.)

JUDGE: Counsel, you may call your next witness.

JACY'S LAWYER: Your honor, I would like to call Chief of Police Raymond Cletter to the stand.

(Raymond walks up to the stand, gets sworn in, and sits down.)

JACY'S LAWYER: Officer Cletter. On the night of September thirteenth while you were out looking for Miss Ellis, did you call Mr. Wilson at his home?

RAYMOND CLETTER: Actually I called him on his cell phone, but he did say he was at home at the time.

JACY'S LAWYER: Mr. Cletter, during your conversation with Mr. Wilson, did you hear any screams in the background?

RAYMOND CLETTER: Yes. I heard Miss Ellis screaming in the background.

MAYOR'S LAWYER: Your honor I object! The witness is speculating. Mr. Cletter was on a cell phone. How could he possibly have known from where, or from whom the scream came?

JUDGE: Sustained. I'm going to ask the jury to please disregard Mr. Cletter's last statement. Counselor, please keep this thing under control.

JACY'S LAWYER: Yes your honor. Mr. Cletter what did you see when you entered Mr. Wilson's bedroom on the night of September thirteenth?

RAYMOND CLETTER: I saw Mr. Burgess in the bed with Miss Ellis, and Mr. Wilson standing at the foot of the bed.

JACY'S LAWYER: Was Mr. Burgess in the bed lying beside her?

RAYMOND CLETTER: No. He was on top of her.

JACY'S LAWYER: And what was Miss Ellis doing at the time?

RAYMOND CLETTER: She was crying and saying no over and over again.

JACY'S LAWYER: Your honor, I have no further questions.

JUDGE: Would the defense like to question the witness?

MAYOR'S LAWYER: Yes your honor.

(He walks over to the witness stand.)

MAYOR'S LAWYER: Mr. Cletter, is it true that on several occasions you've told Mr. Wilson that if you were Mayor of Swamp Fox you could do a much better job than Mr. Burgess?

(Not fully understanding exactly why he asks that particular question, Raymond pauses.)

RAYMOND CLETTER: Yes.

MAYOR'S LAWYER: Did you also tell Mr. Wilson on several occasions that you would love to have Mr. Burgess's job?

RAYMOND CLETTER: Yes.

MAYOR'S LAWYER: Mr. Cletter, how long have you been a police officer here in Swamp Fox?

RAYMOND CLETTER: Almost sixteen years.

MAYOR'S LAWYER: And do you consider yourself to be an honest police officer that obeys the very law you enforce?

JACY'S LAWYER: Your honor, I object! This trial is not about Mr. Cletter!

JUDGE: Overruled.

(Out of frustration, Jacy's lawyer sits down and shakes his head.)

MAYOR'S LAWYER: Please answer the question, Mr. Cletter.

RAYMOND CLETTER: Yes, I do obey the law.

MAYOR'S LAWYER: Mr. Cletter, do you remember ever approaching Mr. Burgess about illegally planting a bugging device in Minister Ragland's hotel room?

(Raymond looks at the Mayor and the Mayor gives him a little smile.)

RAYMOND CLETTER: Yes.

MAYOR'S LAWYER: And how did Mr. Burgess respond?

RAYMOND CLETTER: He told me not to do it because it was against the law.

MAYOR'S LAWYER: And was he right Mr. Cletter? Is it in fact against the law to use a bugging device without a signed court order?

RAYMOND CLETTER: Yes.

MAYOR'S LAWYER: Knowing that it was illegal, did you bug Minister Ragland's hotel room Mr. Cletter?

(Raymond is silent as the entire courtroom stares at him.)

RAYMOND CLETTER: Yes.

MAYOR'S LAWYER: Mr. Cletter, when you planted that bug, did you have a signed court order that gave you permission to do so?

RAYMOND CLETTER: No.

(Everybody in the courtroom starts to talk as they are overwhelmed by Raymond's answer. So the judge hammers his gavel.)

JUDGE: Order in the court! Order in the court!

(After about seven whacks of his gavel and him yelling, the judge finally gets some order.)

MAYOR'S LAWYER: Mr. Cletter, is police brutality against the law?

RAYMOND CLETTER: Yes.

MAYOR'S LAWYER: And have you ever committed this crime, Mr. Cletter?

(Raymond pauses as he stares at Minister Ragland.)

RAYMOND CLETTER: Yes.

MAYOR'S LAWYER: On more than one occasion, Mr. Cletter?

(Pause.)

RAYMOND CLETTER: Yes.

MAYOR'S LAWYER: Mr. Cletter, is one of your victims in this courtroom today?

(Again he pauses as his face is covered in shame.)

RAYMOND CLETTER: Yes.

MAYOR'S LAWYER: And what is that victim's name Mr. Cletter?

(Raymond doesn't answer.)

MAYOR'S LAWYER: Answer the question Mr. Cletter!

RAYMOND CLETTER: Joe Ragland.

(After Raymond answers, the courtroom erupts in chatter.)

MAYOR'S LAWYER: Ladies and gentlemen of the jury. I give you a man of no credibility, a liar, and a lawbreaker who devised a plan to ruin my client's reputation, and his life. And in the process, continued to break the law by involving a minor in a police sting without written or verbal consent from the parents of that minor! He has committed the crimes of breaking and entering, performing an illegal procedure, and assault with a deadly weapon by putting a loaded nine-millimeter pistol in my client's mouth and threatening to kill him!

(At this point the audience is in an up roar. Some people are shouting at Raymond, some are shouting at the Mayor, and some are shouting at the Mayor's lawyer. Jacy's lawyer, who has now reached his boiling point stands up and tries to cut the Mayor's lawyer off as he rambles on.)

JACY'S LAWYER: Your honor, he is out of line!

(The judge, now feeling like he has lost complete control of his courtroom gets extremely upset, stands up, and yells at the top of his lungs as he bangs his gavel.)

JUDGE: Order in this courtroom! I want some order, right now!

(As he yells, everybody begins to settle down, everybody except Jacy's lawyer. He is still trying to get his point across.)

JUDGE: Counselor, I said I want some order!

JACY'S LAWYER: Your honor, he's out of order and you know it!

(The judge yells.)

JUDGE: Counselor, I said be quiet!

(He finally stops talking.)

JUDGE: Counselor, do you know what...

(He cuts the judge off in mid sentence.)

JACY'S LAWYER: Your honor the defense is completely out of line!

JUDGE: Counselor, approach the bench! Now!

(Jacy's lawyer walks up to the judge and the judge leans forward.)

JUDGE: Look, I don't know how you city boys do it back in Charlotte, North Carolina, but here in Swamp Fox, South Carolina, this is my courtroom. You hear me? This is my courtroom. If you ever challenge my authority like that again counselor, as God as my witness, you will be through? Do you understand me?

JACY'S LAWYER: Yes sir.

JUDGE: Don't play with me son. I will show you a bad day.

JACY'S LAWYER: Yes sir.

JUDGE: Now sit down.

(As Jacy's lawyer walks back to his seat, the judge stands up.)

JUDGE: And as for the rest of you! If I hear one more outburst, I'm gonna have every last one of you arrested and thrown in jail for contempt of court.

(The judge looks at the Mayor's lawyer.)

JUDGE: Counselor! Are you done questioning this witness?

MAYOR'S LAWYER: Yes your honor.

JUDGE: Mr. Cletter you may step down. As a matter of fact, I want all of you to step right out of those doors back there. This court is adjourned until nine a.m. tomorrow. I've had enough!

(The judge hammers his gavel, throws it on the desk, and storm off to his chambers.)

BAILIFF: All rise!

(Everybody stands and is dismissed. As the defense is walking out, the Mayor's lawyer smiles at Jacy's lawyer. Pete Wilson walks by with a huge smile on his face and the Mayor does the same, trying to agitate the prosecution. After taking five or six steps, the Mayor stops, turns around, and walks up to Raymond.)

HAYWOOD BURGESS: I'm gonna let you in on a little secret you may not be aware of.

(He steps forward and stands almost nose-to-nose with Raymond.)

HAYWOOD BURGESS: I am the man, I've always been the man, and I'll always be the man.

(Raymond grabs the Mayor by his shirt. Immediately Minister Ragland grabs Raymond.)

MINISTER: Let him go Ray! That's exactly what he wants you to do!

(After Raymond lets go of him and the two of them are separated; Mayor Burgess straightens his shirt.)

HAYWOOD BURGESS: I'm surprised I'm not laying on the floor with my nose broken in a hundred pieces. You're losing your fire Ray. Being a nigger lover is making you soft.

(The Mayor walks away laughing. Meanwhile at the prison, Cynthia Hanks is sitting in the waiting room waiting for her husband. As she looks around the room she hears a door shut, it's Ronald. He comes in and sits down across from her without saying a word. After a few minutes of silence Cynthia speaks.)

CYNTHIA HANKS: Ronald I know you're angry and you're hurting. But you're not the only one. I'm living this nightmare right along with you. I'm being degraded and talked about just like you were. Ronald there are people out there trying to kill me!

(Surprised by what she has just said, Ronald looks up at her.)

CYNTHIA HANKS: That's right, somebody tried to kill me. I didn't want to say anything because you've got enough to deal with. Ronald, somebody planted a bomb in our house, and by the grace of God, we weren't inside when it went off. I'm not the only they're trying to kill Ronald, they're trying to kill Joe also. He's out there every single day putting his life on the line trying to get you out of here, and what kind of thanks does he get? He gets accused of having an affair with your wife. That's a slap in the face for him, and a knife through the heart for me!

(Cynthia starts to cry.)

RONALD HANKS: Cynthia.

(Ronald leans forward and gently touches the side of her face.)

RONALD HANKS: Baby.

(Cynthia looks up at him.)

RONALD HANKS: Please, leave me alone! Stop coming around here putting on your little dramatic performances! I don't care what you do or whom you do it with. All I want is for you to leave me alone! Better yet, maybe I should leave you alone!

CYNTHIA HANKS: What do you mean leave me alone?

(Ronald's comment has Cynthia worried. She's now wondering if he's going to do something to hurt himself.)

RONALD HANKS: Guard!

CYNTHIA HANKS: Ronald, you're scaring me!

RONALD HANKS: Guard!

CYNTHIA HANKS: Ronald, please don't do anything crazy! I need you!

(The guard walks over to the table, Ronald stands up, and they leave the room headed for Ronald's cell. Back at Raymond's house, Raymond, Minister Ragland, and Jacy's lawyer are sitting at the kitchen table.)

MINISTER: So what happens now?

JACY'S LAWYER: Well, it doesn't look good. The whole good cop bad cop thing. When he hit us with that he hit us hard. That's gonna carry a lot of weight, a lot of weight. Not to mention the fact that some of those jurors are probably paid off, knowing him.

RAYMOND CLETTER: Which means?

JACY'S LAWYER: Which means because of a lack of evidence, her blacking out, and the jury thinking you're after his job. They'll probably be acquitted.

(Minister Ragland leans back in his chair and sighs as Raymond buries his face in his hands. Jacy's lawyer looks at his watch.)

JACY'S LAWYER: I need to get going. Joe, you need a ride?

MINISTER: Yeah. Can you drop me off at the church?

JACY'S LAWYER: Sure.

(After sliding their chairs under the table they all head for the door. Jacy's lawyer walks out first followed by Minister Ragland. Before they walk to the car they both turn and face Raymond.)

JACY'S LAWYER: You did the right thing today by telling the truth Ray. No matter how much it hurt, you did the right thing.

(They shake hands.)

RAYMOND CLETTER: Thanks.

(Jacy's lawyer heads for the car leaving Minister Ragland and Raymond alone.)

MINISTER: You gonna be all right?

RAYMOND CLETTER: Yeah.

MINISTER: So that's how you knew I was going to see Tim Joyce that day. You bugged my hotel room.

(Feeling ashamed, Raymond looks away.)

RAYMOND CLETTER: Yeah.

MINISTER: Raymond, since I've been in Swamp Fox, because of you, I've seen some of the worst days of my life. And at times I started to feel broken, but I knew change was coming. You are that change Ray.

(As they stand face to face not saying a word, Minister Ragland sticks his hand out for Raymond to shake. Raymond, who is completely caught off guard by the gesture, hesitantly reaches out and shakes his hand. Minister Ragland then takes his other arm and wraps it around Raymond giving him a hug. After the hug Minister Ragland steps back.)

MINISTER: I'm proud of you Ray. Today in that courtroom, in front of all those people, in spite of the shame you felt when you had to answer those questions, you stood tall and you told the truth. You told the truth Ray, and I respect you for that.

(Minister Ragland taps him on his shoulder.)

MINISTER: You're gonna be all right, Chief of Police Raymond Cletter. You're gonna be all right.

(Minister Ragland walks to the car. As they drive off, Raymond stands on the porch in awe. His heart and mind are overwhelmed by the act of forgiveness he has just witnessed. Back in Cary at Jennifer's house, she has just walked in from school to find her parents sitting at the kitchen table talking.)

JENNIFER MUNDY: What's up?

(Jennifer grabs a soda out of the fridge.)

ANNE MUNDY: Can you believe that?

JENNIFER MUNDY: Believe what?

SAM MUNDY: Raymond's got some nerve. After all that Haywood has done for him!

JENNIFER MUNDY: Hello!

(They both turn and look at Jennifer.)

JENNIFER MUNDY: What are you guys talking about?

ANNE MUNDY: Raymond.

JENNIFER MUNDY: Raymond Cletter?

SAM MUNDY: Yeah. He's trying to pin some bogus rape charge on Haywood. Can you believe that?

ANNE MUNDY: Haywood and Pete Wilson!

SAM MUNDY: Haywood and Pete may be a lot of things, but rapists they are not.

JENNIFER MUNDY: How can you be so sure?

(Both her mom and dad look at her as they are shocked by her statement.)

SAM MUNDY: You're joking right?

JENNIFER MUNDY: No, I'm serious. Unless you were there, how do you know they didn't do it?

SAM MUNDY: Because I know. They're good people and you know that. We've left you alone with both of them many times, have they ever tried anything with you?

(As much as Jennifer wants to tell her parents what happened, she doesn't.)

SAM MUNDY: That's what I thought. If you plan on making it in this world young lady, you had better learn to think before you speak! Do you understand?

JENNIFER MUNDY: Yeah, I understand.

(Jennifer gets up and goes to her room, slamming the door behind her. Back at the church, Pastor Fredricks is sitting in his office when Cynthia knocks on the door.)

PASTOR FREDRICKS: Come in.

(Cynthia opens the door.)

PASTOR FREDRICKS: Well look who's here!

(Pastor Fredricks greets Cynthia with a hug.)

CYNTHIA HANKS: How are you, Pastor Fredricks? I didn't catch you at a bad time did I?

PASTOR FREDRICKS: No, not at all! Come on in and have a seat!

(After they both sit down, Pastor Fredricks notices that Cynthia has been crying.)

PASTOR FREDRICKS: You've been crying, what's wrong?

CYNTHIA HANKS: It's Ronald.

(Cynthia begins to cry.)

PASTOR FREDRICKS: Is he all right?

CYNTHIA HANKS: Not really. He accused me of having an affair with Joe.

(Pastor Fredricks leans back in his chair and takes a deep breath.)

CYNTHIA HANKS: I don't understand any of this. I love that man more than anything else in this world, you know that. Why is he doing this?

PASTOR FREDRICKS: Isolation.

(Cynthia looks up at him.)

CYNTHIA HANKS: What?

PASTOR FREDRICKS: Isolation.

CYNTHIA HANKS: What do you mean?

PASTOR FREDRICKS: Let me explain. Your husband is isolated in that cell by himself and that's exactly what the devil wants; he loves to isolate us. The devil doesn't want us to do things like go to church, have fellowship with other Christians, read our bibles, or pray. He wants to isolate us from those things because he knows that without them we're not as strong. The bible refers to the word of God as our sword and our weapon. Without that weapon we have nothing to fight with when he attacks. Now after we've been isolated, the first thing he does is attack our minds. The devil knows our troubles and he knows our weaknesses, and that's where he'll get you every time. I'll give you an example. Drugs, fear, greed, hatred, deception, strife, lust, they're all spirits of the enemy. The devil can see your weaknesses through the way you live your life, and he can hear your weakness through the words you speak. That's how he knows where in your life to attack you. Without that weapon, you're unable to withstand all of the things he's throwing at you. So what happens is you end up entertaining the temptation in your mind until you finally give in to it. Once he has you down, he spends the rest of the time trying to convince you that you don't have a right to get up after what you've done. What's happening to Ronald is that he's probably not reading, praying, and seeking the Lord like he should, and unfortunately, when that happens your faith starts to weaken. The devil knows the most important thing to Ronald on this earth is you and your son, so what he did was work through somebody, or something, and sent a spirit of deception to attack his mind and now he's battling. The Holy Spirit is telling him you're not having an affair, but that spirit of deception is telling him you are. It's called spiritual warfare. But the devil is a liar and the truth is not in him. The Lord himself said, "that he would never leave us, nor forsake us". Cynthia, don't you dare give the devil victory over your marriage. Don't give up on God. You just keep on praying and believing that God is going to produce a miracle. Stand on his word and watch all of this come to pass, Cynthia. Your breakthrough is coming, and it's coming sooner than you think. You just gotta hold on and stand.

(Cynthia stands up to give him a hug. After the hug she wipes her eyes and smiles.)

PASTOR FREDRICKS: I promise you everything is going to be all right, okay?

(Cynthia nods her head yes.)

CYNTHIA HANKS: Is the sanctuary open?

PASTOR FREDRICKS: It's always open.

CYNTHIA HANKS: Is it okay if I go down there for a little while?

PASTOR FREDRICKS: Stay as long as you want.

(Cynthia grabs her purse and heads for the door. Just before walking out she turns to face Pastor Fredricks.)

CYNTHIA HANKS: Thank you so much, Pastor.

PASTOR FREDRICKS: Anytime, sweetheart.

CYNTHIA HANKS: I'll see you Sunday.

PASTOR FREDRICKS: Okay.

(Cynthia leaves for the sanctuary. She walks down a long hallway, takes a right, goes down another stretch of hallway, takes another right, and ends up right in front of the double doors that lead into the sanctuary. As she reaches out to push the doors open, she looks through the small glass windows and sees Minister Ragland holding his bible to his chest as he cries. Cynthia immediately stops, steps back, quietly lets the doors close, and watches him. Minister Ragland, with tears in his eyes, stands up, looks up towards heaven, and begins to pace around as he talks to God. As Cynthia continues to watch him pour his heart out to God she realizes something that causes her eyes to wail up with tears. She realizes that in spite of all she's going through, there before her, emotionally broken, stands a complete stranger that has suffered and endured more hurt than any one person should ever have to experience, and why? To please, God. In spite of what he's been through, Minister Ragland has remained on the battlefield and faithful to the work God has given him to do in Swamp Fox. It's that very act of obedience that encourages her, warms her heart, and brings a smile to her face as she watches him fall to his knees and cry out to God. Later that same night at the Williams's, Cynthia is sitting in the living room when the phone rings. Although she is the only one at home, she can't bring herself to answer the phone in fear of some bad news about Ronald. So she sits there staring at it until it stops ringing. Still wondering in her mind if that was a call from the prison or not she goes back to what she was doing when the phone starts to ring again. After a few rings she decides to answer it.)

CYNTHIA HANKS: Hello.

(The caller has asked for her specifically, which causes her to take a deep breath.)

CYNTHIA HANKS: This is Cynthia Hanks.

(As she sits there her face goes blank and tears begin to fall. She covers her mouth and begins to shake her head in disbelief.)

CYNTHIA HANKS: When?

(Cynthia drops the phone and falls to her knees screaming.)

CYNTHIA HANKS: Ronald! Ronald! Ronald!

(The next day comes and court is in session.)

JUDGE: Counselor, please call your next witness.

MAYOR'S LAWYER: Your honor, I would like to call Minister Joe Ragland to the stand!

242

(The people in the courtroom begin to talk amongst themselves. But the chatter is a little too loud for the courtroom, so the judge hammers his gavel and immediately gets their attention.)

JUDGE: One more time, and I'm clearing this courtroom!

(He puts his gavel down and sits back in his seat.)

JUDGE: Counselor, you may proceed.

MAYOR'S LAWYER: Thank you your honor. Bailiff, if you will.

(The Bailiff walks over to Minister Ragland and holds out a bible to swear him in.)

BAILIFF: Please place you right hand on the bible and repeat after me.

MINISTER: I'm sorry but I can't do that.

BAILIFF: Excuse me?

MINISTER: I will not swear on that bible. Your honor I apologize. I mean no disrespect to you, your authority, or your courtroom, sir. But I cannot swear on that bible.

JUDGE: Why is that Minister Ragland?

MINISTER: Sir, in the book of Matthew, chapter five verses thirty-four through thirty-seven, the Lord Jesus himself said, do not swear at all, neither by heaven, nor by earth. But let your yes be yes, and your no be no. Anything other than that comes from the evil one.

(The judge takes his glasses off and wipes his eye out of frustration.)

JUDGE: Minister Ragland, are you going to tell the court the truth?

MINISTER: Yes your honor.

JUDGE: Very well. Counselor, please proceed.

MAYOR'S LAWYER: Minister Ragland, is it true that since you've been here in Swamp Fox your car has been vandalized?

MINISTER: Yes.

MAYOR'S LAWYER: And is it also true, that you in fact saw what the perpetrator that vandalized your car was wearing the night the crime was committed?

(Knowing full well where he's trying to go with the question Minister Ragland pauses.)

MINISTER: Yes.

MAYOR'S LAWYER: And what was the perpetrator wearing Minister Ragland?

MINISTER: A white uniform.

MAYOR'S LAWYER: Was it a uniform like this officer is wearing?

(He walks over to one of Raymond's Deputy's and points at his uniform.)

MINISTER: No.

MAYOR'S LAWYER: Was it a uniform like this officer is wearing?

(He walks over and points to the bailiff.)

MINISTER: No.

MAYOR'S LAWYER: Was it a uniform like this one?

(He points to the back of the courtroom and in walks a man dressed in the same uniform Raymond wears. Minister Ragland doesn't want to answer the question.)

MAYOR'S LAWYER: Minister Ragland, could you please answer the question!

MINISTER: Yes.

(The Mayor's lawyer walks over and stands in front of the jury.)

MAYOR'S LAWYER: I'm sorry Minister Ragland, I don't think the jurors heard you clearly. Could you repeat that a little louder please?

MINISTER: Yes, it is!

MAYOR'S LAWYER: Ladies and gentlemen of the jury, this very uniform you're looking at is worn by one man in this town and one man only. Minister Ragland, can you please tell the court who that man is?

(He takes a deep breath before answering.)

MINISTER: Raymond Cletter.

(One of the jurors shakes his head in disgust.)

MAYOR'S LAWYER: Ladies and gentlemen of the jury, this once again proves that the same man who has accused my client of rape is a liar, a scam artist, and a criminal. He has no credibility, and he has no proof.

(As the Mayor's lawyer continues to talk, one of the officers standing in the back of the courtroom hears a light knock on the door. He pushes the door open just enough to see who it is. He then quietly steps out into the hallway to talk to them. After about forty-five seconds have passed, the officer steps back into the courtroom carrying a small piece of paper. With paper in hand, the officer walks up to Jacy's lawyer, leans over, whispers in his ear, hands him the paper, and then walks back to where he was standing. After unfolding the note and reading it, Jacy's lawyer sits back in his seat and covers his mouth. He is in absolute shock over the news he's just received. Raymond is sitting right behind him. He turns around, hands Raymond the note, and again the reaction is utter shock. They just can't believe what has happened. The Mayor's lawyer has just finished questioning Minister Ragland and now it's the prosecutions turn.)

JUDGE: Would the prosecution like to question the witness?

(Jacy's lawyer is so overwhelmed by what he has just read he doesn't even hear the judge talking to him.)

JUDGE: Counselor, would you like to question the witness!

(Again he doesn't hear him so Raymond taps him on the shoulder to get his attention.)

JACY'S LAWYER: I'm sorry your honor, did you say something?

JUDGE: Are you all right counselor?

JACY'S LAWYER: Yes sir, I'm fine.

JUDGE: I asked you if you would like to question the witness.

(He looks at Minister Ragland and then looks at the judge.)

JACY'S LAWYER: No your honor.

(The Mayor and his lawyer both look at Jacy's lawyer. They are surprised and somewhat confused by the fact that he's not going to question Minister Ragland who they feel is the strongest witness the prosecution has.)

JUDGE: Minister Ragland, you may step down.

(Minister Ragland walks back to his seat, which is behind Jacy's lawyer, and beside Raymond. He then leans forward to ask Jacy's lawyer a question. Her lawyer turns to face Minister Ragland.)

MINISTER: What are you doing? Why didn't you question me!

JUDGE: Does the prosecution have a final witness?

(Jacy's lawyer turns around and stands up, never giving Minister Ragland his answer. Leaving him with a very confused look on his face.)

JACY'S LAWYER: Yes, your honor.

(He takes a deep breath.)

JACY'S LAWYER: The prosecution would like to call to the stand…

(Jacy's lawyer pauses and the courtroom is completely silent as all eyes are on him.)

JACY'S LAWYER: Miss Jennifer Mundy!

(With their heads held high and holding hands, in walk Jennifer Mundy and Cynthia Hanks. The phone call Cynthia received the night before that made her so upset was from Jennifer. That's why she began to cry out her husband's name after they hung up. Jennifer told her that she was ready to come forth and tell the truth. Minister Ragland cannot believe what is happening. Raymond, with a look of victory on his face, smiles at the Mayor. Pete Wilson, knowing the end is near, slumps over in his seat, covers his face, and shakes his head. The judge is about to lose his mind. After hammering and hammering his gavel, he still can't get the people in the courtroom to be quiet. He orders the bailiff and the other officers to clear the courtroom. After all of the people have cleared out, the Mayor's lawyer stands up.)

MAYOR'S LAWYER: Your honor, this person was not on the witness list. I never had a chance to question this witness!

JACY'S LAWYER: Your honor, this young lady is the key to my entire case! And the prosecution asks that you please allow her to take the stand!

(As both lawyers talk, trying to prove their point, the judge hammers his gavel to shut them up. After three or four whacks, they finally stop talking.)

JUDGE: Counselor! You know that both the prosecution and the defense are to question the witnesses before the trial. You know that's procedure.

(Jacy's lawyer takes a deep breath and shakes his head.)

JUDGE: But because this witness could possibly put an end to this circus you two keep calling a trial, I'll allow it.

MAYOR'S LAWYER: Your honor this is not right!

(He hammers his gavel.)

JUDGE: Excuse me counselor! Whose name is on this nameplate?

MAYOR'S LAWYER: Yours, your honor.

JUDGE: Exactly. The witness is allowed!

MAYOR'S LAWYER: Your honor, can you at least grant the defense a one-hour recess?

JUDGE: You have thirty minutes, counselor!

MAYOR'S LAWYER: Thirty minutes your honor?

JUDGE: Do you have a problem with that counselor? I can make it thirty seconds!

(The Mayor's lawyer sighs.)

MAYOR'S LAWYER: Thirty minutes is fine your honor.

JUDGE: That's what I thought! This court is adjourned for a thirty-minute recess!

(The judge bangs his gavel and heads for his chambers. The Mayor, along with Pete and his lawyer leave the courtroom. As they are walking past everyone Raymond calls out to the Mayor.)

RAYMOND CLETTER: Hey Haywood!

(He stops to see what he wants.)

RAYMOND CLETTER: You know what guys in prison do to other prisoners that have sexually abused kids? That which you have sown Haywood, you shall now surely reap.

(As the fear of prison settles, Mayor Burgess turns around and walks away. Minister Ragland, who is still in shock, stands up to talk to Jennifer as everybody else is hugging and talking.)

MINISTER: What changed your mind?

(Jennifer looks up at Minister Ragland. And before she can answer, a tear rolls down her face.)

JENNIFER MUNDY: The thought of being free.

(Minister Ragland hugs her. After the hug he steps back and gently grabs her hands.)

MINISTER: I'm really sorry I upset you so much. I didn't mean any harm.

JENNIFER MUNDY: You didn't upset me. The truth did.

MINISTER: I'm so proud of you Jennifer.

(As Minister Ragland steps forward to hug Jennifer again, the blast of a gun shot is heard just outside the courtroom doors. The bang of the shot causes all of them to jump.)

RAYMOND CLETTER: Everybody get down!

(They all get down on their knees.)

RAYMOND CLETTER: You guys stay here!

(Raymond pulls his gun out and slowly walks up to the door. He pushes it open just enough to peek out. He sees a woman crouched down on the floor and gets her attention.)

RAYMOND CLETTER: Where did that shot come from?

WOMAN ON FLOOR: Down the hall that way!

(Raymond and Minister Ragland ease out of the courtroom and slowly make their way down the hall. As they move further down the hall Raymond asks another officer.)

RAYMOND CLETTER: Where did that shot come from?

OFFICER: The bathroom!

(After the officer answers Raymond's question, a noise comes from the bathroom.)

RAYMOND CLETTER: Joe, get these people out of here!

(Minister Ragland moves some of the people standing near the bathroom further down the hall. Raymond, with his gun drawn, slowly enters the bathroom. He gets down on his knees and looks expecting to see someone standing in one of the stalls, but instead, he finds a large puddle of blood, and the Mayor lying in it with a bullet hole in the top of his head. Knowing that Jennifer's testimony would surely land him behind bars, Mayor Haywood Burgess put a fully loaded nine-millimeter pistol in his mouth, pulled the trigger, and took his own life. Raymond stands up and walks out of the bathroom.)

MINISTER: What is it?

(Raymond turns to face Minister Ragland.)

RAYMOND CLETTER: It's over.

(Realizing there's no way out, the next day, Pete Wilson decided enough was enough. He confessed that both he and Haywood had raped Jennifer, attempted to rape Jacy, and rigged the Hanks trial. With his confession and Jennifer's testimony, the courts declared Ronald Hanks a free man. As Ronald is sitting in his cell playing with a deck of cards, totally unaware of the fact that he has just been cleared of all charges, a guard walks up to his cell door.)

GUARD: Ronald Hanks.

(Ronald stops his game of solitaire and looks up at the guard.)

RONALD HANKS: What?

GUARD: Pack your stuff, you're going home.

(Ronald stares at him for a second and then chuckles.)

RONALD HANKS: Yeah, right.

(Ronald resumes his card game ignoring the guard.)

GUARD: Hey!

(Ronald sigh's and looks up at the guard.)

GUARD: I'm serious, it's over.

(The guard's comment has sparked his interest. So he puts the cards on his bed and stands up.)

RONALD HANKS: If this is your idea of a joke, you've got one twisted sense of humor.

GUARD: It's not a joke, read the front page.

(The guard opens Ronald's cell and hands him a newspaper. Ronald reads the front page and almost immediately a tear falls from his eye. Ronald looks at the guard.

GUARD: Go ahead and get your stuff together so we can get you out of here. Your ride is waiting out front.

(The guard walks away leaving Ronald in utter shock. After gathering his things, Ronald and the guard are on their way to the front desk where Ronald will sign out and collect the rest of his belongings that they took from him when he arrived.)

FRONT DESK CLERK: Here you go Hanks, one watch, one leather wallet, and one pair of sunglasses. And from the state of South Carolina, here's one hundred dollars to help you on your way.

(Ronald puts his belongings in his bag, the one hundred dollars in his pocket, and walks away.)

FRONT DESK CLERK: Hey, Hanks!

(Ronald turns to face the clerk.)

FRONT DESK CLERK: You stay away from them white girls, you hear?

(The clerk laughs.)

GUARD: Don't listen to him. He's just mad because he can't get one himself.

(As the clerk's laughter comes to an abrupt halt, Ronald smiles, turns, and walks away. As Ronald and the guard are walking down the hall towards the front gate the guard stops.)

GUARD: I almost forgot.

(The guard pulls some papers out of his inside jacket pocket.)

GUARD: Here's your bus ticket.

(He hands Ronald the ticket leaving him confused.)

RONALD HANKS: Bus ticket? I thought you said my ride was waiting for me out front.

GUARD: We are your ride Ronald. The prison van will take you to the bus station and you'll go to Swamp Fox from there.

RONALD HANKS: My wife, is she not here?

GUARD: No. We tried to get in touch with her but we couldn't, I'm sorry. Nobody showed up.

(Saddened by the news, Ronald picks up his bag and continues down the hall. Once they get outside of the front gate Ronald drops his things and looks around as he gets his first taste of freedom in almost two years.)

GUARD: Sure smells a lot better on this side of the fence doesn't it?

RONALD HANKS: Yeah.

(Because of Ronald's facial expression, it's obvious he's feeling down about his wife not being there.)

GUARD: You gonna be all right?

RONALD HANKS: Not without my wife. I can't make it without her.

(As Ronald begins to cry he looks up at the guard.)

RONALD HANKS: God blessed me with the greatest wife on the face of the planet and I ran her off. All she ever wanted to do is love me, and I just ran her off. What

250

have I done?

(The guard put his hand on Ronald's shoulder to comfort him.)

RONALD HANKS: I chased her away, man. The only woman that ever truly loved me; I chased away.

(Ronald wipes his eyes.)

RONALD HANKS: At least I still have my son. I haven't ruined that yet.

(The guard looks at his watch.)

GUARD: We had better get going or you're gonna miss your bus.

(Ronald takes a deep breath.)

RONALD HANKS: The trip to nowhere. Let's go.

(Ronald throws his bag in the backseat and climbs in the van. As they take off down a little service road that runs along the East Side of the prison parking lot, Ronald is convicted in his heart for what he did to his wife. When they reach the street and take a left, headed for the bus station, Ronald gets one last look at the prison as they pass in front of it. But the prison isn't the only thing he sees. Sitting to his left, in front of the prison, in the parking lot, is a freshly painted black Nissan Maxima. And standing on the passenger side of that Nissan Maxima, with tears streaming down her face, is the one person that never gave up on him, even after he had given up on her. There beside that Maxima stand his wife, Cynthia Hanks.)

RONALD HANKS: Stop, stop, stop! Stop the van!

GUARD: For what?

RONALD HANKS: Look in the parking lot.

(The guard looks to his left, sees Cynthia, and pulls into the driveway that runs along the West side of the prison parking lot. As soon as the van comes to a stop, Ronald jumps out and runs around the van to the edge of a forty yard stretch of grass. On the other end of this stretch of grass is his beautiful wife. While the thoughts and memories of all the pain he caused his wife run through his mind, Ronald slowly opens his arms and begins to cry not knowing what to say. After a few seconds go by his emotions take over, his heart falls, and the conviction literally breaks him down to his knees. When Cynthia sees her husband go down into a kneeling position in tears, she immediately takes off running towards him screaming his name, but she gets no response. All she gets is a back and forth rocking motion from him as he covers his face and weeps. When Cynthia finally reaches him she falls to her knees, which puts her at eye level with him. Cynthia kisses him on his forehead, tells him she loves him, and then wraps her arms around him with the intentions of never ever letting him go again.)

CYNTHIA HANKS: It's okay baby. It's okay.

(As Cynthia is cradling Ronald rocking him side to side, he searches deep down in his heart for the right words to say. But in his mind he is constantly reminded of the damage he's done. For that reason alone, he is so emotional that he is unable to say a single word. Minister Ragland, who is leaning on his car watching this beautiful reunion take place, can only cry. He is reminded once again, that with God, all things are possible. As the very prayer he prayed for is answered right in front of him, Minister Ragland looks up towards heaven and whispers.)

MINISTER: Thank you, Jesus.

(Later that same evening at the Williams's home, everyone has just finished eating. Cynthia and Jean cooked a welcome home dinner as a surprise for Ronald.)

JEAN WILLIAMS: Would anybody like some dessert?

MINISTER: I think I'm gonna pass. But I tell you what, I would like about two hours in that old hammock in the backyard if you don't mind.

EARL WILLIAMS: Knock yourself out.

(Minister Ragland excuses himself from the table.)

MINISTER: I don't mean to be a party pooper, but it is naptime!

(A few minutes after Minister Ragland has been gone, Cynthia leans over and whispers to her husband.)

CYNTHIA HANKS: Now would be a good time to talk to him.

RONALD HANKS: Cynthia, the man is going to take a nap!

CYNTHIA HANKS: Go talk to him.

(Ronald takes a deep breath.)

RONALD HANKS: All right.

(Ronald stands up.)

JEAN WILLIAMS: You finished too?

RONALD HANKS: Oh no, I'll be right back!

(When Ronald gets outside he finds Minister Ragland swinging back and forth in the hammock with his hat over his face. Not quite asleep yet, Minister Ragland hears Ronald approaching him so he uncovers his face and looks up.)

MINISTER: I guess I'm not the only one that country cooking got the best of.

RONALD HANKS: Yeah, it was good. Actually I came out here to talk to you.

MINISTER: Well, have a seat.

(Ronald sits down in a chair that's next to the hammock.)

MINISTER: What's on your mind?

RONALD HANKS: I just wanted to say thank you.

MINISTER: For what?

RONALD HANKS: Helping me get out of prison, I can't thank you enough.

MINISTER: You shouldn't thank me at all. You getting out had nothing to do with me. If I had tried to get you out on my own, you'd still be there, and I'd probably be in there with you. I just happen to be the vessel the good Lord used to get you out. He deserves all the thanks, not me.

RONALD HANKS: Yeah, you're right. But I just…

(Minister Ragland chuckles as Ronald tries to find a way to thank him for not giving up on him.)

MINISTER: Hey look, I know what you're trying to say, and I appreciate it. You're welcome.

(Ronald smiles as he sits back in his chair.)

RONALD HANKS: Joe, you do any fishing?

MINISTER: Not as much as I would like to.

RONALD HANKS: I tell you what, tomorrow morning I'll pick you up, and take you to my favorite fishing spot out at Grant Lake. We'll fish until about noon, and then we'll slide on into town and grab some lunch. What do you say?

MINISTER: I say you're on.

RONALD HANKS: And you know what, it's all on me. The bait, the lunch, everything, it's my treat.

MINISTER: Now you're absolutely on!

RONALD HANKS: Good. Well, I'm gonna go on back in and have some of that chocolate cake. Are you sure you don't want any?

MINISTER: No, thank you.

RONALD HANKS: All right.

(Ronald stands up.)

MINISTER: Was there anything else you wanted to talk about?

RONALD HANKS: No, I just wanted to say thank you.

MINISTER: Are you sure?

RONALD HANKS: Yeah.

MINISTER: Okay.

(Minister Ragland covers his face with his hat and pushes off the ground to swing the hammock as Ronald walks away.)

MINISTER: Hey, Ronald!

(Ronald stops and turns to face him.)

MINISTER: Welcome home.

(Ronald smiles.)

RONALD HANKS: Thanks.

(Again Minister Ragland covers his face with his hat and Ronald continues on towards the house. Once Ronald is inside he turns, looks through the window in the door and smiles, as he watches Minister Ragland peacefully swing back and forth).

CHAPTER TWENTY-THREE

(After spending the early morning fishing at Grant Lake, Ronald and Minister Ragland are on their way into town for lunch.)

RONALD HANKS: Man, you talk about strange. I haven't seen this town in almost two years.

MINISTER: Are you sure you're ready for this?

RONALD HANKS: Ready for what?

MINISTER: All of the pointing and whispering.

RONALD HANKS: That doesn't bother me. I know I'm innocent and so do they.

(As they pull up in front of Breakfast Time and park, people sitting beside the window start pointing as soon as they spot him.)

MINISTER: There they go.

RONALD HANKS: I don't care, it doesn't bother me.

(Minister Ragland and Ronald are greeted with complete silence as they enter the restaurant. Not one customer is saying a word. Once they sit down at the counter Ronald looks around. Seeing black people and white people separated in the restaurant bothers him.)

RONALD HANKS: I can't believe what I'm seeing.

MINISTER: They're confused Ronald.

RONALD HANKS: What do you mean?

MINISTER: They're confused; all of them. They've spent the last year and a half tearing each other down over absolutely nothing. They're all ashamed and embarrassed, and not one of them knows how to go about saying they're sorry.

RONALD HANKS: So you're saying what I see in this restaurant right now is the future of Swamp Fox? This is how it's going to be?

MINISTER: I hope not. We just gotta pray for God to…

(In mid sentence Minister Ragland stop's talking as his face goes blank.)

RONALD HANKS: What's wrong?

(Minister Ragland doesn't answer.)

RONALD HANKS: Joe, what's wrong?

(Minister Ragland turns and looks at Ronald.)

MINISTER: Lead by example.

RONALD HANKS: What?

MINISTER: Lead by example.

RONALD HANKS: What are you talking about?

MINISTER: Our job, as Christians, is to lead unbelieving souls to Christ so they can be saved, right?

RONALD HANKS: Right.

MINISTER: Well unfortunately, that job gets harder and harder everyday. There are so many people out there claiming to be Christians, but the way they live their lives looks nothing like Christ, and in the eyes of those that we're trying to reach, we look like hypocrites. Through words, Christians can sometimes portray themselves to be above sin and others, but we're not. We're in no position to judge another person because of their wrongs; we're all sinners. That's why we must put more effort towards living God's word, and not just talking God's word. We've got to lead by example.

RONALD HANKS: So what do you suggest we do?

MINISTER: We teach them how to say I'm sorry.

RONALD: How?

MINISTER: We lead by example. Come on, let's go.

(As they drive through town, Ronald's curiosity gets the best of him.)

RONALD HANKS: So where are we going?

MINISTER: To see Raymond.

(Ronald immediately pulls the car off the road and stops.)

MINISTER: What are you doing?

RONALD HANKS: Raymond Cletter?

MINISTER: Yeah!

RONALD HANKS: Forget it! I don't want to have anything to do with him!

MINISTER: I know what you're thinking and you're wrong. Raymond had nothing to do with you going to prison.

RONALD HANKS: That's not why I say that. When I was locked up Raymond came to see me. You know what he told me? He told me that my wife was having an affair, with you.

(Minister Ragland laughs.)

RONALD HANKS: I believed him.

(Minister Ragland's laughter comes to an abrupt halt.)

MINISTER: You believed him?

RONALD HANKS: I know I should have known better, and I'm sorry. But the point I'm trying to make is that he can't be trusted. We can't count on him for help!

MINISTER: MINISTER: He's not the enemy Ronald. Now I know Raymond has done some shady things, believe me I know. But he's changed. As a matter of fact, he put his entire career on the line to help me take Haywood down, which, in turn, led to you getting out of prison. Now that doesn't sound like the enemy to me.

(Ronald leans his head back on the headrest.)

MINISTER: He can and he will help us, Ronald. He's all right.

RONALD HANKS: All right. You've been right so far, let's do it.

(As Minister Ragland knocks on Raymond's office door, Ronald starts to feel uncomfortable.)

RAYMOND CLETTER: Come in!

RONALD HANKS: I don't know about this Joe.

MINISTER: Relax.

(Minister Ragland walks in first. As soon as Raymond sees the Minister he stands up, extends his arm, and they shake hands.)

RAYMOND CLETTER: How's it going Joe?

MINISTER: Pretty good, Ray. Ray, you know Ronald.

(Raymond pauses before he says anything as they lock eyes for the first time since he visited him in prison. Hoping to break the ice, Raymond extends his hand for Ronald to shake. But instead Ronald just sits down in the chair next to Minister Ragland, leaving Raymond standing with his hand out. After a few seconds, Raymond sits down, still locked eye to eye with Ronald.)

MINISTER: Ray, I need your help.

(Raymond turns his attention from Ronald to Minister Ragland.)

RAYMOND CLETTER: With what?

MINISTER: I want to call a town meeting. And I want the meeting to take place at Pastor Fredricks' church.

RAYMOND CLETTER: A town meeting for who?

MINISTER: The whole town. I'll put flyers in mailboxes, store windows, or wherever I need to put them to bring the people in.

RAYMOND CLETTER: Are you crazy Joe? What are you trying to do, start a war?

MINISTER: I'm trying to bring these people back together Ray. There are no more excuses for hating each other now. That's over and done with, the man's innocent, and they know it.

RAYMOND CLETTER: Joe, I know peace is what you want, but a catastrophe is what you're going to get if you put all of those people in the same building.

MINISTER: It's not going to be a catastrophe Ray. It'll be okay.

RAYMOND CLETTER: And how do you know that?

MINISTER: Because God is not going to allow a catastrophe. Not in his house.

RAYMOND CLETTER: And once you get all these people in, "His house," what then? What are you gonna do?

(Minister Ragland takes a deep breath.)

MINISTER: I don't know.

(Raymond sits back in his chair and chuckles.)

(RAYMOND CLETTER: You don't know? I'm sorry Joe, but I can't allow it. It's too dangerous man.

(Minister Ragland scoots forward to the edge of his chair and leans on Raymond's desk.)

MINISTER: You can't allow it? I didn't come here for your approval Ray; I came here for your help. This meeting is going to take place whether you want it to or not. You see, this has nothing to do with me, and it has nothing to do with you. It's all about God's perfect will. And that, my friend, is something neither you, that badge you're wearing, nor that gun strapped to your side can stop. The will of God cannot be stopped Ray. Now if you don't believe that, then just take a look in the chair next to me.

(The mere fact that Ronald is sitting in his office a free man proves to Raymond that Minister Ragland is right. God's perfect will cannot be stopped. Raymond sits there for a few seconds and then stands up.)

RAYMOND CLETTER: Just let me know what you need Joe.

(Raymond and Minister Ragland shake hands.)

MINISTER: Thanks, Ray. I'll call you.

(Minister Ragland heads for the door with Ronald following. As Minister Ragland opens the door, Raymond calls Ronald.)

RAYMOND CLETTER: Hey, Ronald.

(Both the Minister and Ronald turn to face him.)

RAYMOND CLETTER: I'm sorry.

(Raymond extends his hand to Ronald in hopes of making peace. Ronald looks at Minister Ragland, looks Raymond in his eyes, and then slowly reaches out and accepts the peace offering. Putting all the negative things that happened between them, behind them. Bright and early Monday morning, Minister Ragland and Ronald begin to post flyers about Saturday's town meeting all over town. They hang them in store windows, on telegram poles, car windshields; they even put them in mailboxes. As the week goes by, people all over town are talking about the meeting. It's the main topic in all the beauty salons, barbershops and restaurants. It's now Saturday and the big day has arrived. As the people of Swamp Fox pour into the church, at Minister Ragland's request, Raymond and some of his deputies are sending them in different directions to prevent all of the white people from sitting together, and all of the black from sitting together. Some of the people are a little upset when they get to their seat and find out that they have to sit next to someone of the opposite color. But after a little hesitation and sighing, they decide to sit down anyway never saying so much as hello. The attendance of the meeting is so large, that it fills all of the pews on the floor and in the balcony. Even after putting chairs in the aisles, some people are still left standing up along the walls. Once everybody is in place and settled, Minister Ragland walks up to the podium in the pulpit, stands there for a second, looks around the church, and then begins to speak as eight hundred pairs of curious eyes stare at him.)

MINISTER: Exactly one month ago today, I left my home in Charlotte, North Carolina, with the intentions of surprising an old college friend of mine that lives in Bailey, South Carolina. Somewhere along the way I missed an exit, got lost, and ended up here in Swamp Fox. I stopped at a restaurant to grab a bite to eat and hopefully get some directions. But what I ended up getting was the shock of my life. Here we are in the year 2006, and in this restaurant, the black people are sitting on one side, and the white people are sitting on the other. I knew right then and there something strange was going on, and I wanted to know what it was. I decided to take a little walk around town to observe the people, to observe their interactions with each other, and again I was blown away. People of different races were sitting on park benches a foot away from each other and not saying one word. All I could do was shake my head in disbelief. I just couldn't believe it. In the distance I kept hearing a ball bouncing. I looked around to my right, and there he was, Corey Williams. He was a tall, thin, good-looking young brother that seemed as if he had it all together. He was smart, he was respectful, he had his head on straight, and he had dreams. Dreams of going to the University of North Carolina to become a lawyer. But unfortunately, he never got the chance to see those dreams come true. Two weeks before his eighteenth birthday, on a Tuesday afternoon, Corey Williams was nearly beaten to death out at Grant Lake and left for dead. He lived for exactly fifteen minutes after arriving at the hospital, and then at the age of seventeen, he died. I said all of that to say this, get used to it. Children dying before they've ever had a chance to see their dreams come true, get used to it. If you people, all of you, don't do something about the hate that festers in this town, the death angel will frequent this place. I have seen kids that couldn't have been any older than six years old calling each other nigger, and white trash. These kids, in the end, are going to pay the ultimate price and you adults, all of you, will have to answer to God for it. Kids are not born racist, and they're not born with hate. That's something they're taught. There are some of you that have turned your back on friendships that have lasted for over thirty years. Thirty years people! Not because you've been wronged, but because everybody else was doing it. You didn't have the guts to stand up for yourselves. You didn't have the guts to say, regardless of what has happened, he or she is still my friend. You were too busy worrying about what people might say. Worried they might call you a nigger lover, or call you an Uncle Tom. Enjoy your children while you can. Hug them, kiss them, and tell them you love them everyday, because if things don't change around here, and change soon, Corey Williams won't be the only child buried outback that never lived to see his dreams come true. Forgiveness is where it begins. Put your pride down and do the right thing. The good Lord above said we should love our neighbor as we love ourselves. He also said that when He returns, He would return as a thief in the night. Don't get caught with that poison seed in your heart when he returns, because the price you'll pay for it is far greater than you could ever imagine. Make up in your minds today, in your hearts, right now, that you are not going to allow the devil to send you out of this church, the same way you came in. The hate, the anger, the revenge, let it go. Let it out, and allow love, and forgiveness, to come in.

(As Minister Ragland takes a seat in the pulpit, the church piano player begins to play. After about ten seconds, a strong powerful voice blares from the speakers throughout the church. As the people in the audience are looking around to see who is singing, a door on the left side of the church beside the choir stand opens, and the voice is revealed. It's Bobby Medlin. Bobby comes out, stands in front of the pulpit before the audience, and sings one of four solo parts of a very special song. As the second soloist begins to sing, people in the audience begin to look at each other. The familiar angelic sound that penetrates their ears causes their eyes to grow wide, and their hearts to skip a beat. Again there is no face to go with the voice, and then, on the other side of the church beside the choir stand a door opens, and through that door walks none other than Jennifer Mundy. Cynthia Hanks, as she sits on the front row, slowly rocks side to side with a smile on her face as she watches Jennifer walk past her to stand beside Bobby Medlin down in front. She is moved to tears as she reflects back on all she's been through and how God has blessed her by bringing her husband home. On the fifth row from the front, Pastor Fredricks is standing up with his hands clasped together under his chin as tears fall from his eyes. He is so overwhelmed, and so happy to hear Jennifer's beautiful voice again, all he can do is weep. After the crowd is swept away by Jennifer, another beautiful voice rings out, the voice of Corey's mom, Jean Williams. When she walks through the door singing, again the people are moved. As Jean Williams makes her way to the front of the church to join Bobby and Jennifer, some of the people begin to stand up and clap as they cry. They are inspired, and encouraged by her strength. To see her standing there with her hand extended towards heaven, tears in her eyes, and a smile on her face, after all she's been through; they are touched in ways they've never been touched before. Eight rows back on the left, Jacy, who is sitting next to the aisle, is with her mom and dad. As Jean Williams continues to sing, Jacy's father Clint begins to cry. While his emotions take over, in his heart, he wishes that he could somehow take away all of the pain his son has caused her by killing her only child. Seeing that her dad is suffering inside, Jacy reaches over and gently grabs his hand to comfort him. As the fourth and final soloist begins to sing, a spine tingling blanket of silence covers the entire audience. The voice they hear is a familiar one. It's also a voice they thought they'd never want to hear again. On the right side of the church, beside the choir stand, a door opens. Through that door, walks the most inspiring soloist of them all. Through that door, singing from the depths of his soul, walks Ronald Hanks. As he makes his way down front, the entire church erupts. Some of the people are leaning forward in their chairs resting their head in their hands. Joy, happiness, and tears overcome them. Some of them are sitting in their seats straight-faced and astounded as their tears fall in their laps. Most of the people are standing up. Either with their hands covering their mouths as they cry, or with their hands waving in praise, thanking God for the healing that is taking place. As Jennifer Mundy watches Ronald sing, she is reminded of how she wronged him, and how it almost ruined his entire life. As the guilt wears on her for what she did, Jennifer finally breaks down in tears. She covers her mouth and looks down feeling so ashamed, and then it happens. Ronald walks over to her and puts one hand on her shoulder. She looks up at him, he smiles at her, and then the two of them embrace in a hug as he continues to sing. Cynthia Hanks is sitting in her seat crying as she stares at Ronald and Jennifer. Over Cynthia's right shoulder, out of nowhere, appears a tissue. Cynthia looks back to see who is offering her the tissue, and to her surprise, she sees her lifelong friend she thought she had lost forever. It's Jennifer's mom, Ann Mundy. Ann walks around the pew and stands in front of Cynthia, gently grabs her hand, and slowly pulls her up. For the first time in almost two years, they stand face to face.)

ANNE MUNDY: I'm sorry Cynthia. I'm so sorry for not believing you.

(The two of them embrace in a long hug of forgiveness. Jacy is leaning forward crying as her father rubs her back. Jean Williams begins to walk towards Jacy, but Jacy doesn't see her approaching because her face is buried in her hands. Jacy's father Clint watches Jean as she walks toward them not really knowing what to expect. When Jean finally reaches the pew where Jacy is sitting, she extends her hands. Clint looks at her, and whispers to Jacy who still doesn't know she's standing there.)

CLINT ELLIS: Honey.

(Jacy turns to her father and he points at Mrs. Williams. When she turns and sees who's standing there, she is shocked, and completely lost for words. Jean Williams says something to her that's guaranteed to heal any wound she may have caused that day at Corey's funeral.

JEAN WILLIAMS: Its okay baby. I know it wasn't your fault. I'm sorry I blamed you.

(Jacy takes hold of her hand and stands up. As they stand face-to-face for the first time since Corey's funeral, Jacy is so lost for words that all she can do is cry.)

JEAN WILLIAMS: Because of you, my son was blessed with the opportunity to experience what true love is all about before he died. You didn't care about his color, you cared about him, and he knew that. I cannot thank you enough, for giving him that.

JACY ELLIS: I'm so sorry.

(Jean reaches out and wipes a tear that is running down Jacy's face. Then, with all eyes on them, Jean wraps her arms around Jacy, and holds her tight as they both, in their hearts; finally lay Corey to rest. Minister Ragland walks up to the podium and looks out into the crowd. As he watches people who once hated each other shake hands and hug, his chin starts to quiver. His eyes fill up with tears as he whispers to himself.)

MINISTER: Thank you Lord for your blood. The blood, that has cleansed every heart and soul in this building today. Thank you.

(After wiping his eyes he speaks to the people.)

MINISTER: Let us all stand for prayer.

(Everybody stands.)

MINISTER: To touch and agree, please join hands with your neighbor.

(Some of the people are a little hesitant about holding hands with someone of a different color, but that hesitation is short lived. Eventually they all slowly join hands and stand as one in prayer.)

MINISTER: Let us bow our heads as we pray.

(Just before Minister Ragland begins to pray, he looks out over the crowd of bowed heads and is emotionally moved, as the choir softly sings. To see both black, and white, standing in the Lord's house, as one, in peace, he is reminded that nothing is impossible for God. But amidst all of the bowed heads, he sees only one set of eyes staring back at him. Standing at the very back of the church at the door is Raymond. As they lock eyes, a tear falls from Raymond's face. He then turns, opens the door, and walks out, yearning for his own healing. The next day, the Williams', the Hanks', and the Mundys take Minister Ragland out for a farewell lunch. Afterwards, as they're standing beside the Minister's car, which is parked in front of the restaurant, they begin to say their goodbyes.)

CYNTHIA HANKS: Are you sure you can't stick around for a few more days?

MINISTER: Yeah I've got to get back, I've got a million things.

(Minister Ragland looks at his watch.)

MINISTER: As a matter of fact, I should probably go ahead and get on the road to beat that five o'clock traffic.

CYNTHIA HANKS: Well, as much as we'd like to, we won't keep you any longer.   '

(Cynthia steps forward and gives him a hug.)

CYNTHIA HANKS: You take care of yourself Joe.

(Cynthia steps back and gently touches the side of his face.)

CYNTHIA HANKS: You have been an absolute blessing to this town. If you ever, ever need anything, don't hesitate for one second to call us. We'll always be here for you.

MINISTER: Thank you, Cynthia.

(Ronald steps forward and hugs Minister Ragland.)

RONALD HANKS: I love you, Joe. Thanks for everything.

MINISTER: I love you too Ronald.

(After Cynthia and Ronald say their good-byes, both Jean and Earl Williams step forward and hug him at the same time. Just as they did in the emergency room the night Corey died. Minister Ragland whispers to them.)

MINISTER: You will see him again one day.

(Almost instantly, both Mr. and Mrs. Williams begin to cry.)

JEAN WILLIAMS: We love you, Joe.

MINISTER: I love you too.

EARL WILLIAMS: Our home will always be your home.

MINISTER: Thanks, Earl.

(After an emotional embrace with the Williams', he hugs Mrs. Mundy.)

ANN MUNDY: It was a pleasure meeting you, Minister Ragland.

MINISTER: The pleasure was all mine.

(Next he and Sam Mundy hug.)

SAM MUNDY: You make sure you come see us the next time you head this way.

MINISTER: I will.

(Last, but not least, he hugs Jennifer Mundy.)

MINISTER: I am so very proud of you, Jennifer.

(After the hug Jennifer steps back to ask him a question.)

JENNIFER MUNDY: Will I ever see you again?

MINISTER: You can count on it sweetheart.

(Jennifer hugs him again as she too begins to cry.)

JENNIFER MUNDY: Thank you so much for never giving up on me.

(After the hug he pulls his keys out of his pocket.)

MINISTER: I have all of your phone numbers and addresses. I'll keep in touch.

CYNTHIA HANKS: Please do.

MINISTER: I will. You guys take care of yourselves.

(Minister Ragland gets in his car.)

JEAN WILLIAMS: You drive careful!

MINISTER: I will.

(He starts his car and slowly pulls off as he blows his horn and waves. While driving through town, Minister Ragland notices that things are starting to get back to normal. To his left he sees a black child and a white child playing together in a sand box as their mothers sit on a bench and talk. To his right, on the very same court he met Corey, he sees a young black kid coming down court with the ball. He throws an alley yoop to his teammate who is white, and his teammate dunks the ball. As the white kid comes back down court, his black teammate that threw him the pass gives him a high five and a pat on the rear. Minister Ragland can only smile as he slowly pulls off. Just before making his way to the highway, Minister Ragland looks to his left and sees his favorite restaurant, Breakfast Time. Immediately a huge smile stretches across his face as he decides to see his favorite waitress one last time. Just before Minister Ragland enters the restaurant, he looks to his left, and sitting off to the side are an old black man and an old white man playing checkers. It's the same white man from the barbershop that insulted him when he asked for directions. When the old man sees Minister Ragland looking at him, he takes the small wet cigar out of his mouth, and gives him a thumbs up. Minister Ragland, who is somewhat amused by the gesture chuckles, gives him a thumbs up, and then walks into the restaurant. The very first thing Minister Ragland does when he walks in is look around. No longer are the black and white people separated. There's a beautiful mix throughout the restaurant.

FAYE WATERS: How are you, Minister Ragland?

(Minister Ragland stands there in shock with his mouth wide open. He can't believe that Faye is actually being nice to him.)

MINISTER: Hold on for just a minute.

(Minister Ragland walks outside and looks up at the sign on the front of the restaurant, suggesting that he's in the wrong place. Faye, knowing he is being sarcastic, laughs when she sees him look up. When he turns to go back in the restaurant, the old man that gave him the thumbs up before does it again. Minister Ragland laughs, gives him another thumbs up, and walks back into the restaurant.)

FAYE WATERS: Very funny. Get in here and sit down.

MINISTER: I just wanted to make sure I was in the right place.

(Minister Ragland sits down at the counter.)

FAYE WATERS: The usual?

MINISTER: You got it, and a BLT to go.

FAYE WATERS: Coming right up.

(While waiting for his food, Minister Ragland looks around the restaurant and thinks about how bad things were the first time he sat in that very same seat at the counter. To see the same people that once hated each other sitting together and getting along brings a smile to his face.)

(Faye returns with his food.)

FAYE WATERS: There you go.

(Minister Ragland opens his bag to make sure everything's in there. As he's looking, three young men, two white, one black, are on their way out of the door. One by one as they pass him they all speak.)

FIRST KID: How you doing, Minister Ragland!

(Minister Ragland turns to see who is talking to him.)

MINISTER: I'm good.

NEXT KID: How's it going?

MINISTER: Pretty good.

LAST KID: Take care.

MINISTER: I will. You guys do the same.

(As the last kid walks out, Minister Ragland turns to face Faye who has a huge smile on her face.)

MINISTER: What may I ask are you so happy about?

FAYE WATERS: A week ago there's no way you would have seen those three boys hanging out together. Now look at them.

(Minister Ragland turns around to look at them. The boys are shaking hands and giving high fives as one of the white kids walks off in one direction, while the other white kid and the black walk off in the other direction. Minister Ragland turns back to Faye.)

MINISTER: It's a beautifuf thing isn't it?

FAYE WATERS: You know you saved this town, don't you?

MINISTER: I know that God used me to save this town. I don't deserve any of the credit for what's happened here.

FAYE WATERS: Well, I tell you what, God sure does know how to pick 'em.

MINISTER: Thank you Faye, that's very nice.

(Minister Ragland looks at his watch.)

MINISTER: Well, I've really got to get going. How much do I owe you?

(Again Minister Ragland looks through his bag.)

MINISTER: Faye, I think you made a mistake. There's a piece of pie in here. I didn't order pie.

FAYE WATERS: Well, I know how much you like our apple pie. I figured I'd throw you a couple of pieces in there for your trip home.

MINISTER: How did you know I was leaving today?

FAYE WATERS: Bad news travels fast.

(He smiles at her.)

FAYE WATERS: I'm sorry for being so nasty to you.

MINISTER: It's okay. So what do I owe you for the food?

FAYE WATERS: A hug will do. Don't worry about the food, it's on me.

(Minister Ragland reaches across the counter and they hug for the very first time.)

MINISTER: You take care of yourself, Faye.

FAYE WATERS: You too. Please be careful driving home.

MINISTER: I will.

(As Minister Ragland makes his way to the door, Faye watches him with a smile on her face.)

FAYE WATERS: Come back and see us!

MINISTER: You bet.

(Minister Ragland walks out of the restaurant, gets in his car, backs out of his parking space, and heads for the highway. As he slowly makes his way through town, he sees Jacy walking with one of her friends. He blows his horn to get her attention as he calls her name. After turning around to see who is calling her, Jacy waves and yells hello.)

MINISTER: Can you hold on for just a second? I'd like to talk to you!

JACY ELLIS: Sure!

(Minister Ragland parks his car and walks across the street to talk to Jacy.)

MINISTER: How are you?

JACY ELLIS: I'm fine, how are you?

(Minister Ragland and Jacy embrace in a hug. After the hug, Jacy steps back and introduces her friend.)

JACY ELLIS: Minister Ragland, this is my friend Tiffany King, Tiffany...

TIFFANY KING: You don't have to introduce us, I know who he is. Minister Ragland, it is so nice to have finally met you.

(Tiffany steps forward and hugs him. After hugging him she steps back and smiles.)

TIFFANY KING: Do you have any idea what you've done for this town?

MINISTER: Yes I do. I also know that I couldn't have done it with out God. He made it all possible.

TIFFANY KING: I agree one hundred percent.

JACY ELLIS: So what are you up to?

MINISTER: I'm on my way home.

JACY ELLIS: Right now?

MINISTER: Yeah, I've gotta get back to the Queen City. But I was wondering if I could talk to you for just a minute.

JACY ELLIS: Sure. We were just about to have some lunch, would you like to join us?

MINISTER: I'd love to, but I really need to get on the road. All I need is just about five minutes.

TIFFANY KING: Jacy, I'll go on in and get us a table.

JACY ELLIS: Okay!

TIFFANY KING: Minister Ragland, you drive safe!

MINISTER: I will, sweetheart. It was nice meeting you.

(Tiffany leaves the two of them alone)

JACY ELLIS: So what's up?

MINISTER: I just wanted to check on you and see how you're doing.

JACY ELLIS: I'm doing okay.

MINISTER: Are you sure?

JACY ELLIS: Yeah.

MINISTER: How are your parents?

JACY ELLIS: They're good, especially my dad. Corey's mom and my dad talked on the phone last night for almost four hours. She and her husband are having dinner at our house tonight!

MINISTER: That's wonderful Jacy!

JACY: I know, I can't believe it. Corey would be so happy.

MINISTER: He is happy honey.

JACY ELLIS: Yeah he is.

(They smile at each other.)

MINISTER: Well, I'm not gonna to keep you any longer. I just wanted to make sure you're doing okay.

JACY ELLIS: Thanks, I appreciate that.

MINISTER: You stay sweet.

JACY ELLIS: You too.

(Minister Ragland steps forward and they hug.)

MINISTER: Be good.

JACY ELLIS: I will.

(As Minister Ragland crosses the street, he remembers something.)

MINISTER: Oh! I almost forgot!

(He reaches into his glove compartment and grabs a small velvet box, wrapped in a Carolina blue bow. He walks back across the street to where Jacy is standing.)

MINISTER: This is for you.

(Jacy looks at the box and then looks at the Minister.)

JACY ELLIS: What is this?

MINISTER: I don't know, it's something Corey bought for you. He was going to give it to you on his birthday. He asked me to pick it up from the store for him. I forgot it was locked up in my glove compartment.

JACY ELLIS: He was going to give me a gift, on his birthday?

MINISTER: That's what he said.

(Jacy looks down at the box as her eyes fill up with tears.)

JACY ELLIS: That sounds like something he would do.

MINISTER: Go ahead and open it up.

(Jacy takes the Carolina blue lace bow off of the little dark blue velvet box. After opening the box she immediately covers her mouth in shock.)

MINISTER: What is it?

JACY ELLIS: It's a bracelet.

(Jacy pulls the bracelet out of the box and looks at it.)

JACY ELLIS: It's a sterling silver bracelet.

(She holds it out for Minister Ragland to see.)

MINISTER: Oh my goodness, it's beautiful. What's engraved on it?

(Jacy reads the inscription to herself, as a tear rolls down her face. Then she reads it to Minister Ragland)

JACY ELLIS: My Biz.

MINISTER: What does that mean?

JACY ELLIS: That's the nickname Corey gave me when we were planning our picnic for Grant Lake.

(As the memories of that fatal day return, Jacy begins to cry.)

JACY ELLIS: I miss him so much. Am I ever going to get over this?

MINISTER: It's beautiful, isn't it?

(With tears in her eyes, Jacy looks down at the bracelet.)

JACY ELLIS: Yeah, it is.

MINISTER: I'm not talking about the bracelet.

(Jacy looks up at Minister Ragland.)

MINISTER: I'm talking about the fact that Corey Williams, at the age of seventeen, was blessed with the opportunity to experience something a lot of people won't experience in a lifetime. He experienced true love. Love that you gave him Jacy. That Tuesday we lost Corey was, and always will be a tragedy. I know you miss him, we all miss him, but life has to go on. There are so many people out there that need what God has given you Jacy. There are millions of people out there that are hurting, millions. In your lifetime, God is going to send a lot of them your way. Not because of, Jacy, but because of everything that God has put in, Jacy. Like a caring heart, a peaceful spirit, respect, and most importantly, love. Love is the main one. Everybody wants to be loved. So you carry on with life, just as Corey would want you to, and the world needs you to.

JACY ELLIS: Okay.

(He gives her a hug.)

MINISTER: I love you.

JACY ELLIS: I love you too.

(Minister Ragland steps back.)

MINISTER: Take care of yourself, and stay strong.

JACY ELLIS: I will.

MINISTER: And I want you to do me a favor.

JACY ELLIS: What?

MINISTER: Don't forget about your brother. In spite of what's happened, he still has a heart.

JACY ELLIS: I know. I won't forget about him.

MINISTER: Go on in and have lunch with your friend.

(Jacy gives him one last hug.)

JACY ELLIS: Good-bye, Minister Ragland.

MINISTER: Good- bye, Jacy.

(After the hug, Minister Ragland watches Jacy as she walks away. And just before she's out of sight, he whispers to himself.)

MINISTER: The only thing you're missing are the wings.

(After getting on the road and passing the sign that reads, "You are now leaving Swamp Fox," Minister Ragland leans his head back, takes a deep breath, and exhales. Then the unthinkable happens, a police officer pulls in behind him and turns on the lights to pull him over.)

MINISTER: You have got to be kidding me.

(Minister Ragland pulls over and the officer gets out of his car. As the officer is asking for his license and registration, he begins to laugh hysterically. Recognizing that laugh, Minister Ragland looks to his left, and there stands Raymond grinning from ear to ear. Minister Ragland is so amused by what has happened he can only shake his head.)

RAYMOND CLETTER: You come to my town, you stir up all kinds of trouble, and you're just going to up and leave without saying good-bye?

(Minister Ragland gets out of his car.)

MINISTER: I went by your house and your office this morning. I must have just missed you both times.

RAYMOND CLETTER: So today is the day, huh?

MINISTER: Yeah, I gotta get back. God's got work for me to do there too.

RAYMOND CLETTER: Well, take this with you.

(Raymond pulls out his wallet and hands Minister Ragland one of his business cards.)

RAYMOND CLETTER: Here's my card, my cell phone number, and my office number. And I wrote my home number on the back.

(As Raymond flips the card over to show Minister Ragland where he wrote his phone number, Minister Ragland notices a picture of Raymond's family in his wallet.)

MINISTER: May I?

RAYMOND CLETTER: What?

MINISTER: See the picture of your family.

(Raymond looks down at the picture and then slowly hands it to Minister Ragland.)

MINISTER: They were beautiful.

(After looking at the picture Minister Ragland looks up at Raymond.)

MINISTER: Were Raymond. They're gone now, and they're not coming back. When are you going to move on with your life?

(Feeling somewhat uncomfortable about the conversation, Raymond reaches for his wallet.)

RAYMOND CLETTER: Look, I gotta go.

(Minister Ragland stretches his arm out to his right so that Raymond can't grab the wallet.)

MINISTER: Answer my question, Ray. When are you going to lay them to rest?

RAYMOND CLETTER: Joe, not now.

MINISTER: No Ray, right now.

RAYMOND CLETTER: Look, I've had about enough. Now give me my wallet!

MINISTER: Not until you answer my question! When are you going to let go and live your life?

(Raymond, who has now reached his boiling point, begins to yell.)

RAYMOND CLETTER: I can't let go! I tried and I can't do it! You think I like my life? You think I like living this way? I hate my life! I hate what I've become! Every stinking day I wake up, the first thing I think about are those three burnt bodies I saw in that morgue!

(Raymond begins to cry.)

RAYMOND CLETTER: In my mind, when I see my little nine year old daughter Marie lying in that body bag, a trigger goes off inside of me that turns on this rage and anger I can't control! When my family was alive, and something went wrong, or I would have a bad day, I would think about them and it made everything okay! Now when I think of them all I can do is rage! Because of that rage, people purposely avoid me! They don't talk to me because they never know which Raymond they're going to get. I feel like I'm all by myself in this world! I feel like nobody loves me! I don't have anybody Joe! I don't have anybody!

(While listening to Raymond, Minister Ragland's eyes fill with tears.)

RAYMOND CLETTER: If this is how my life is going to be, I don't want to live anymore.

(Minister Ragland, feeling every ounce of his pain, reaches out, and wraps his arms around him. After a brief heartfelt embrace, Raymond steps back and wipes his eyes as he continues to cry.)

MINISTER: Enough is enough Ray. It's time to let it all go man. It's time to live again.

RAYMOND CLETTER: I want to let go, but I don't know how! I just don't know how!

MINISTER: I do Ray.

(Raymond looks at Minister Ragland with tears dangling from his chin.)

MINISTER: Raymond, do you believe that Jesus is the Son of God?

(Completely caught off guard by the question, Raymond is left speechless.)

MINISTER: Do you Ray?

(Raymond pauses for a second and then answers.)

RAYMOND CLETTER: Yes.

MINISTER: Do you believe that Jesus died on the cross to save us from our sins and rose on the third day?

(With his head down and crying, he answers.)

RAYMOND CLETTER: Yes.

MINISTER: Do you know you're a sinner, Ray?

(Short pause.)

RAYMOND CLETTER: Yes.

MINISTER: Ray, I want you to repeat after me.

(Again Raymond looks at Minister Ragland.)

MINISTER: Dear God please forgive me for all of my sins.

(Realizing what is taking place, and knowing the end of his pain is near as he accepts Jesus Christ into his heart as his Lord and Savior, Raymond again begins to cry as he repeats after Minister Ragland.)

MINISTER: I need your forgiveness to make me whole.

(Raymond repeats.)

MINISTER: Jesus, please come into my heart and my life as my Lord and Savior.

(Raymond repeats.)

MINISTER: Make me your child and use me as a vessel to do your will all the days of my life.

(As Raymond begins to repeat, he stops because he is so emotionally moved by what is happening.)

RAYMOND CLETTER: I'm sorry Joe.

MINISTER: It's okay. Just take your time.

(After gathering his composure, Raymond repeats what Minister Ragland said.)

MINISTER: I thank you Lord, for saving my soul.

(Raymond repeats.)

MINISTER: In Jesus name I pray.

(Raymond repeats.)

MINISTER: Amen

RAYMOND CLETTER: Amen.

(Minister Ragland again embraces his friend knowing that he can now live his life in peace with God. As he holds him he whispers in his ear.)

MINISTER: You're free Ray. You're free.

RAYMOND CLETTER: Yes, I am.

(As they let go of each other Minister Ragland begins to laugh.)

RAYMOND CLETTER: What's so funny?

MINISTER: I'm truly convinced now, that God definitely has a sense of humor. Because never in my wildest dreams, did I think that you and I would be standing on the side of the road, hugging and crying as brothers in Christ? He really does move in mysterious ways.

RAYMOND CLETTER: It just goes to show that it's never to late.

MINISTER: You're right. It's never to late.

RAYMOND CLETTER: It's gonna be dark soon. You better get going.

MINISTER: Yeah, I better.

RAYMOND CLETTER: I wrote my name and address on the back of the card. I figured I'd save you some money.

MINISTER: Save me some money? What do you mean?

RAYMOND CLETTER: I mean the next time you head this way don't bother wasting your money on a hotel. Next time, you stay with me, at my house, where you'll always be welcomed.

MINISTER: I appreciate that Ray.

(Raymond and Minister Ragland shake hands.)

RAYMOND CLETTER: You take care of yourself, Minister Joe Ragland.

MINISTER: You do the same, Chief of Police Raymond Cletter.

(The two hug one last time and Raymond heads for his car. Just before Raymond gets in his car, Minister Ragland calls his name.)

MINISTER: Hey Ray!

(Raymond turns to face him.)

MINISTER: Everything in your life is about to change.

(Raymond smiles.)

RAYMOND CLETTER: It already has.

(As Minister Ragland smiles back at him, Raymond gets in his car, turns around, gives one last wave, and drives off. After getting on the highway and driving for a little while, Minister Ragland decides to have a bite of the pie Faye gave him. While pulling the napkins out of the bag, out of the corner of his eye, he sees some writing on one of the napkins. He picks it up with his right hand as he drives with his left. The napkin reads: Matthew chapter 17, verse 20. "If you have faith the size of a mustard seed, you can say to any problem, move, and it will. Nothing will be impossible for you." Love, Faye.

(Minister Ragland smiles, places the napkin on the seat, and whispers.)

MINISTER: Thank you, Jesus.

(As he continues down the road heading home, Minister Ragland is looking through the bag of food when the unbelievable happens. He accidentally misses his exit again, and is now heading towards a town called Cilas, where a young man and his grandmother have just... Well, until next time.

TO BE CONTINUED

ABOUT THE AUTHOR

After losing the battle with crack cocaine, which I tried to fight on my own, I turned the addiction, the robbing, and the stealing over to Christ and instantly He set me free. With my mind clear, my eyes focused, and my soul where it should be, I now see my purpose in life. Using the gift to create love and peace on paper, I will spend the rest of my life tearing down the walls of racism that sadly divides us. I want to teach the world that forgiveness and love will always produce peace.

Printed in the United States
51208LVS00004B/106-432

9 781425 923587